They returned to the bunkhouse. Cowboy hastily retired for the night, quite exhausted; but not randy Randall! He was still a-quiver, wild with an excitement that would kindle any man, no matter what his pretensions to virtue.

There were other young men working at the Bar Star Ranch, some almost as vigorous and attractive as Cowboy. Randall lingered at the bunkhouse door. He forgot his intention to preserve an ideal. To use his own words in telling of what he later described as the greatest night of his life, "What I did is just nobody's business." Suffice it to say, he awoke in the predawn light in a great heap of denim shirts and pants, leather chaps, riding boots, and well over a thousand pounds of assorted sweaty, snoring, masculine flesh. Whatever it was, he had done it.

The Scarlet Pansy

ANONYMOUS

A BADBOY BOOK

First BADBOY Edition 1992

First printing April 1992

ISBN 1-56333-021-0

Cover Photograph © 1992 Daniel Perry
Cover Design by Eduardo Andino

Manufactured in the United States of America
Published by Masquerade Books, Inc.
801 Second Avenue
New York, N.Y. 10017

CHAPTER
1

Randall Etrange lay dying on a battlefield in France, dying in the arms of the man he loved.

Young Lieutenant Frank, much younger than Randall, tenderly drew him closer. At that time he did not sense that Randall had sacrificed his life to save him. Though Randall had revealed his true self, in his gratitude for his recent ministrations Lieutenant Frank truly thought he loved this man. Perhaps he did. Perhaps he was even broad-minded enough for that. At least, in the long years after, he was heard to speak reverently of Randall.

Randall was beautiful, had always been beautiful, from babyhood onward. Whatever feature is to be admired in a babe, he had possessed: skin of the softness and bloom of a dainty blush rose; eyes of deepest blue; ringlets of spun gold. And later, at the age when growing boys are thin and gangling, he had been pleasantly rounded and winsomely lovely. Even at the time of his death, when he was well past thirty-three, his beauty had not begun to fade, but with each year had seemed to take on an appropriate maturity. Best of all, he had never realized that he possessed beauty. He had studied his mirror but little, except when making up for some grand function. This was due to an overwhelming interest in others and in objects about him, a trait manifested early in life.

Though Randall belonged to the emotional type, nevertheless, he was possessed of a marked interest in science. Thus his life had developed along complex lines.

Randall was born in a quaint little white cottage at Kuntzville, in the lower Pennsylvania hills. Here he lived with his father, mother, two sisters and his brother Bill. His parents were of that superior type which in a past generation has been called so proudly "good American stock."

His first loves were idealized, and each disillusionment was followed by a sense of keen self-condemnation and by a long period of hopelessness before again attempting to grasp happiness through love. If they later became more frequent and promiscuous, perhaps it was because of the attempt to find in the many a summation of the attributes which love craves.

Until late in adolescence, he had no frankly sexual experience. He did have frequent "crushes" in his first contacts at school, and these, as with all children, were sometimes directed towards the young, sometimes toward mature people; sometimes towards the opposite sex, sometimes toward his own. Aside from his physical beauty, he was always a marked child, never interested in the games of other children, always dreaming, so absorbed with some inner urge that he often seemed stupid to normal children. Yet his school fellows always went to him for advice and sought him out for aid when lessons were difficult.

Randall loved all animal life, human or otherwise; the difference was only in degree, and this motivated his future career. From his mother he inherited a love of service. As much as possible he followed that good woman about on expeditions to nurse sick neighbors, or to render other kindly offices, though the father demanded much of Randall's time for work in the fields or about the barns.

Early Randall learned to feed the smaller stock and to nurse any sick baby animals. As he developed sturdily, he was obliged to give him time and strength to the rough field work, doing quite as much as his older brother Bill. He would have somehow preferred to be with his mother in the house, doing the more domestic tasks, cooking, sewing, beautifying the home, but his father resented any such attempts. Thus the instincts that were normal to Randall were somewhat thwarted in his home life.

The years of work, school and play sped by. The village school and the town high school were soon finished. Then the need of earning money was forced upon him. Debt had piled up. The summer after finishing high school, Randall worked side by side with his father and brother Bill, plowing, planting, harvesting. At sixteen he could pitch as much hay as his father, could plow more land in a day, and could lift heavier burdens. He was strong and healthy. But there was that in his cheeks, his eyes, even his hair, that proclaimed him sexually different. Mentally there was a hidden unrest, dimly perceived by his brother Bill, who resented his difference from the common herd and frequently taunted him on his manner of speech or his graceful movements—the antithesis of the boyish ideal.

Randall realized that the farm was not his place. He determined to go to the nearest large city, which happened to be Baltimore, to make his own way at least, and to try to stand as a buffer between his family and the hardships of the world. With Randall, thought was quickly followed by action.

'Twas a dull day in February when Randall left home, left it to return only for such dreary events as family funerals. After the hard summer's work on his father's farm, or about the community, doing whatever he could to earn a dollar here or there, harvesting crops, picking fruits, peddling produce of all kinds to the neighboring towns, his efforts had failed to do more than pay his share of the expenses at home and provide a rather scanty cheap wardrobe. The most important thing was that he had learned to work, to work hard, and to be independent of others. So he was off to Baltimore. Money! The family must have money! He must hasten and earn. He could not bear to see his mother becoming more bent and tired-looking, denied many of the necessities and most of the pleasures of existence, for Randall's affection for his mother colored all of his early life.

The sun was sinking as the train which was to bear Randall away pulled into the station at Kuntzville. Any sentiment he might have called up at this parting was dispelled by the presence of a neighbor's boy, who was going to the nearest small town to take a job, and attached himself to him. They sat together on the train. The boy urged Randall to stop in the town where he was going and to attend a theater and afterwards go to a dance hall, explaining in great detail how "a fellow can pick up a girl." But Randall's mind was on essentials. At the railway junction they parted.

Randall had to wait an hour for the Baltimore express. A dowdy old woman sat beside him, asked "Where you goin'? How long you got to wait?" and finding that the wait was ample started out to sing a saga of the family Ritter. Once Randall interrupted to get a drink of water. On his way to the cooler he observed a well-dressed man looking at him intently. It was but a moment before this dapper gentleman was at his side offering assistance, seeking to engage him in conversation. Randall sensed something wrong about him. Perhaps he was a pickpocket! Indeed, short moments later, this man had slipped his long, slender fingers into one of the front pockets of Randall's pants! Were it not for the tight-fitting manner in which Randall wore his breeches, he would have only realized this gentleman's crime too late, and the damage would have been done.

But this man was no pickpocket. Despite Randall's protests, he drove his nimble hand deeper still into the pants, not stopping until his fingers came upon the substantial carriage at the fork of Randall's legs. Poor Randall was horrified! And to his greater terror, his till-then limp and shriveled member leapt to life, growing and hardening under the caresses of this lecherous pocket-bandit.

"Oh!" said Randall with his high and trembling voice. The well-dressed gentleman grinned lasciviously, but this was too much, and Randall forcibly pulled the man's hand from around the enflamed cock, and tugged it with great strength from the trousers.

"Whoops-my-dear!" mocked the molesting suit. Randall hurried back to the old woman, where he would suffer the rest of her story, as well as the unusual pain in his groin, which he would later learn was the result of pressures unreleased. This first meeting with a strange man was almost prophetic. For the rest of his life he was to meet this kind, wherever and whenever he traveled—always seeking him and the favors he could bestow.

At last the Baltimore express arrived and Randall and his small packages were stowed into half of the seat of a day coach. The car was dimly lighted by gas. Every seat was filled and it seemed to Randall that each occupant was possessed of a distinct and repellent odor. All of them were untidy and most of them more or less dirty. Randall felt a sensitive recoil, which but accentuated the loneliness that was beginning to well up within him.

The train jerked along. Randall alternately waked and dozed and dreamed horrible dreams. At dawn they dragged into the suburbs of Baltimore. There was no snow, but the ground was bare and frozen; the air was smoke-befouled, the landscape dreary; it formed an unpleasant contrast to the clean wintry aspect of his snow-clad Pennsylvania hills. When he alighted from the train he felt a damp chill which was more penetrating than the dry cold of the higher country. He left the railway station and looked about. Already the sun, which at peep of day had promised gay sunshine, was beginning to be obscured by a dull gray fogginess bringing twilight at early morn.

The city was bewildering.

For several blocks Randall could see only warehouses, freight stations and horsedrawn drays going back and forth. A long way up the street, and in the direction which most of the travelers pursued, higher buildings were in evidence. He reasoned that there he would more likely find a stopping place. As he started forward, a policeman who had observed his hesitancy stepped up and asked, "What's botherin' you? Don't you know the town?"

"I would like to find a place to board," he explained in his too-musical singing type of voice.

At once the cop was all kindness and waved his stick in the direction of a spire with the admonition—"Keep that thar spire in sight and right besides it you'll come to the Y. There they c'n tell you of plenty places."

Randall picked up his suitcase and started forward while the cop muttered to himself—"Nice lookin' youngster. Nice lookin' country youngster."

How disagreeable the air was to Randall! Those were the days of horses, and all cities reeked of the odor of equine effluvia. Then too, sanitation in general was not so good as today. In the poorer parts of towns a smell of horse, sewage and garbage prevailed.

Randall picked his way carefully across the street and onward toward the spire that was to be as a beacon to him for the next year. He arrived at the Y, a building of brick with a low, arched doorway placarded "You are welcome." Randall smiled. He entered and approached the nearest desk. The professional welcomer arose and initiated him to the usual overly-ardent handclasp. Questioning, he learned Randall's mission and piloted him to an official for enrollment as a new prospect for the Christian welfare workers of the city to guard and watch over, and, if possible, bring into the fold of the righteous.

The official was a thin, wrinkled, sallow, sandy Scotsman, bent and spectacled, half-bald, a man of about thirty-five, of the type Randall later learned to classify as "born old." He greeted Randall effusively—"We are pleased to welcome you to our midst. You refreshing young country people, you buoyant adolescents who bring an air of health and verve with you! Our cities would decay unless they were replenished and constantly rebuilt by the fair youth of the countryside." Randall listened with amazement. Much useless language was an unfamiliar thing to him. Sandy was very flattering and patted his arm.

11

Then he gave him a list of boarding houses "on the approved list," and spoke gushingly of the hope of seeing him again and the hope that he would avail himself of some of their night classes. Night classes! The very things he had hoped for! There was no fee for finding him a boarding house but there was a fee for filing with the employment agency. He learned too, that there were other employment agencies, and with anxiety also learned that a young person who is without specific training in some one branch of work "is very difficult to place."

Randall found a boarding house, a dark, dingy, ugly house, not too clean, situated on a street which was still respectable but which abutted on the edge of the less reputable part of the city. The landlady, Mrs. Foreman, was a small dark Virginian of lovely manners but of shabby attire. Randall noticed the unaired smell of the house as he was guided to his room on the top floor. The room had one window, and that opened on an airshaft; there was a shade but no curtain. There was a small bed, a washstand with a tarnished-looking bowl and pitcher, and a single chair. He was instructed that when he needed better light, he should turn on the gas. The landlady illustrated. The sickly flicker seemed to add to rather than to dispel the dreariness of the dimly lighted room. The linen, though recently washed, looked gray and unclean. The carpet was spotted and dirty. The room's one virtue was extreme cheapness. The landlady quickly recounted the advantages of this house and its location and added a brief description of the good companions whom Randall would find there; these included "a splendid young man from the Eastern Shore"; a farmer-politician who was a member of the legislature; a wonderful young man who was a gym teacher; Mr. Strong, who was a boss carpenter (and, incidentally, the lady's secret lover, as Randall later learned); and Mr. Shorthorn, who was a motorman. Randall would meet them all at the evening meal. Meantime he could pay a week in advance and make himself at home. "At home!" Already he loathed this place, as he was to loathe all of his city dwellings for the next five years to come—cheap, dirty, depressing. The landlady was all kindness. Truth to tell, generosity had been and always would be her undoing. She gave shelter and food to those who failed to pay; she gave love to those who used it and failed to reciprocate. She looked at Randall with pity and sympathy. So many had she seen come to the city, only to be transformed into hardened, selfish human animals. To Randall's anxious inquiry about prospects for work, the lady assured him—"No one who wants work will fail to find a job." She cited case after case of her young men who were "successes," young men who had come from the country and taken positions in offices and factories and in a brief two or three years become head bookkeepers or chief clerks or foremen of departments—and gone to live elsewhere. She ended, "Yes, indeed, you will find work and success."

It was to be but a brief time before Randall would forget that Mrs. Foreman was a slattern and incompetent and remember only that she was the embodiment of generosity. Later in life, when Mrs. Foreman's bright prophecies of success had in some degree been realized, Randall was to meet the cream of American society and titled Europeans aplenty; but never did he meet one who was always such a perfect exemplification of kindliness and good manners as was this little dark Virginia woman.

At the evening meal, Randall met the assembled paying guests. He listened to them, avid to learn.

Years later he could recall that supper of ham, cabbage, corn pone and talk, much talk, and afterwards a banjo boldly played, and games of euchre before a pungent smelling soft coal fire in an open grate in the "parlor."

At bedtime Randall counted his depleted hoard, which had shrunk to less than ten dollars.

CHAPTER
2

To anyone who has ever been stranded in a strange city, this part of Randall's life would seem familiar. His second day he made the round of the Y, the employment agencies and every shop and office within a certain district of the city. The third day was like unto the second, with the exception that he invaded the blocks adjacent. The fourth and all the days up to the end of two weeks were the same and still there was no work offered to him. Hope steadily sank. His lovely face became drawn and paled from terror. The landlady had not yet asked him for another week's rent. The beginning of the third week was at hand. He had scarcely tasted food, feeling that he had no right to eat that for which he could not pay.

At last it would be his lucky day. At his third call, a coal dealer told him he would give him work. He looked at him closely and seemed to sense that he was in dire need of employment. Randall could never decide whether pity or the desire to take advantage of his necessity induced Mr. Rush to give him a job. But he was thankful for an opportunity to labor, even

15

at the pittance offered him, which allowed a margin of fifty cents each week after all expenses were paid. At once he took his place in the line of laborers. In those days all coal was handled by means of shovels and barrows. But Randall was young and had always worked hard, and muscular effort did not trouble him. He kept pace with Irish Mac and black John and never guessed that they were trying to tax his staying powers. That night he hurried home joyfully to tell the good news of having found something to do. After that it did not seem hard to ask Mrs. Foreman to give him credit for a week. And in the coal yards Randall passed two years, a brief part of that time at hard manual labor, till his office value was discovered.

It was shortly after Randall began working in the coal yards that his first love experience in Baltimore occurred. Queer too, to one knowing Baltimore!

Randall realized that he must do something to procure more remunerative work. He talked it over with his friend the practical Sandy. He advised Randall—"Take up some night study, both for intellectual betterment and to find profitable social contacts."

Randall laughed at the idea of "social contacts." Sandy laid out a business course for him—bookkeeping, shorthand, typing. Before he enrolled for the classes, Sandy suggested that he come up to his rooms, and look over some of the books and give further thought to the matter.

Bashfully, Randall followed Sandy to his room in a tower. He had no feeling of insecurity, but he did experience a deep feeling of embarrassment. Sandy gave him a book and pinched his cheek playfully as he excused himself, ostensibly to go down to his desk, but in reality to see if the coast was clear. Sandy was not bold enough to attempt a quick seduction, but he was so madly enamored that he had worked himself up to a state where he dared, at least, to attempt an awkward kind of lovemaking. By degrees, and by book after book, he arrived at the point where he had the courage to sit down and put a loving arm about Randall's shoulder. He endured!

Physically the man was repulsive to Randall, but at that time of life he was not experienced enough to know what to do. He could only blush as Sandy's hands alternately caressed and squeezed his biceps, drawing his plug-ugly face closer and closer to Randall's own. Though short and stubby, Sandy's fingers were talented with a massage, and they rubbed at the muscles of Randall's shoulder as they crept closer to the more tender areas on his neck.

Before long, this man was placing soft kisses near Randall's left ear, this being the first time he had been kissed by a man in such a way since he had reached adulthood. He was mortified, but his embarrassment was not yet complete. Suddenly, just as Sandy's puckering, fishlike lips had begun to nibble at the corners of Randall's mouth, the gym instructor, wearing rubber-soled shoes, bounded into the room. His only remark was, "Oh! did I interrupt you?" Then tactfully he fled. Randall disengaged himself.

On his way homeward he pondered the incident, recalling the flushed and excited feeling he'd experienced, despite his molester's generally unattractive qualities. He felt regret that he could not reciprocate Sandy's very evident love—the man had been so kind to him. But then he dismissed the sweatiness in his palms and the stirrings in his loins to the basic confusion of the moment, and tried to forget the entire incident.

Shortly afterward, Sandy was transferred and

Randall heard veiled gossip of his suspected misconduct with others.

He took up his night courses with determination. Thus he occasionally met the gym instructor, who always looked on him with a kindly eye, too kindly. Randall could only return his wordy salutations with a bashful nod of his head and a deep blush. He did not read aright the yearning that was in this lecherous man's eyes. But he was becoming more accustomed to city ways and also more accustomed to the admiration and attentions of all types of men.

One Sunday, when visiting a military camp and watching the men march by, one jocose militiaman yelled, "Look at pretty standing there by that tree." At once the whole company took up the refrain—"Pretty! Say there pretty!" And one called out "Oh, you peaches and cream, meet me tonight in the moonlight"; another one—"Oh, you fairy, will that complexion rub off?" "Razzing," he learned to call such conduct later on in life. At that time Randall was so innocent that he did not grasp the evil intent that lay behind their words. But he was beginning to realize that he was different from the majority of his sex.

CHAPTER
3

When the commercial courses were completed, the
Y, ever anxious to advertise, held a "commencement," at which the prize pupils wrote somewhat
familiar business dictation on a blackboard, display-
ing their accomplishments to the assemblage. The
businessmen, the chief contributors to the Y activities, thus could see that their money had been well
spent. Randall, all blushes as usual, and more strikingly beautiful than ever, did his part along with the
others of his classes, and felt a perfect fool while
doing it.

Mr. Rich, a banker, with an eye to pulchritude as
well as to efficiency, asked for an introduction to
Randall and straightaway offered him a position in
his bank, a leading one in Baltimore. Randall
demurred, well knowing that he was not sufficiently
expert to do good work.

Randall was entirely ignorant of all the possibilities that lay behind such an offer. Then he did not
know that his peculiar beauty would offset poor typing; that one glance of his dark and lovely eyes would

give the banker a rejuvenating thrill for which he was willing to pay a high price.

A knowledge of "johns" and to what extent they would put themselves out for a good-looking young man had not yet been vouchsafed to him. At that time, a compliance which he would have shunned, a very little compliance, such as allowing this employer to touch his knee or feel the firmness of his thigh; or that supervisor to lean closely behind him over some nonsense work such that the swelling cock within his trousers might thrill to a rub or two, would be enough to overlook a shortfall. Heaven knew what the surrendering of a manly kiss—or kisses to very private places—would have gained him. For more than a few handsome city boys, fresh out of school and eager to get ahead in business, a good sucking or even the opening of a dirty hole for probing could provide not only an ample income, which they could have gone through the formalities of earning, but also a home, a course at college, or any of the better things which they craved. Randall had not the cupidity to take advantage of all these possibilities; nor had he any thought that such a compliance, even to the complete and utter surrender of his virgin body, would soon be yielded to another in return for nothing but remorse, heartbreak and a sense of shame.

The next evening, Mr. Fisher, the successor to Sandy, called Randall into his office to learn why the business opportunity had been refused. Randall explained to him that his work as a typist was too far below the standard required. This was his opportunity. At once he suggested that Randall do extra copying for him evenings; he would pay him liberally. Randall, ever eager to improve, and also earn, gladly consented.

He began the next night. After he had been working an hour, Mr. Fisher came to his desk and suggested that he come with him to a nearby restaurant for a "bite," and then return to finish his work. Innocently Randall exclaimed, "But I cannot afford to eat at such an expensive place."

"This time you are coming as my guest. Now, don't refuse!" he urged him.

He accepted, his heart thumping wildly from an excitement which he did not understand.

There was music at the restaurant, music which Randall loved. This brought the topic into their conversation and Randall spoke of his own modest achievements as the church organist at Kuntzville, while Mr. Fisher in turn told of his courses in Boston, courses both in music and painting. Randall was awed.

To the haunting strains of a Chopin waltz they left the restaurant. Randall was more pleasantly excited than he had ever been before. The typewriter seemed to bound along magically when he returned to his tasks. By nine o'clock he had finished. Mr. Fisher came to the doorway. He complimented him on the work he had done, then asked pleasantly if he would like to hear him play, and suggested too that they try a duet together. He explained to him, "I have to go out your way to see a sick man and I'll call a cab afterward. You'll arrive home just as soon as if you relied on the cars." He was a man prolific with plausible schemes.

Poor, lonesome Randall! Happiness seemed to beckon. Innocently he thought Mr. Fisher the most considerate man he had ever met. He was considerate enough; considerate of every angle and possible move in a dangerous game. Too, he knew just when to be reassuring and just how far to move. He wanted Randall in his arms, in his own room, behind locked doors, but he sensed that any inopportune suggestion might startle him and drive him beyond his reach. He led him to one of the semi-private parlors. There he waited while Randall went for some books of music and some of his drawings. He returned quickly, and without comment he turned to a difficult Chopin nocturne and played with the ease of the born artist. The man had been properly schooled. His playing was far beyond anything Randall had theretofore heard. He was entranced.

"Why are you not a concert pianist?" he asked, spontaneously paying him a high and deserved compliment.

"I have tried that too," he answered, "but the work with the boys of the Y gives me more satisfaction than concertizing would yield. Besides, I have some means of my own and do not have to submit to all the unpleasantness of travel and the inconveniences of public life."

Then he asked Randall to try a duet. He read quickly enough, but all of his musical work had been at the organ and he was not at ease at the piano. Mr. Fisher was surprised when he learned of the disadvantageous circumstances under which Randall had acquired that knowledge. He begged him to play more. Wily one, he chose Liszt's "Liebestraum" and for an encore Chopin's deliciously sentimental waltz, Opus 70, No. 1.

Then it was time for the ride home. Mr. Fisher directed the driver to go by way of the park. It was moonlight, nearly the full of the moon. Randall was strangely moved by this evening full of unusual delights. Mr. Fisher was not crude. When the cab rolled around a curve he pressed against Randall, who observed that he did not find it unpleasant and breathed a little faster. They neared Randall's door for a final handshake. Randall felt the intensity of Mr. Fisher's grasp, and then he was shocked to find his palms were being lifted to his new friend's lips.

They did not embrace, only Mr. Fisher held Randall's hand tightly as he helped him from the cab. Solicitously he asked if Randall could come the following Saturday night and finish the task he was engaged upon.

That night, before sleep came to him, Randall pictured himself in Mr. Fisher's arms, being kissed on the lips instead of on his hand. So dignified and fatherly was this Mr. Fisher, and yet so handsome and attractive. Randall imagined himself stroking his silvering hair, and kissing his cheeks, his ears, his chin, and again his lips. How Mr. Fisher would care for him, treating him as he would a precocious child, rewarding him for good behavior with gifts and kisses and sweet caresses. But when Randall would be bad, Mr. Fisher would chastise him, calling him naughty words, and demanding that he drop his drawers for a good spanking, that he would learn his lesson. How that spanking would smart, and Randall would cry out his apology to Mr. Fisher with each firm swat upon his red and trembling buttocks.

Randall groaned with pleasure at his revelry. It did not occur to him that he was indeed toying with his own body, caressing and stroking himself as he thought of the punishment Mr. Fisher could dole out to him for bad behavior. He did not perceive that these romantic dreams were manifesting themselves in the lengthening of the nipples upon his blushing chest, or the rapid growth of his thick and reddening cock.

How Randall would please the fatherly Mr. Fisher! He would feed him scrumptious meals, fetch his slippers in the evenings, and kiss him again and again. He would bounce on his great lap and they would laugh until some mistake was made—a glass of milk spilt, the newspaper dampened—and it would be time for a spanking once again!

"Oh dear!" cried Randall as the big, throbbing penis he had been holding so firmly over his navel suddenly seemed to explode upon him. Hot jets of sperm were fired across his belly and almost to his chest, and he nearly swooned with the electrical feel of the ejaculation. It had been so long! But even as he gasped with indulgent pleasure he knew that this was wrong. What had he been dreaming? What kind of thoughts were those? This must never happen again, he stated flatly to himself as he cleaned and then recleaned the semen from his flushed torso.

CHAPTER
4

Saturday, the end of a week filled with back-breaking, muscle-torturing labor!

Monday, under the broiling sun, they had begun the task of unloading a fleet of coal barges, and even the office force had been impressed. Randall held his end up with the most robust of them. All day long, hour after hour, he formed one of a line of laborers trundling barrows of coal. He did his work smilingly, for he knew that at last he was to leave it and advance to a more profitable occupation.

Most lovers of beauty are not good workers or good students; they are commonly of the type that loves to look on. There are a few exceptions, but even these are usually capable only of sustained effort along their chosen lines. Randall could work either mentally or physically, and continue at it, till others would be exhausted. His subsequent career was due to this ability.

But the hopes that sustained him that day had no concern with ambition, but with an all-consuming emotion—love. Love comes to all who are normally constituted (and to most of those, alas! who are abnormally constituted), comes in some guise or other. The one who loves recks not of ambition; when love begins to wane, perhaps then ambition may influence, and degrade.

Randall had not yet tasted real love, unless his childhood adoration of the family physician could have been termed love. Even as a youth, he had gone to sleep of nights thinking of the handsome doctor and wishing he was there to take him up in his arms and kiss him while he looked into his lovely eyes. All day Randall was buoyed up by his dream of being with his trusted friend of the Y, after the day's work was finished.

At last the week's labor was over. Randall hastily bathed beneath a hose, donned his street clothes and hurried to the boarding house he called home. There he completed his toilet, doing everything over and over, that he might be the more presentable.

The street cars seemed to creep. At last the Y was reached and then his courage failed him as he bashfully stammered that he wished to see Mr. Fisher. Soon Fisher sauntered up and greeted him in a casual, disarming manner.

They went to the lovely old Southern Hotel and entered the cool Palm Room. While Mr. Fisher handled the terrifying bill of fare with ease, Randall scanned one after another of the items, all so highly priced. Secretly he was looking for something cheap. Pressed to state a preference he made the usual decision of the socially inexperienced and murmured, "I'll take whatever you do."

So began Randall's first acquaintance with *hors d'oeuvres*, cold chicken soup, lobster *à la reine*, salad with Russian dressing, and Biscotto Tortoni. Even the bread, though still bread, was different and seemed all delicious brown crust.

In the interlude between the musical numbers, they talked of things beautiful. When they had finished, Mr. Fisher suggested that they go to the park and sit under the trees and listen to the orchestra. Moonlight and music! Nothing could have given Randall greater pleasure or made greater appeal to his romantic nature.

On their way to the park their hansom passed an automobile. Mr. Fisher expressed his envy of the possessor of such wealth and trappings. Poor Randall! At that moment he envied no one; he possessed the greatest thing in the world.

Twilight faded quickly. By the time they had reached the park, Randall's sturdy, muscular, hardworking brown hand was grasped in Mr. Fisher's effeminately white, soft, weak paw. Randall thrilled to this touch. Well Mr. Fisher sensed this, and was satisfied—for the time being. Then they left the cab and wandered out into the park beneath the trees. Here they found a secluded bench. The music drifted to them and answered for language. They were half in shadow, and when the full moon passed behind a cloud Fisher wasted not this opportunity but put his lips to Randall's neck in a caress that aroused desires Randall thought well-suppressed. Impulsively Randall threw his arms about him, and for a moment their lips were pressed in a passionate kiss. An ecstatic waltz was being played, just suited to their mood.

Fisher drew Randall away from the bench to the shadow cast by the trunk of a great oak, and with that at his back he sat on the ground with Randall's head cuddled against his chest. The music had ceased. The crowd had left. A gentle breeze sprang up and fanned them. The moon sank from sight and the darkness stole upon them as he kissed Randall's ears and whispered his desires.

Randall seemed sunken in a stupor of acquiescence, an automaton as without volition as a subject of hypnosis. He received Fisher's kisses joyously, and ran his fingers through the elder man's hair just as he had done in his evening fantasies. Only when the moist tip of Fisher's probing tongue invaded his mouth did Randall begin to question his passion, though he still proceeded. Before long, his lips and tongue were pressed hungrily against Fisher's exposed chest, and he thrilled to the feel of the man's warmth, the beat of his heart.

So enraptured was Randall that he failed to hear the jingling of Fisher's belt buckle as it was undone by the old man's pudgy fingers. Soon enough, Randall came face to face with the enraged priapus of his night's date. Though not inordinately large, Fisher's cock seemed almost purple in the darkness. His desire was overwhelming and he was pushing Randall's head downward toward it. Seeing no other choice, flushed and dizzy against the speed of the event, Randall took hold of Fisher's member and gulped it whole down his throat. This strange movement and the repeated suckings which followed seemed to come naturally to Randall, though he did not know why. What only was certain were Fisher's soft cries of ecstasy, effeminate mewings which culminated in a stifled shout as blobs of white semen rose from his balls to be deposited in Randall's eager mouth.

Thus began his degradation. Morally, from then on, he was to go down, down, down. Not till Fisher had completely defiled him and sated his lust did Randall come back to his normal self.

Then he moaned in anguish of spirit at his debasement. Nor could consolation be derived from the realization that he had experienced no pleasure from his compliance, but seemed to have been goaded on by forces which demanded his complete abandonment to another's will. So strong was his instinct!

Randall's emotional reaction was so violent, he frightened even Mr. Fisher, practiced seducer of the young though he was. Randall could only shudder with horror! Now he realized that he could with justice be called the loathsome name which at times and with horror he had heard the coarse workmen use, a name from which he recoiled—a "cocksucker."

"Think what I have done!" he exclaimed over and over again.

Mr. Fisher tried to induce forgetfulness by caresses calculated to arouse a new compliance. But Randall arose and walked madly toward the gates of the park. Though Mr. Fisher caught up with him, all attempts to engage him in conversation were met with the reiterated plaint—"Think what I have done! Think what I have done!"

He did not shed tears, too tortured by conscience even for that. He wished to escape, from Mr. Fisher, and more, from himself. A homeward-bound street car, the last for the night, came into view. Madly he ran from him and scrambled aboard.

It was two o'clock when he reached the end of the car line, and another half hour before he reached his home. He tried the front door. It was locked, and he was too ashamed to ring. Huddled on the doorstep he slept and awoke when the milkman made his rounds.

He walked down the street till he came to a leaky fire hydrant. There he washed his face and hands and freshened his appearance as best he could. At seven he knew the landlady would be up for the early breakfasts. He went back with the morning paper, entered by the back door, went to his room, rumpled the bed to make it appear used, came down and announced that he had decided to go to a special early church service.

Then he stole away to the park and, hidden there, slept till his wearied body was refreshed.

He awoke to realize that he must adjust himself to a new conception of his personality.

CHAPTER
5

A week of dreadful self-realization dragged by. Randall worked with a zeal that should have brought exhaustion and sleep, but did not. His self-respect had been annihilated. In his need to regain his self-esteem, he decided to see Mr. Fisher again and talk with him of the horror he now felt for his conduct. He wondered if Fisher even still respected him. So with the coming of another weekend he went to the Y. There Mr. Fisher received him with unusual warmth, for he had begun to have some fear of the consequences of his most recent seduction, the sudden disappearance of his new sweetheart and the ominous silence. Thus his welcome was perhaps more fervent and his expressions of pleasure at seeing Randall more sincere than they would otherwise have been. Mr. Fisher's manner alleviated to some extent the ache within him, and Randall regained a part of his old-time composure.

As he shook hands he said, "Wait while I finish some work and then we can go to the Southern and dine."

"But I'm not hungry."

"You will be by that time. So wait for me!"

"Very well."

Soon they were at the Southern, and as they talked things over in a none too specific fashion, Mr. Fisher's lightness of manner helped him to forget and seemed to bring back some of the atmosphere of things as they were before "the awful deed." He was almost happy again. The soft lights, the delicate food, the lovely music and the skillful flattery of the subtle Mr. Fisher dulled the thoughts of the act that had so cruelly wounded Randall's soul.

During a lull, when the music stopped, Randall looked up at him and murmured, "Then you do still respect me?"

"Why, of course!" he made quick reply. "That was nothing. I love you more than ever."

"How good of you to say that; you don't know how tortured I have been all the week. I did a terrible thing!"

"You mustn't feel that way about it. You have harmed no one. You are feeling morbid about something that is perfectly natural—to you!"

Then Mr. Fisher proposed a play, a gay hodgepodge which was then classed as a comic opera. He knew that a series of fresh impressions would help to deaden these too sharp reactions.

In the theater, a pressure of knee against knee, and handclasps in the dark, were all that were needed to kindle anew the violent infatuation Randall had conceived for him.

After the play they walked for a while and Mr. Fisher told Randall of the acting he had seen in New York, of the operatic singers he had heard, and of the symphony concerts, at one of which he had substituted as pianist. Cleverly he piloted him by a roundabout way to the vicinity of the Y and then he abruptly suggested that Randall come up to his room, adding, "There we can talk over all the things about which we feel so bad."

By that time Randall had forgotten to feel bad. For the moment, at least, he was perfectly happy. The Y was dark and Mr. Fisher let himself in with his latch-key. He guided Randall by the hand, and carefully they tiptoed up the stairway to his den. Then he adjusted the windows and curtains and turned on a rose-colored light, which put them in shadow but illuminated the room sufficiently—for his purpose. Mr. Fisher led Randall to a great old-fashioned comfortable sofa, and with his arms about Randall's waist and his lips kissing that tantalizing kiss on the nape of Randall's neck, he drew him down once again.

He spoke in a tender tone of voice—"Now tell me just why you feel so bad. You know I love you, don't you? And you love me? And after all, love is the only thing in the world that matters. You don't feel so bad now, do you? Aren't you happy with me?"

And Randall did feel everything he suggested. Eager to coincide with his opinions and just as giddy as when he first felt love for this sweet man.

With his skill, and Randall's hypersuggestible state, the culmination could only be as before, though this time, Randall attacked his subject with an even more passionate fervor. The buttons on Fisher's shirt were all but torn away in Randall's effort to once again lick and bite the flesh of his breast. Fisher's soft moans and firm caresses only furthered him to his goals, and soon Fisher's pants were about his ankles, and his undershorts were pulled in an unseemly manner about his thighs.

Falling to his knees before the quivering Fisher, Randall paused for a mere instant to study the enflamed cock before him. The light was better in these quarters than it had been in the park that time, and he was curious. Even as Fisher begged for him to continue, he gazed at the erect penis and pulled at it until the foreskin had come up over the shiny red mushroom of a head. Randall was fascinated. How could it be—he thought wildly to himself—that so many were attracted to a sex which did not possess between their legs one of these grand, fleshy devices? Then he was upon Fisher's cock as a starving dog to a bone.

Again Fisher gasped, looking down upon this angel darling nursing his cock to a raging stand. It seemed Randall was possessed; devouring then pulling out this dripping erection, licking the head with the tip of his tongue as would an expert in the field. Randall then took Fisher's cock in hand and began to slide it down and up with the lubricant of so much saliva, much as he had done to himself some nights ago. In doing this, he made Fisher come in glorious jets, and hot sperm landed with a splash over his chest and belly before Randall took the last of it into his own mouth.

Then it was over. An almost automatic compliance with Fisher's desires was then quickly succeeded by a return of normal self-assertion, in which Randall again felt his debasement and defilement. It is always thus with people who have been highly idealistic. Even marriages are sometimes shattered by the too sensitive attitude of one of the partners. Curiously, he did not blame Fisher then; not till much later.

With horror Randall regarded himself in a great mirror on the opposite wall and burst out, "Oh, I am going away. I am going away where this can never happen again. I do not know why I do this. I must not do it. I must not!"

He outlined a plan for going to New York—New York, for reformation!

Fisher, perhaps a little conscience-stricken, tried to give him good advice. He even suggested introductions to people in New York, people who might be of value to him.

Randall rose suddenly and held out his hand to bid him a stiff, formal goodbye. Mr. Fisher, probably thinking it appropriate to carry out the role of devoted lover, drew him close and give him a farewell kiss, but now he avoided Randall's lips—he gave him only a cold pressure to his brow.

Randall left him, fired by determination to rid himself of a loathsome practice. He had the feeling that sensitive "sinners" often experience, that his character was stamped upon his face.

Then, he began to attempt to cultivate a new outward self.

CHAPTER
6

Sunday morning Randall decided to attend the church to which the banker, Mr. Rich, belonged, and to meet him after the service.

Randall was in the vestibule as he came out, and Mr. Rich greeted him more than cordially and presented him to his wife and daughter, both of whom were impressed by Randall's good looks. Later they made flattering comments about "the handsome Yankee." Randall asked permission to call on Mr. Rich at his bank the next day, and the happy man, thinking that at last he was to have a loaf, a delicious loaf, float back on the waters of philanthropy, gladly assented.

Randall lingered to hear the organ. It soothed him, as it always had.

Monday dawned hot, bright and clear, as so many Baltimore summer days do. Randall donned his best clothes and arrived rather late at the coal yards. The "boss" was late too, and all of the workmen were standing about, waiting for orders. Briefly Randall told them that he intended to leave Baltimore and go to New York. Irish Mac burst forth—"So that's what's eatin' ye? I thought all that stoddyin' was doin' somethin' in yer brain!"

And all, with one quip or another, which they deemed killing wit, told him they knew he had been planning something new. In their rough way they had been kind. Though it was a relief to escape from the phase of life they represented, still he felt a twinge of sorrow at leaving even such friends, and an unaccustomed emotion crept into his voice as he bade them farewell.

What was late for these laborers was early for the banking house, and Randall arrived there before the portly, red-faced, reddish-haired, successful Mr. Rich.

There was a marked stir, an exaggerated attempt at activity when Mr. Rich arrived. Because Randall was so anxious to please him and gave such unstinted evidence of it, the junior officers and clerks regarded with wonder this young person who could work such a transformation in the usually flinty old gold-worshiper.

Almost with menial servility, Mr. Rich ushered Randall into his private office. He seated him in a chair, closed the door and then with one hand on his shoulder and the other on his knee and with the look of a cannibal on his face, gloatingly asked, "So you have come to take the position I offered?"

Randall read that look instantly and replied, "It is imperative that I go to New York. I came to see if you could give me some introductions. When I arrive there I must find work without delay."

"But you are not leaving today?" grieved the banker. "Can't I prevail upon you to accept a position here?"

"No, not in Baltimore."

"Then do promise to visit us at our home for a few days before you go," he urged.

Randall thought quickly. He realized that if he was to have Mr. Rich's influence he must accept his invitation and favor him with his society, the luxury for which he hungered. With Mr. Rich he felt safe, knowing well that he could never be induced to yield to him, and that he could not be overpowered through the manipulation of his emotions. Mr. Rich was a different man. Randall felt no attraction for him. Too, he was vaguely aware that he could "wind him about his finger," so to speak, though he had no desire to do so. He did not feel curiosity as to just how far he would dare to go. He did not follow that thought far, for he knew that no matter what Mr. Rich's goal was, it was not his too. So he accepted.

And while Rich was still tasting the joy of having Randall with him, he deferred not, and soon possessed himself of a sheaf of letters of introduction to give this beautiful young man, letters which any high financier might have been glad to have.

Thus, Randall became a guest for three days in the home of a member of Baltimore's so-called "aristocracy," and drove and rode with the unsuspecting wife and daughter. The old banker played his part with surprising self-repression, considering the ardor of his desires. He had lived long, and perhaps had become used to being thwarted. One does! Then too, he had no intention of jeopardizing his chances of success by too hasty an avowal of his purposes, and he could not read this cool, apparently self-possessed young person who appeared never to have been awakened sexually.

His usual plan was first to kindle a firm friendship, and when sufficient obligations had been imposed, to force friendship a step further. He spoke of meeting Randall in New York. Randall assured him, "That would be nice."

There was no danger of this friendship getting out of bounds. For three days Randall kept Mr. Rich talking of affairs of commerce, learning what he could that might be of service in a business way. And Rich, with such a willing auditor, enjoyed to the utmost expending his ideas. Randall had not yet learned that the most subtle flattery one can give is to listen intelligently. The old man was happy; he was being understood; he was being looked up to for his wisdom. The more flattered he felt, the more maddening became his infatuation; even his wife and daughter laughingly commented on his crush.

The daughter, Lola, with that frankness which is so often a part of the charm of young Southern people, and also with that sagacity which is a part of the endowment of the socially successful, endeavored to interpret Randall.

The last evening of the visit, after Randall had been playing the pipe organ for them for an hour, Miss Rich urged them to go out on the balcony and enjoy the cool breeze. She looked at Randall earnestly, then spoke frankly. "Do you know, Randall, I must declare, you are the most wonderfully attractive young man. There is even something thrilling about your voice. I do not believe you realize fully how fascinating you are, and it is not only because you have good looks but because of some quality in you which I cannot define; Mother feels it and so do I, and you have simply infatuated dear old Father. With it all, I believe you do not know yourself; not yet. Some day you will awaken and if you do not become self-conscious, you will have your own way with everyone."

Randall slowly raised his eyes, sat erect, drew a deep breath, scarcely compressed his upper teeth against lower lip, then let escape a sigh. Slowly he relaxed, leaned back in his chair, gazed afar off, and simply remarked in a tragic voice—"I wonder!"

Never did he forget that remark, "You do not know yourself." It served to increase his desire to understand this new self which seemed to be developing with maturity. He felt a certain shyness and to hide it went back to the organ and played a largo, a *Nachtstück* and even part of a sonata which lent itself to organ. Randall had the gift of feeling music and making others feel it too. The too-French strain often shows itself that way. At Mr. Rich's request he ended with a medley of "old-timey" songs, then quietly wandered back to the balcony as if in a dream. Something new, a half-vision, had come to him.

The next morning the *adieux* were said. Mr. Rich himself offered to drive Randall down to the depot. He chose a roundabout way through the ever fateful park, and stopped the horses where the view was best. He told Randall how much he had enjoyed his sojourn with them and added, "You were wonderful last night. But then you are always wonderful. It is a part of you to be that way." His emotion overcoming him completely, he threw his free arm about Randall and drew him close in a fierce embrace. Over and over he repeated, "You don't know how I love you! You don't know how I love you! I'd do anything for you." And when Randall remained calm he added, "Oh, make me happy, make me happy for just a little while. Don't go away. Stay here with me! I've loved you ever since the first time I saw you. I've never loved like that before."

Randall had read him aright but he had expected no such sudden outburst in broad daylight in a public park. He did feel sorry for the poor old man. His own suffering had been so great 'twas easy to extend pity to him and for the time being, forget that what he called love was nothing but mad lust. He petted Rich's flabby, fat hand and assured him that he liked him very much; that he would never forget him; that he would write often and would surely come to see him again, and urged him to visit in New York at any time. Randall kept his word later, but Mr. Rich never bothered to go all the way to New York to visit him. When Randall again went to Baltimore he found Mr. Rich had consoled himself with someone more amenable and also much more convenient.

The rest of the journey to the train continued with more decorum. Mr. Rich insisted on presenting him with a ticket to New York and a seat in the Pullman. When Randall hesitated to put himself under what he felt to be a financial obligation, Rich waved his objections aside. "But you have given us your society, your music and the inspiration of your presence."

Not to prolong the embarrassing situation, he accepted without further demur. It was a relief when the train pulled out of the station and he had left Mr. Rich forever.

Randall turned this episode over in his mind. Was he always to be pursued by some man? Then the only hope of escape was the cultivation of the utmost reserve. Quite unconsciously he was laying the foundation for one of the greatest charms of any person. He suppressed himself; a faint smile took the place of laughter, and thus he forever escaped that prevalent bane, the society grin.

CHAPTER
7

No sooner was the train well in motion than a rather oldish, prosperous looking, somewhat overfed man seated himself near Randall and tried to engage him in conversation.

How quickly is youthful beauty observed by the hungry wolves! The man made Randall uneasy. He did not wish to be abrupt or rude; that was not a part of his nature. He did sincerely wish to be rid of the individual. The plump man detected his lack of experience and hoped evidently by persistence to break down his polite, but nonetheless determined, resistance to his advances.

Randall excused himself and went to the washroom to brush his teeth. No sooner had he come back to his seat than did the man return to the attack. Four drinks of water, two brushings of teeth and constant unnecessary attentions to his toilet still failed to dislodge this unwelcome suitor. Randall's voice made him conspicuous. Even the porter had observed him, and watched him to see what would happen. When Randall next went to the washroom, the porter suggested that perhaps he would find it agreeable to visit the observation platform. This suggestion was gratefully followed.

There was but one empty place on this platform, and in going to the seat, Randall found it necessary to pass others, excusing himself several times along the way.

When loose males are gathered together their tendency is to dwell on anything even remotely feminine which presents itself. Randall's voice was a challenge. He had not yet learned to control it; in fact he never did succeed in controlling it absolutely. It was quite a revealing voice!

The men became boisterously offensive, all but one, a traveling salesman who suggested that the sun was hot and that a chair inside might be more comfortable. Then looking at his watch he suggested luncheon. Randall accepted the invitation, anxious to escape the pointed remarks of the other men. His sharp ears did not miss the comments that followed his departure—"Unless I miss my guess, that's one of them!"—"Too good to be true!"—"How would you like to meet that in the dark!"—"My Gawd, Percy, did you notice that voice!"—"Easy to pick up too!"

In the dining car the salesman exchanged cards with Randall; his read, "Henri Voyeur, Ladies' Hats." The name was as French as Randall's own. Mr. Voyeur was to prove a valued acquaintance. He confided, almost apologetically, to Randall that he had tried various lines of trade but that ladies' hats seemed to be the one for which he was fitted.

"Oh, well," he said, "one must be satisfied and do that for which one is best fitted, no matter what that may be."

Then he told him in a very low voice—"I understood you even before you had come out on the platform—your gait! You are inexperienced. You do not yet understand yourself! But you'll have to learn and you may as well begin at once. You say you are going to New York. That city will crush you unless you master it, and a thorough knowledge of life is the only thing that will give you the upper hand. You must learn to be quick at repartee. A wise one would have made those men feel ridiculous."

Then he dashed into a description of phases of the night life of New York, just as wild then as now, in some respects wilder, and much more open, wide open. "Reform" had not yet struck the town. He described the old Hay Market, which might have lived up to its name in a distant past, but which at that time was a market where the merchants were hot young men and the merchandise somewhat tarnished women.

Randall said, "That doesn't interest me."

"I didn't think it would, but I wished to feel you out, to be sure. I think I know just what pleasures would appeal to you in New York."

"Pleasures? I am not going to New York to seek pleasures. I'm going to seek work and opportunity."

"You'll find plenty of both, and sometimes when you are tired of work you'll seek pleasure, the same as the rest of us. In New York it is sometimes even possible to combine work and pleasure." He laughed mischievously. "Better let me wise you up. I'm not after you, but others will be. Not my type! Don't be afraid of me. All I want is companionship. You'll need a straight friend; you'll need plenty of friends. Better let me help you out. I remember the mistakes I made when I first came to town. No use you making them too. I understand you completely. Your voice tells me everything."

"My voice? Again my voice!"

"Yes, your voice: too soft; too genteel; too caress-ing. There's not a man back there who's not wise to you. Don't be afraid to open up to me. I look on you as a brother."

Randall shuddered. Were his recent experiences as an open book to others?

There are some natures marked for definite expe-riences, marked clearly and absolutely. His was one of these peculiar personalities!

As they entered Jersey City, they finished their long, drawn-out luncheon. Before they parted Randall had promised to let Voyeur hear from him again.

So Randall entered the great city, with the doors of one type of society open to him and with precious letters of introduction to the men of the financial center.

CHAPTER

8

Settled in a boarding house in the old twenties of New York, Randall was quickly swallowed up by the town. Easily he found a position as stenographer to a bank president, Mr. Rule, a man who appreciated one who could take dictation rapidly and accurately and spell correctly without the aid of a dictionary or prompting from the valued and highly paid other clerks who had their own duties to perform. Also Randall had the ability to relieve him of practically all letter writing, once he had absorbed his style. As time went on the banker found Randall invaluable and later on took him along again and again on his summer trips to Europe.

Randall was quickly classified at the bank as a queer sort; and the other clerks let it go at that. His employer took him for granted. He did not interest him any more than any other efficient clerk. The Baltimore banker's letters vouched for him. That was enough. Outside of paying the bills of his society wife and daughter, the banker was interested in a member of the Floradora Sextette. Randall was a cog in his machine.

At the boarding house he was popular because he could now afford to be generous with money, and further because he was possessed of an innate desire to please and make others happy. People circumstanced much like himself, his neighbors were not overcritical of others. Most of them were poor. Their entertainment consisted of walks along Fifth Avenue, watching their "betters"; conversation in the boarding house parlor; innocent games of cards; and an occasional evening when some visitor would drop in who could play and sing.

A man named Bryant occupied what the landlady styled "the back parlor room." His formal education had been obtained at one of those newer denominational Western colleges, St. Something-or-Other's. 'Twas not of good quality, nor of much depth. Superficially he could pass for a gentleman.

Through Randall's good offices a clerkship had been found for his brother Bill in the bank where he was employed.

Bill and Bryant soon became devoted friends. They were entirely congenial. Bill seemed to hark back to his Irish ancestry; had little ambition for aught but pleasure; would accept only what came easily; drank too much; saved nothing. As a family asset his value had been nil, whereas generous Randall was ever sending money and gifts home. Always Bill was borrowing small sums of money from Randall which he never repaid and for which Randall could never get up the courage to ask him. His overdrinking and his improvidence had worried both Randall and their mother. Randall had not yet learned that this type of man sometimes marries, changes, settles down to business and becomes one of "the backbone of the country," as intolerant as any of the other members of a well regulated "Christian" community. He disapproved entirely of Bill's lack of thought for the family welfare. He did not realize yet that Bill as strongly disapproved of *him*, seeming to sense in him the latent sexual aberrations which would shame Bill before his male companions. Already he was objecting to Randall's voice, constantly admonishing him not to talk, or to change his voice and talk like other people. Randall did talk like other people, but not the other people Bill meant.

Bill approved entirely of Bryant, because Bryant appeared to have a wide knowledge of worldly affairs. For the same reason he approved of Fred, one of the other clerks at the bank, a somewhat older man who had made the mistake of marrying one of the spoiled virgins of his small Connecticut town. Bill, Bryant and Fred, along with Fred's somewhat dissolute wife and her bosom friend, a kept woman, made wild parties about town. Randall did not dissipate—then. Dissipation interfered with ambitions, and his ambitions, though difficult of fulfillment, were by no means petty.

One Saturday night, wishing to rouse Randall out of his serious mood, and, too, desiring his financial contributions to the entertainment, Bill insisted that he accompany them on a slumming tour. Finally he consented. He anticipated no delight in the thing; drinking was nauseous to him. But downtown and the great East Side were being featured in the papers and slumming parties were then beginning to be the vogue; he succumbed to the urgings of the party. The tour embraced an old place of disrepute on MacDougal Street where Fred's wife seemed quite at home and called various of the males "Lily," and "Maude" and "Fanny," all of which seemed to titillate most of the party. To Randall it seemed common and low. The place was dirty and the air stifling. He was glad when Fred suggested that they go on down to Chinatown. Here they ate Sino-American messes and then went to a "hop-joint"; such dives were fairly open then. Fred and his wife smoked opium freely, and Bryant and Bill even took a few puffs "just to see what it was like." Randall refused and longed to leave the place and get the trip over with. But then they had to see East Broadway and the Jews overflowing the sidewalks, and after that Fred announced what was to be the crowning event of the evening, a visit to a "fairy joint" in Christie Street.

They came to what was apparently an ordinary saloon, but instead of entering the main door they stepped through a side door and followed a long narrow hall which finally gave on a brilliantly lighted back room. On the face of it, the place appeared orderly. The usual beer was served, with a soft drink for Randall, and then Fred's wife pointed out to them the various characters of the place. There were men and boys who called themselves "Kitty," or "Minnie" or "Maude" (a favorite name). By way of being sparkling they indulged in imitation spats with each other, exchanging all the vile epithets of the gutter and brothel. Fred's wife giggled, and though she said, "Ain't they awful?" she was delighted.

At an adjoining table sat a handsome dark-eyed refined-looking young Jew. His seat almost touched Randall's, and when a waiter, to make more room, pushed the table back a few inches further, the young man's chair was tilted and he fell heavily against Randall. There was a moment of confusion, and the beautiful stranger's hands somehow came into Randall's lap. A moment of connection in their gazes shot fire to Randall's loins, and an immediate erection became noticeable to them both.

The stranger smiled and apologized, and that

paved the way for a few courteous and general remarks. Randall was conscious of an aesthetic attraction the man had for him. When he excused himself and went elsewhere, Randall remarked, "What an unusual man to be in such surroundings. He really seems to be a gentleman."

Fred's wife giggled at this "good one" as he informed Randall that the young man was in fact one of the queers, the gays, the man-lovers who frequented this lurid place. From that time onward Randall was discreetly silent. He was glad when the party broke up; glad to leave the half-besotted and half-doped Fred and his wife.

Randall was beginning to find Bill unsettling. So one fine day he announced his intention of living alone, that he might study in peace. Bill, despite his somewhat irregular social life, was doing well at the bank. Randall had done all he could for him. Bill needed him no longer.

Up near one of the colleges, Randall found a tiny room. He enrolled for all of the evening courses they would permit him to carry. Now he was joyously happy. Every spare moment was filled with useful endeavor. Thus the time sped.

CHAPTER
9

Randall was progressing. The piano lessons he took through the university night school helped him improve his technique. The language courses brought promotion at the bank also. Then too, he was learning of favorable investments. His savings were beginning to amount to a substantial sum.

And because of his position others were beginning to ask his advice about investments, seeking a "tip" about one stock or another. He pondered this. His earliest training at the bank had taught him not to disseminate information. Finally illumination came. Patiently he cultivated the acquaintance of the small local tradesmen. They wished to make money rapidly. So did he, and he had the opportunities but not the capital. Finally, he evolved a practical, safe and honest plan. Whenever he saw an occasion for a quick safe turnover, he would approach one of the tip seekers, borrow the five hundred or thousand dollars which the man had saved to gamble with, exchange simple contractual notes, and promise to share the profits of the investment with him. The details he kept to himself. In due time, six weeks, a month, or even a shorter period, he repaid the loan and gave the lender the interest and a fair share of the profits. It was not long before he was able to control a fair amount of capital. He never traded on margin. It was all safe, sure.

Randall was generous. Soon he was able to do all and more than he had planned for his mother and the family, and was looking forward to the gratification of his own ambitions.

He had almost forgotten his Baltimore episode. When he did recall it, he no longer thought with love but with contempt of the man who had humiliated him; the man who instead of seeking the best within him had sought only to debase him. There is a fundamental difference between true love and passion. The one looks deeply into the soul of the beloved, tries to read aright and aids in the unfolding of the best within that person; the other seeks only to lead on to physical sensation and emotional enslavement. But try as we will to forget that we are sexual beings first and other things afterwards, we usually end only in deceiving ourselves, and the more deeply we are deceived the more in danger are we of suffering disastrous consequences. Randall had ceased to acknowledge sex. He failed to realize that it was as much the sexual candor of the orchestra leader as the beauty of the music which attracted him to certain concerts; also he failed to realize that a man's shoulders, his legs encased in puttees, a certain dark Vandyke beard, were all powerful fetishes to him. He was frank in his outspoken admiration of the musician's conducting, of the mounted policeman's appearance astride a horse, of the masculine beauty of the one or two physicians whom he occasionally met in society. He thought "studying types" in public conveyances was an innocent pastime; its disguised sexuality was well hidden from him.

He again changed his abode and went to live at a boarding house where his piano teacher lived. Here he also met other musicians and people either studying or interested in music. It was long since he had seen his brother Bill, who had been transferred to an uptown branch of the bank.

A students' concert was scheduled. Randall was to play, his first appearance in the role of pianist. He thought to surprise Bill, as he was always proud of anything that tended to exhibit the family in a favorable light.

Randall invited him to dine at the boarding house and attend the concert. He came. He gave short answers to Randall's queries and to everyone else; he was churlish. After the concert, when pressed for an opinion, he expressed himself forcefully and to the point: "The music was fine, but these men are a bunch of sissies. Such lisping I've never heard before, and you talk like them. Do you like such people? God, sometimes I wonder whether you are going to be one of them! How can you stand that old bearded lady [referring to a physician who was also a guest that evening]? Get educated, but get out of this. And change that damned voice of yours; it's getting worse instead of better. I heard some of the boys down at the bank telling about the bunch you hang out with."

Randall was crushed. His sexual transgression had not endowed him with the ability to read people and thus sift the worthy from the unworthy. Besides, he could not change himself; he could not see himself. His only defense was—"Well, Bill, God made us all. Blame Him!"

Afterwards he thought, "Can Bill be right?" He reviewed his list of acquaintances. None of them meant much to him. He determined gradually to withdraw from them and to cultivate new, circumspect acquaintances. Instead of drifting socially he would apply the same careful tactics that he used in his business life.

So Randall decided to call on Henri Voyeur and ask his advice. Voyeur told him briefly, "Be yourself and to hell with the rest of them! You are as your were born. You will never change. You may deceive others—quite unlikely; you may even deceive yourself—very likely; but innately you will be the same."

Randall's dearth of social life outside of the office turned him to the theater for diversion. There, quite unconsciously he lived the part of the heroine and in the actress identified himself as the one held in the passionate embrace of the stage lover. He was having many, many love affairs; true, all vicariously, but through them he was perhaps laying the foundation for the promiscuity he was later to manifest.

The process of acquiring a desirable social position in New York then was a difficult and also a painful one. Now, thanks to night clubs, dances and more or less open doors at country clubs, and commingling at various affairs, it is easy. Then there was one main channel, church work and its associated charities.

At an early age, even before his misfortune in Baltimore, Randall had ceased to accept the validity of his mother religion, relinquishing one idea after another as childish and much on a par with the fables regarding Santa Claus; this had led in turn to a critical examination of some of the offshoots of the faith. Electing to take religion as one of his college courses, he had obtained a wide knowledge of the teachings of the East. Practically all began with assumptions of infallibility, which, though unproven, the disciples then proceeded to teach as basic facts. Their leaders, he found, ignored the selfish reasons which led them on and caused them to set aside reason and endeavor to inculcate blind faith. He had no faith. He could see no reason to have faith. He was happier without it. Nothing was explained ultimately; why accept puny, childish explanations? Certainly this attitude gave him great mental freedom and his logical-mindedness probably saved him in the end from the frightful and hopeless remorse from which so many of his kind forever suffer, and which even he underwent for a time. Randall then turned to some of the newer manifestations of religious faith, wondering if there was any comforting knowledge they could give him. He listened to long harangues on Spiritualism, Theosophy, New Thought, Christian Science, and Hindu philosophy. What was good and useful in them he found reduced to two very simple practices—self-control and auto-suggestion—the rest was harmful. They did not teach him a tithe of the wisdom he found in a study of psychology.

Mentally Randall was fearless and not afflicted with the cowardice which obsesses the great majority of human beings and causes them to fear theological conclusions, always devastating to the previous childish ideas with which the thought of the whole race is cluttered. The teachers of new religions he found to be wholly selfish and their followers of the suggestible, emotional type. The combination was less satisfying than the organized and regulated practices of the old religious bodies.

It is well recognized that religious experience and sex are closely interwoven. The wild outcroppings which manifest themselves at intervals in some of the newly inspired cults but serve to bring out this feature of religion more clearly.

It is probable that Randall was unconsciously seeking sexual experience and that his desires disguised themselves as yearnings after truth.

Deliberately setting aside his lack of faith he again took up attendance at the church of his childhood. He accepted no part of the tenets, but he reveled in the pageantry and the music. He laughingly told one of his acquaintances of a Sunday morning that he was on his way to a performance of grand opera.

"In the morning? On a Sunday? What grand opera?" the man asked.

"High Mass at St. M's," answered Randall. Though superstitions no longer bound him, things aesthetic had come to exercise a greater and greater sway over his emotions.

He affiliated himself with some of the church's charity workers. It did him good to be of service to others; also he met many congenial souls. To one of these, Theodore Wemys Cocke, a young Englishman, he was strangely drawn. The man, who was somewhat older than Randall, had left home to seek opportunities in the less fettered America, where one can embrace trade, or anything except openly recognized fraud, and be highly respected for any financial success. Quite unaccountably to Randall, but not to the Englishman, he found himself on some committee or other with him.

Mr. Cocke's ideas were quite as liberal as his own, but the social call had always kept him from making any out and out break with the church.

There was the usual groping after topics of mutual interest. Their thoughts ran along much the same lines. Perhaps Randall's mind led him more toward an interest in abstract science, while Mr. Cocke fancied applied science. Both loved art, or rather objects of art, both loved music, both loved the theater. So together they visited all of the good things with which New York abounds. Mr. Cocke, except for the Englishman's manners and accent, was anything but British; in fact he was more of the French type, dark, intense, quick in his decisions and actions. His suavity was delightful; his *savoir faire* was phenomenal. He had traveled extensively and had the ability to relive and retell and make others share his abundant experiences.

Randall began to feel that all of his scant leisure was ill-spent unless he and Teddy were together. They called each other up on the phone at luncheon time and made appointments; they telephoned at five, and later dined together if possible. Randall did not acknowledge that this was love, but spoke openly and much of their friendship. Love, and its peculiar manifestations in Baltimore, had meant so much disillusionment, that he refused to admit that love could touch him again. Teddy had been born promiscuous-minded; he had the faculty of being in love with many at the same time, an accomplishment which if not natural, can be acquired in time. To him love was an amusement. Perhaps it should be so for many people. His affair with Randall was but one of three he was developing at the same time. Even to himself he admitted that he loved Randall most. Despite the fact that he was showing marked and rather expensive attention to a youthful member of an English theatrical company, he sought Randall whenever possible and applied himself only enough in the other quarters to keep interest alive. He found Randall delightfully economical and valued to the full his ability to get the utmost for the minimum of expenditure. With this as excuse, he changed his place of residence to Randall's boarding house. Perhaps he was becoming impatient and wished to hurry to the climax and then pass on to yet untasted, but imagined, other joys.

At last Randall awakened to the fact that he was in love. He had been disillusioned and defiled before, but past experience should serve as a warning. With youthful idealism he vowed to keep this love on the highest planes of purity and not suffer it to be dragged down by lust. Often he would say to himself, "Love is the greatest thing in the world." So it is. Perhaps even chemistry is love, or perhaps it is the other way about.

It was upon an early fall day, one of those crisp, sunny, cheerful days when New York seems to blossom in anticipation of the greater winter season; a time when all are freshly costumed; when the business houses flaunt anew all their temptations; when there are new plays in town, new faces invading old haunts; when the town in every way seems to take on added life.

Randall's employment had been transferred to the private home of the president of the bank. His duties had become progressively fewer and more important. His time was almost his own during the briefer business hours. He was even able to arrange a few day courses at the university, some early and some after business hours. With greater leisure he even found more time to give to love. He found himself thinking of Teddy between his tasks, planning everything with reference to him; Teddy wanted to see certain shows, he provided the tickets for the following Saturday; Teddy liked him best in dark blue, he bought blue; Teddy did not care for this and did not care for that; Teddy! Teddy! Teddy!

Teddy had invented a new type of automobile. He

was anxious to try it. Also, this day, he was anxious to get Randall out into the secluded romantic country where he could feel more free with him. In the city there was the ever-present crowd, at the theater, at the restaurant, on the street, anywhere. Even the halls of their boarding house were constantly being invaded and there was no opportunity to caress at ease. He knew intuitively that Randall would have to be won unsuspectingly—taken unawares.

So this lovely fall day he planned to try out his automobile and also to try out Randall. He suggested a run up the Hudson. The novelty of the thing was appealing. Randall was tingling with excitement, the thrill of his new love, the sense of novelty, the stimulation of the wonderful fall day. Life seemed glorious. He would love Teddy always and Teddy would love him and that would be all there was to it, love, love, love—purest love!

They turned from Thirtieth Street onto Fifth Avenue. Randall waved gayly to several acquaintances. Any automobile was a novelty then. He felt a pleasant sense of importance in being different from the crowd, an admired and envied something different. They passed through the park, over to the Drive and up the Hudson where the foliage was all brilliant reds, yellows, oranges and purples. Teddy's car was a success. 'Twas a glorious ride, of wonderful distance—for those days! They were far out in the country and finally arrived at an eminence where the view of the Hudson was superb. Here Teddy halted. They alighted to enjoy the scene and also to have a picnic supper.

The dead, dry grass, sunned all day, was delightfully warm. They sat down, even as the sun was beginning to redden the sky. They ate their sandwiches lingeringly and quietly. Words seemed unnecessary.

Randall's face, as he gazed on the beauty about him, wore a look of exaltation. The sunlight on his short, curly hair turned it to reddish gold. A faint happy smile played about his lips.

Teddy too was affected by the scene. Also, he was experiencing the happiness which comes from satisfied achievement. He was stirred by Randall's youthful beauty as never before. Also, he had become increasingly aware of Randall's excellence. For the time being he thought himself capable and eager to renounce all other loves for the sweetness of this, the most entrancing affair of his life. There are times when sex dominates completely. Such a time had arrived!

As the sun sank, a chill wind sprang up. Teddy went to the car for robes, one to sit on, the other to wrap about Randall. As he enveloped his companion's slender body with the robes, he closed his arms about him, and meeting no resistance gave him a long lingering kiss.

"Oh, Teddy, Teddy, how I love you!" he whispered, though there was no one to hear had he declaimed it aloud. Randall almost swooned in his arms.

Teddy, to do him justice, had never been so much in love as at this moment. He kissed Randall over and over again and they made repeated avowals of their love, just as all lovers do.

The sun set in a glorious burst of flame that encompassed the whole horizon. They were alone; the world, the entire world, seemed theirs. As the sun disappeared from sight, the moon came up casting its dark blue shadows. Teddy pleaded. The almost hypnotic compliance invaded Randall. He felt no emotion other than the compulsion to do Teddy's bidding.

Before long, the two of them were nude to the world, and the cool evening air whispered across their bodies. Teddy was younger and more handsome than Mr. Fisher had been. Though pale and somewhat soft about the edges, Teddy was better fleshed, and Randall thrilled to the musculature of his upper arms and shoulders. Then they were upon each other.

The feeling of embracing a naked man in the wide open astonished Randall and he became overwhelmed with emotion. They wrestled about passionately, kissing one another in the grass, stroking and petting one another as their cocks grew large and stiff between their bellies.

"Dear Randy, I want to taste you," murmured Teddy. "Let me please you, I beg you."

"Oh Teddy!" cried Randall. "I am yours to do with as you like."

They turned in upon each other at once; their heads moved into the lower regions of one another's nudity. Randall examined Teddy's thick-headed cock only briefly before taking it into his mouth for a delicious sucking. But he was taken completely by surprise with Teddy's simultaneous reciprocation. The feeling of Teddy's lips wetly creeping over his cock nearly made Randall swoon, and for a moment, he lost hold of the member he had been nursing himself. So shocking was this pleasure that Randall cried out despite his efforts to stifle himself, and he could only but continue to rub Teddy's engorged penis with the palm of his hand. In seconds Randall was brought to a fiery climax, and he released a pitched scream as great jets of come exploded from his throbbing erection. Instinctively, Randall grabbed and pulled at Teddy's cock even as he still convulsed with passion, and, crying out with sheer joy, Teddy came fully into Randall's face.

The ride home was very quiet. Teddy was beside himself with glee. Far from feeling satiation, his experience had served to make him more truly in love with Randall than ever. On every possible occasion he stole one hand beneath his lover's robe and caressed the still-trembling cock within.

Teddy came into Randall's room to bid him goodnight. Then he took him again into his arms and gripped his new lover's body madly as if, with such viselike force, he would fuse them into one being. God! How he loved him!

"Teddy," Randall whispered, "you do love me, don't you?" and when Teddy answered that he loved him more than ever Randall begged, "Then don't let me ever forget my better self again!"

Teddy laughed as he said, "Oh, you've been there before. You're too good at it."

"Stop, stop," whimpered Randall. "Go away before I hate myself and you too."

Puzzled, Teddy gave him a perfunctory embrace and hurried to his own room.

For hours Randall lay awake thinking alternately of his love for Teddy and his new fall from grace, with its accompanying sense of shame. But this time he was calmer in the face of self-realization.

CHAPTER
10

The next morning, Sunday, Randall felt ashamed to meet Teddy at breakfast, and planned to remain in his room. But Teddy's actions showed that he experienced no such qualms. His attitude was entirely matter of fact. He was in love with Randall and he cared not who knew it or what others thought; this was Randall's affair and his; it was for them to seize happiness when it presented itself, in whatever form, and make the most of it as and while they could. In after years Teddy was wont to relate with pride that this was the great love affair of his life. True, he was ten years older than Randall and also came from more sophisticated people. Ten years more of experience did much to develop Randall's character; at the end of that time he would have been quite a match for Teddy. Complete revelation had not yet come to Randall. To too many it never comes at all; else the world would be much more tolerant and kindly.

Teddy arose bright and early. Randall could hear him whistling in his room above, whistling gaily. What would he think of him? Would he tell on him?

He had forgotten to make him promise not to tell. He was terror-stricken at the possibilities. As he sat gazing into space, imagining all of the horrors of such a situation, he was startled by a knock on the door, followed by Teddy's cheerful call, "Hello! Are you coming to breakfast?"

"In a minute!" he answered as he realized thankfully that Teddy still desired his companionship. He put the finishing touches to his toilet, then opened the door. "Come in Teddy!"

Teddy stepped into the room and closed the door quickly, then gathered Randall into his arms. Randall did not resist but welcomed this demonstration of Teddy's continued interest in him. "Teddy," he murmured, "Promise me that you will never tell anyone about yesterday!"

"Of course not! That is for me and you alone to know. But you take things too seriously," he whispered as he kissed his ear. "Don't you wish to make me happy? Are you not happy loving me? Let us make the most of life while we can. I love you. You love me. What else matters! Now come along and eat breakfast."

So they went down to the dining room and Randall found enjoyment in the luscious late peaches with cream, the hot waffles and the coffee which Jinny, the cook, set before them. Jinny too could have told a tale of love—of loves, of many loves, in which conscience had not been the least bit troublesome to her. She had survived them and had been and still was happy. After all, we are beginning to question whether repression, with its frequent dire consequences, is the desired thing that the priesthoods of all nations would have us believe it to be.

Teddy wished to rush off at once to church so they might enjoy the music together. With their automobile, it was almost a triumphal tour to the church of St. M's, where the music and pageantry at that time were unrivaled and where the senses were lulled into sweet dreams that answered well for religious sentiments when one was too advanced in thought to accept either Judaism or any of the teachings of its many, and even more childish, Christian offshoots.

The music was exquisite. Randall was ecstatic. All through the service he and Teddy held hands under the overcoat thrown across his knees. They did not accept communion; they never did.

They dined in the Park, a special dinner in celebration of their happiness. The afternoon they spent driving up and down the avenue in the novel car, astonishing the onlookers and earning the curses of the cabbies whose horses had not yet become accustomed to the newfangled machine. At night they returned to their boarding house, tired and happy. Teddy, perceiving that he must not proceed too fast and too suddenly with Randall, or perhaps satisfied enough with his conquest, gave Randall a chaste goodnight kiss as they parted in the hallway before his door.

CHAPTER
11

Except for an occasional sigh at the thought of his peccadillo of the afternoon along the Hudson, Randall was wildly happy during the following week. Teddy gave him every evidence of being in love with him, and he in turn loved Teddy—in fact thoughts of him almost excluded all others. Every evening they met for a short turn on the avenue in the new car and later they would always slip into Café Martin for Teddy's "nightcap."

Already Teddy was planning for another weekend. They would run up to New Haven in his car, see a theatrical tryout and put up with mutual friends there. He proposed this one evening as they were walking home from the old barn where he stored his automobile. Randall snuggled close to his side. He agreed that it would be delightful but added, "You must promise to be good, Teddy. Our love must be kept above all sordidness. We must keep it ideal and pure." Teddy, having never experienced the novelty, acquiesced. Joyfully Randall exclaimed, "Oh, Teddy! I never thought love could be quite so beautiful. I am the happiest person in the world." Then, "We are the happiest people in the world," he amended.

In sex matters Teddy was quite unmoral. His opinion was that what people do with each other is only their own personal concern, a tenet which seems to have become more and more a part of the teaching of the present generation, when one is likely to hear sex, normal or abnormal, openly discussed by adolescents at fashionable luncheons, or tea dances, or between dances at an evening gathering. Teddy lived for the joy of the moment. Kindly, and certainly a gentleman by instinct, he would not intentionally have hurt anyone. He had been spontaneously attracted to Randall, and Randall was attracted to him likewise. It was all very simple. Thus he reasoned. Saturday came. Randall had never visited New Haven before. He was eager with anticipation; he almost fluttered, his movements, unrestrained, taking on the mannerisms that are so revealing of one of his kind.

It was another perfect fall day. The ride was enjoyable from almost every point of view, despite the fact that roads had not yet been improved to their present smooth stage. They arrived in good time and wandered over the campus. They visited some student friends of Teddy's, and though these admired some of Randall's characteristics, they laughed, one and all, at the unusual timbre of his voice once he was out of earshot. Perhaps Randall, a little forgetful and excited by the novelty of everything, failed to repress what his brother Bill had characterized as "that damned voice."

They had luncheon. They attended a frat dance. They hurried to the theater. The play was the premiere of a musical piece that later became famous. The young men and women of the cast had been chosen not alone for their singing and dancing ability, but also for their pulchritude. Teddy was outspoken in his admiration of the physical attractions of various members of the cast. Randall felt a quickening sense of jealousy, admitted their good points, and then gushed forth in praise of some of the wonderful Yale men they had met earlier in the day. Teddy sensed his own jealousy, and he was annoyed with himself for the ill-suppressed emotion.

After the theater, they rejoined some of Teddy's college friends and together went to a rathskeller, a haunt of the students and the theatrical people. Teddy was busy acting as toastmaster. Randall was neglected and a trifle bored. To make the time pass more pleasantly he engaged in conversation with a young instructor who was seated at his left. This man had made his own way in life, even as Randall was doing. He drew Randall out, his true self, as no one else had ever troubled to do. He was interested to hear of Randall's college extension work, of his desire to give up business and earn a degree in science. Mr. Wright, of the many men who were attracted to Randall, was drawn not by sex, but by the quality of his mind. He gave him valuable advice, outlining easy ways for the accomplishment of his ambitions.

The evening wore along. Randall did not drink. Teddy, though he carried his liquor well, was unduly exhilarated. He was sufficient master of himself to realize this and suggested that they take a long walk before appearing at his friend's apartment. They wandered out into the country. The houses were fewer and fewer. Teddy removed his hat and complained that his head was hot and throbbing. Sympathetically Randall laid a hand to his brow. As he let it drop Teddy caught it to his lips, "How sweet you are, Randy!"

71

They nestled close, and in but a moment their arms were about each other. Teddy's kisses were wild and furious, and he fairly tore the clothing from his companion's lean and supple body. This time Randall felt a mad desire for compliance, a conscious enjoyment. They brought their newly awakening cocks to bear upon one another and sandwiched them between their bellies. Randall felt Teddy's nipples strike up against his own, and it was as if they were electrical conduits, throwing sparks as they touched then moved away.

Randall's senses became enveloped with Teddy's body. He drew in each of his masculine odors; felt the different skin textures in his bearded face, his soft neck and his firm breast; tasted the salt of the sweat from his brow. He did the same with each part of Teddy's anatomy, and so expert were his probings that Teddy soon came with such intensity that pearlescent sperm lay across their bodies like morning dew. But then Randall moved to please himself upon his lover's body, and straddled Teddy so that he could run his long, thick member forward and back upon the supine and panting man's soft belly. As Randall abandoned himself to this act, Teddy grabbed his lean and tender thighs with terrific force, and, after a few soft swats delivered by Teddy's open palm, Randall shot come to reach the lower edge of his lover's vandyke.

More calmly they walked to Teddy's friend's apartment. As they bade each other good night Randall said almost lightly, "Teddy, we must stop being naughty."

To this Teddy answered, "We only obeyed something stronger than ourselves—instinct." He was quite sincere when he added, "I only love you all the more for it."

During the night Randall heard a stealthy tapping at his door. He understood. Without hesitation he opened it. Teddy was upon him in an instant, his dressing gown fluttering open to reveal the intensity of his passion raised between his legs. Randall was fairly knocked onto his own bed, and their bodies writhed in a tangle of desire. So lost was Randall in the sea of emotions, in excitement at the danger of their love-making even as the room's door stood slightly ajar, that he did not notice as his thighs were parted and his legs were splayed. He did not notice till it was too late what Teddy's true intentions entailed.

It was as if a lighted torch were run up the hole of Randall's backside. Teddy's cock head had pressed upon it, making it tingle and itch, and then it had started its inevitable invasion. Randall was being deflowered. He was being fucked. Shrieking with anguish and delight, Randall tore at Teddy's chest with his nails, and grabbed hold of his waist with his legs, the better to receive his lover's pounding rhythm. Again, his innate proclivity betrayed his innocence. The feeling of being so filled and refilled was more than he could have dreamed possible, and he brought Teddy to a thundering crisis, even as his own overwrought member truly burst of its own accord, sending a stream of come to run over the flat plane of Teddy's belly.

Thus began their more intimate clandestine relationship.

CHAPTER
12

Randall was contented as he had never been before. With his emotional life thoroughly satisfied, the quality of his work both in business and at the university improved. For the time being, at least, he had let go of his inhibitions. And with that there was a noticeable change in his personality; more and more frequently his voice broke beyond the bounds of proper restraint. One day he chanced to meet Bill. He was happy to see him, fluttered gaily up to him and burst out rapturously, "How wonderful to meet you, Bill. You are looking perfectly marvelous."

Bill took a turn about him as if to look him over well. "For God's sake, keep quiet!" was his answer. "Why can't you act natural?"

His rebuff hurt. He had been so sincere. But Randall understood perfectly—perfectly at last. "Very well, Bill, goodbye," he said in a low, heartbroken tone of voice.

Randall felt his brother's condemnation. It symbolized to him the voice of the rest of the world. He had sacrificed much for Bill and in fact for all of his family. The thought came suddenly that all this counted for nothing. The iron began to enter his soul.

Slowly he walked homeward. After dinner Teddy came to sit with him in his cozy homelike room. He observed Randall's depression, noted the lack of his usual buoyancy, his quiet and absorption.

Randall sat staring straight ahead, lost in deep sad thought. Teddy kissed him with what was meant to be compassion, but when Teddy kissed Randall this did nothing but arouse within him a fiery desire. As his caresses became more intense Randall begged, "Not tonight, Teddy, not tonight. You ridicule my conscience. I do not know what it is, Teddy, whether it is conscience or a sense of loss of self-respect. I must get away from all of this, Teddy. I'm going away."

Teddy knew how firm he could be; that anything he might say would not shake Randall's decision. He had begun to love him madly, to the exclusion of all other love episodes. He felt the need of Randall. He couldn't lose him. He protested that they would keep their relation one of purest friendship, but he must not go. He shed tears. He promised Randall what to a mercenary person would have been tempting gifts. No one move did he leave untried. He threatened to follow him. At last he realized that for the time being his pleas were useless. He kissed Randall one last time, and left.

The next morning Randall arose much earlier than usual. Quickly he packed his bag and trunks. More bulky belongings he left behind to be sent for later. He hailed a hansom, then the common mode of conveyance about the streets of New York, and asked to be taken to the Chelsea Hotel. After he had registered and given a few directions regarding his luggage and boxes to come later, he turned to follow the bellhop. As he did so the room clerk gave a knowing wink to one of his fellows. Randall happened to catch this reflected in a glass. "Does everybody see me as I am?" he thought. Then defiance came to his support—"Well, I'm as God made me, if there is a God, or whatever it is that creates human mistakes."

A dreadful week of remorse and loneliness followed. The day's work now seemed arduous. He looked and felt ill. A pompous young physician who had his bronze sign prominently displayed at the entrance of the hotel, observing Randall announced, "There's a praecox case," knowing that though his auditors would not understand they would marvel at his erudition. But Randall was not "a praecox case." His mind was keen, sound and sharply analytical.

Habits once formed are difficult to break unless something especially engrossing is substituted. Teddy had become a habit. At the end of a week, Randall cast conscience, or remorse, or whatever it was, aside, and as abruptly as he had left returned to the boarding house—and to Theodore Wemys Cocke.

CHAPTER
13

Teddy greeted Randall with tears in his eyes, succeeded by violent sobbing as he gathered him into his arms.

The Christmas season was approaching. Teddy begged Randall to let him know what he could get for him. The vanity of testing his infatuation, more than desire of possession, prompted Randall to name some extravagant thing which he did not need. Teddy brought it the next day. After it was received, he did not experience the satisfaction which he had anticipated. Somewhat remorsefully he told him, "Teddy, I really did not wish you to spend so much money on me. I only wanted to see if you were willing to do it. Take it back."

Teddy of course did not fathom Randall's whims, and felt wounded. Probably from that time the inevitable estrangement set in. Teddy had sacrificed to make this gift. He felt that it was not appreciated. Their conduct toward each other, from then on, began to be less even. There were lapses of politeness on both sides. Teddy's attentions began to wander to others. Randall began to have more fits of remorse. At the end of the winter he suddenly left Teddy again. This time he put so much distance between them that return was more difficult. He spent a wretched week of loneliness, and at the end of that time his craving for some sort of affection was so great that he felt almost beside himself with longing. The weekend took him to Boston for the bank. Saturday afternoon he attend the Philharmonic concert. On the way to the hall he was more than once conscious of being noticed by attractive men. He wept quietly through the more sentimental numbers of the concert, and somehow there concluded that he must have love. He could not live without it.

As he left the concert hall he made up his mind. This time he did not bother to return to Teddy.

Randall's new friend stretched beneath the hotel room sheets and reached over to the night table for a cigarette. He was older, somewhat broad-shouldered and muscular. The sweat on his body was only now cooling and drying. He complimented Randall on his sophistication. It was not often he'd encountered such tenderness with such expertise in an anonymous fucking. Randall shrugged his shoulders and threw out his hands in a Frenchified gesture as much as to say, "What's the difference?"

His work held him in Boston for the following week. He did not even seek to find himself his new lover again, but night after night, handsome substitute was followed by handsome substitute in a careless succession of experiments. Their sizes and shapes did not seem to matter, simply that they be clean and willing. At times Randall would take control, delivering his insatiable cock into the hind orifices of men he encountered in local taverns. But Randall found he preferred to receive the affections and penises of these so-called stand-ins. He made his way through them as if in a voluptuous trance, bedding them and then ridding himself of them before light of day, only to bed another the following night. On more than one evening, there would be two or three of them in a row.

At the end of the week, when he returned to New York, from his new lodgings he telephoned to Teddy quite casually—"I'm back; you may as well come up."

CHAPTER
14

Teddy came. He was very considerate, very tender, but not excessively emotional as on their former reconciliation. They spent the afternoon driving, stopping for tea at the lovely old Jumel Mansion. After tea they took a walk along the Drive, drinking in the fresh spring air, feeling elated by the beauty of the season and the renewal of their companionship. They discussed the future. Randall admitted that he thought he understood himself better and could be happier than before. As they passed along the drive, Randall began to indulge in what, at times later on, was almost an obsession with him, the studying of the various types they saw. So absorbed did he become in watching the face of one well-dressed, tall, vandyke-bearded man that Teddy asked sharply that he stop staring at people. Reproofs from Teddy too? Oh, well!

They agreed, after much discussion, to take an apartment together and at once set out to find a furnished place. This they located somewhere in the fifties, cozy, not too expensive, and convenient to the life of the town.

Some months afterwards the bank president sailed for Europe, practically making Randall free for the spring and summer. So habituated was he to routine useful occupation that time hung heavily. Summer courses at the university were not yet open. He decided to take private lessons in French, German and Spanish. The best teachers were within easy walking distance. April and May are lovely months in New York City; even early June, before the parks have become sere, gives one the feeling of living in an enchanted land. Randall spent hours afoot, going from one place to another. He had formed the curious habit of carrying on two distinct trains of thought, almost simultaneously. He lived a life of actualities and a dream life. In this dream life he was successful, financially at ease, the center of a deferential admiring circle of people. Curiously he never pictured any real women in this circle.

The avenue seemed full of gay people those days, persons who were happy as he. At intervals were stationed the mounted traffic police. Their splendid figures, their neat well-fitting uniforms, their highly polished puttees protecting perfectly formed legs, the delectable penis clearly defined through the fabric, the thigh outlined by pressure against the horse's side, all combined to make a picture which he found irresistibly appealing.

He found himself looking for the mounted police. He formed preferences for one or the other, and enjoyed fantasizing about what loving one would be like. He thought of the Aztecs with their idea that the men astride horses were some kind of god, and he smiled to think that his poetic sense was interpreting these horsemen in the same light. He liked especially to view the officers from the back: the torso, the carriage, the outline of the leg all accentuated. He tried to chastise himself for gazing at such men in public streets and thinking of stripping them and moving their great cocks into his rear canal, but he could not help himself.

In Boston one of his more exquisite sexual experiments had been with a handsome, muscular, athletic young Irishman, a cop in plain clothes, off for the evening. Randall had felt a peculiar satisfaction in giving him caresses, an intensity of excitement which Teddy, perhaps too refined and not sufficiently virile, had failed to arouse within him. He found himself, when admiring these lovely young policemen, reverting to the Boston experience and wondering about what techniques would be necessary to seduce these as well. But that was only occasionally. He was too busy with his studies to give too much thought to them. He found himself laughing when he compared these virile types with so many of the men he met daily, teachers of French, or Spanish, or German, or music; or overly fat brokers and businessmen, all a bit physically degenerate.

June came and with it all classes ceased. Of course later he would enroll for the summer sessions at one of the universities. Teddy knew he would be busy at the summer schools and suggested that they take a trip together before that time. "We'll call it our honeymoon," he said.

The forerunner of the Tin Lizzies was made ready. They were to have two weeks of June along the Hudson, the Mohawk Trail and the Adirondacks. The first days were delightful. Teddy was trying an odometer he had invented. Whenever it registered a new fifty miles he stopped and kissed Randall. He was very playful—in the beginning.

One week had sped by. They had been very happy, laughing and fucking, and playing with one another's cocks like toys. Perhaps they had been too unre-

strained. Certainly satiety breeds enervation, and enervation breeds antipathy, the reaction of the wearied
body in its attempt to repair itself.

They had reached their goal, one of the pretty
lakes with which the Adirondacks abound. They
camped on a grassy slope.

Randall was tired. He felt nervous, irritable and
dissatisfied with himself as much as with Teddy.
Teddy's continued insistence led to rebellion.
Suddenly he burst forth: "You think of me for one
thing only! You did not even respect me! I hate
you! I hate everything!"

He started away. Teddy called on him and when
he did not turn cried out angrily, "Then go, damn
you, and don't ever come back."

Randall ran at first, then settled down to a
steady walk. It was miles to a railway. That was no
task. His overwrought nerves needed the relaxation
exercise would give them. After he had covered a
mile, Teddy overtook him with his machine. But
Randall would not ride with him. Teddy pleaded to
take his confused and distraught lover wherever he
wished to go. He knew it was fifteen miles more to
the railway station. Randall's only reply was "Keep
away from me. I never want to see you again."
Even though he would not talk to him, or ride with
him, Teddy kept him in sight. He would not leave
him unprotected till he saw him safely at the railway station.

Aboard the Pullman Randall sobbed most of the
night. He put Teddy out of his mind. He felt that he
was grieving for a dead self, an idealized better self.

In a city as big as New York, one is quickly lost.
It was years before Randall saw Teddy again. In the
meantime his point of view had shifted completely.

It was on 125th Street. Teddy was so intent in trying to "make" a blond that he did not see Randall, who laughed gaily as he looked on and thought, "The same old Teddy, bless his heart, and up to the same old tricks."

CHAPTER
15

Randall went to work with a vengeance when the summer session opened at the university. The work at the bank was slight, and with the consent of the president he had broken in an assistant, a young, ambitious man from Brooklyn, who was able to do the work as well as Randall could. His conscientious services were appreciated and the officials gave him permission to take six weeks of leave without pay; this covered the summer session at the university.

In view of his record in previous courses, the dean gave him permission to carry an almost impossible number of points.

Randall's reaction from the Teddy episode, far from unfitting him for intense mental application, seemed to have left his brain in so receptive and sensitive a condition that he could grasp his subjects with one reading or one hearing. He did the best scholastic work of his life; his accomplishment was so remarkable as to attract the attention of the dean. At the end of the session he called him to his office, complimented him on his successful performance, and asked what was his incentive. Finding that he was not attempting to make up points flunked at some other college, he tried to fathom the reason for his industry. "Surely," he said, "you have some definite aim in view in studying so systematically?"

Randall had a well-defined aim but even the dean's kindly sympathy could not induce him to put "the goal of his ambition" into words. The dean suggested that if finances were bothering him, the university would see that he had ample opportunity; they would give him a scholarship if he would enroll as a full-time student. "That will make your financial burden an easy one to meet," he assured. He was astonished when Randall revealed the extent of his more than ample funds. A fortunate investment the past spring had netted a clear one hundred percent profit, and several other turnovers of his capital had brought the amount up to an even fifty thousand dollars. He felt safe. But until he had achieved a measure of success in his chosen field, he had no intention of telling anyone of his plans, not even the dean. None other than a psychologist would have been able to understand his motive in giving up what was already a successful business career for a life of drudgery in a difficult branch of science.

So he thanked the dean and fled quickly to take advantage of the one day of vacation that remained.

The need of relaxation pressed upon him. He decided on a trip by the day boat for West Point as being the most restful recreation he could have. He chose a deck chair on the shaded, breeze-swept deck and at once fell into a heavy sleep from which he was awakened half an hour later by the boat swinging from the dock. A little self-indulgently he thought smilingly of the summer's studies. Suddenly he realized that he could scarcely recall any part of the work he had covered. Puzzled, he groped in his mind for the key that would unlock remembrance, but to no avail.

Two young men were standing near. One had a fishing rod and a basket. The other carried a common old tin can. As if in answer to his wondering gaze, the larger of the two announced, "We are going fishing when we get to West Point. Buddy has the worms in the tin can. Don't you want to see the worms? We got up last night and took candles and went out on the grass and grabbed them before they could get back in their holes," and with that he picked out "the greatest biggest one" for prideful exhibition.

At once Randall began to chant inwardly, "The common earthworm, *Lumbricus terrestris*, is one of the most interesting of all the species which we will study in this course. In it you see a perfect exemplification of hermaphroditism, that is, both male and female, perfect in every sense, in the one body. You will do well to remember this as you study the higher species and compare what you see today with the rudimentary appendages which will be found even in man. Those of you who will study medicine will find that the human female has an appendage designated the clitoris, which is the analogue of the male penis; conversely the male has within him the analogue of the female uterus. By some authorities it is even held that the hidden hermaphroditism of some human individuals accounts for various sexual vagaries. The female organs of *Lumbricus* are complete; likewise are the male organs. Mutual cross-fertilization probably always takes place. Some of you may be fortunate enough to find two specimens in your day's supply that are copulating. If so, you will observe that the more cephalad organ of the one is joined to the more caudad organ of the other, and vice versa. That is, they do not lie head to head and tail to tail, but the head of each is directed toward the tail of the other. The embryos…," etc.

He recalled the entire lecture, word for word, every question, every answer, the dissection with the etherized worm stretched out on waxed plates; every detail up to the end of the lecture hour. Then there was a balk. He could not remember what came next. Uneasily he left his chair to stroll about. Passing a French couple he caught the word "*aller*." At once he seemed to hear the effeminate old French professor intoning—"*Les parties principales du verbe aller*," and that lecture came to its close. He laughed at himself. "You press the button, we do the rest. Anyway, it's evidently still there. I didn't spend my money for nothing at the knowledge factory. I'll not worry about it."

When the boat stopped he elected to remain at the Point instead of going further up the river. He climbed the hills to the old fort, and later lolled about beneath the shady trees surrounding the parade ground. He was disappointed; there was no drill. Instead, a group of young officers was engaged in polo. How wonderful their poise astride a horse; how beautiful the muscles of their arms! Nearby stood a group of tall young men in service uniforms. Their slim erectness, their slender legs encased in shining puttees made their usual disguised sex appeal, which Randall acknowledged to himself only as admiration for physical development. One of them looked him over critically, almost superciliously. "I'm an earthworm," it dawned upon Randall. "*Lumbricus terrestris!* Army officers! What connection is there between army officers and earthworms and myself?"

His mind wandered to his course in zoology as he

pondered the relationship that exists between all forms of living matter. One of the young officers whispered to another as he looked at him, but then Randall failed to notice them further. He became engrossed in the polo again and tensed as he observed a difficult play. Gradually he became aware of a uniformed man close beside him. He was not a commissioned officer, and as he began to speak, it became evident he was trying to become friendly, or else wished to appease his curiosity.

Without any self-consciousness, Randall answered all of the questions the man so laboriously led up to and by the end of half an hour had informed him that he was there for the day only; that he did not visit the place frequently; that he knew no one, either of the enlisted or the commissioned personnel; that he came there only because the excursion trip happened to offer the Point as a stopping place; that he held a position in a bank and still had one day of leave; that he could smoke but did not care anything about it; that he did not drink, though he had liberal ideas on that, and in fact on all subjects, that he had no booze with him, he did not think drinking a wise habit; that this, that that. That he would not care to meet any of the soldiers, they were too crude; that he did not think he would care to know any of the cadets, they were too immature; that he was not especially anxious to meet anyone socially, officers or otherwise; that he did not think he would care to have him look him up when he came to New York, and he added with veiled sarcasm, "My time is too taken up with things of importance."

Randall was really too tired at the time to fathom the young soldier's motive in asking him all these questions. He did remember seeing him later talking to one of the group of officers, then looking at him, and when he reviewed the episode thought, "They saw me as I am; they were after me. God! They must think themselves tempting!" In later years, retelling it at an afternoon tea in New York, one of the tempting buds of the season volunteered, "They wanted to make you."

"Not at all," corrected the hostess, every inch a *woman* of the world, "they wanted to get him!"

The return trip to New York was quiet, blissfully quiet and uneventful. Randall took the recently built subway home. He crawled into bed and slept as if drugged.

CHAPTER
16

A beautiful fall followed. Randall was assigned anew to the bank president's uptown library. The work was confidential. He learned of accumulated dividends, uncut "melons". All this formed the basis for wise investments. No longer had he anything to fear financially. And now, when he was able to do so much for his mother, he received word of her sudden passing away. Randall was alone! His brother Bill had taken pains to estrange the other members of the family.

Randall enrolled for extension courses to fill out certain subjects required for the major work of his life—unless his subsequent love episodes, adventures, conquests, should be considered the major work of his life.

Even with a busy routine, at intervals a kind of loneliness invaded him. This proved disturbing. Work, activity, theatrical entertainment, music, art, nothing quite submerged the vague longing which possessed him.

He found himself studying types again. Randall now realized that he had fetishes, as he had learned to call them: vandyke beards and strong-looking men with thick matte flesh and closely shaven blue-black beards showing through the skin attracted him especially. He found himself comparing one type of man with another, on the street, in the bus, on the El, in the subway, at the theater, wherever he might be. He found himself yearning anew for comradeship. But he determined that this time there would be no enslaving infatuation connected with his life.

He bethought himself of Henri Voyeur. At intervals he had run across him in the Waldorf-Astoria, and they had occasionally attended the theater together. He called him on the telephone. Henri had always found Randall unusual, agreeable, and to him entirely congenial. He responded at once.

The banker subscribed for countless theatrical and musical performances, as well as for the opera. Always Randall had tickets, as many as he could find time to use. He and Henri formed the habit of going to these entertainments together. Henri never presumed. He was not in the least interested in Randall physically. Together they satisfied that craving for intellectual companionship which is needed to complement all lives, and which, alas! is not always found in one's immediate family, or even in marriage. Henri too had the habit of studying and admiring types. They compared notes. They became frank and outspoken. Randall told him in detail of his affairs of the heart (and head) and vowed he was through with all love forever.

To this Henri responded, "I hope this is true, dear Randy, but my experience leads me to believe that those of a certain type will continue to seek the ever evasive and baffling happiness of love, and not finding it in one affair will, as the years go by, take the bit they can find in one place, and the bit they can find in another and thus pick up here and there in their lives sufficiently varied experience to make in the aggregate enough to satisfy." He confessed to his own promiscuous adventures.

Randall drew back from becoming again a slave of sensation. "No, Henri, I have gone too far already," he told him. "I shall never play at love again. I realize what I am. I must reform. I've had enough!"

"Randall," Henri warned, "if you mean that, you will have to cut out all friendship with the people to whom you are attracted, you will have to live as a hermit. You cannot even see me. Your conversation with me always turns to this subject. You are seeking a vicarious enjoyment. You can only satisfy your craving by indulgence. There is no happiness in this so-called sublimation. For your own sake I hope that you can live without love, for society is not organized with a view to the exceptional individual and makes no allowances for the variations from the conventional type. If you can foreswear your own kind, you may not be exactly happy, but you will at least breathe more easily. Even now you are interested in various men without acknowledging it to yourself. Why do you comment on the splendid physique of the traffic squad, for instance? I think you deceive yourself."

It was shortly after this that Randall and Henri began to habituate the gay Bohemian places of the town. A famed chop house was one of them. Here, after opera, they frequently sat to nibble a sandwich and have some innocuous drink. Not long after they took to supping at the place, Randall observed a dark, mustached, unusual man at a nearby table. He tried to place him. Finally he remembered; he had seen him at one of the parties which he and Henri had attended in the basement of a 55th Street apartment house where the famous and beautiful Lillian Russell and other well-known theatrical people lived.

Randall looked at this sleek, expensively dressed man. There was much that was unusual about him. Then he remembered more; he had seen him at the opera too. He called Henri's attention to the fellow. "Looks like a grafter to me," Henri remarked curtly. At that time the society blackmailer was beginning to make his appearance again in New York The man did look the part. Randall dismissed him from his mind.

The next Friday evening, forgetful of his resolution to reform, Randall dropped into the 55th Street place. It was a rainy night. Few people were there. The dark chap of the chop house was sitting by a window he had to pass. Randall was startled. The strong and handsome man looked up laughing as he carefully rearranged his white blouse and said, "What frightened you? You needn't be afraid of me." When he smiled and when he talked, his face was transformed.

Randall felt that he had shown his feelings too plainly. He retorted gaily, "The only thing I am afraid of here is a cop. Hope there'll be none tonight. But why should I be afraid of you?"

"To prove that you are not, you must have supper with me after the opera next Friday instead of with your friend, the one you call Henri. I wish to know you better. For a long time I have been wishing to speak to you, but did not dare. I am Billy Pickup. Almost anybody who steps out the least bit in society knows all about me. God knows I'm notorious enough. You've heard of my father too, I am sure. We are stopping at the Holland House this winter. I hope you are going to be generous and make it possible for us to see each other again."

Randall knew his father, had met him in the bank frequently. He studied the strapping man's face a moment; the eyes, the nose and forehead were the same as those of the father; the mouth, somehow, was different, not so strong, not so determined. Small wonder the fellow could dress exquisitely! Quite safe! He accepted.

When he told Henri he blurted out, "Who'd have thought it? So hard to tell the genuine from the imitation these days. I've heard of him. He gives remarkable parties, the gayest in town. If he invites you, don't fail to attend, for you'll meet the very elite of our young set."

Friday night came. There was a double bill. Randall came in late for *Il Pagliacci*. He had called young Pickup on the telephone and told him to look for him. He was sauntering about the lounge when he entered. Billy insisted that he come to their box. As the act started and the house was in darkness, he placed his chair close to Randall's, grasped one of his hands and pressed it tensely. Randall's emotions were mixed, but the flattering satisfaction of being desired by Billy Pickup probably was dominant.

By the time they had reached Jack's Restaurant, where they were to sup, they were like old friends. Pickup appeared to be madly infatuated, but that meant nothing, for infatuations new and frequent were a commonplace in his life. At first Randall was rather indifferent emotionally, but his long practice in lovemaking had schooled him in the art of insidious flattery, and as a love affair is in great part founded on self-love, 'twas not long before Randall thought he was again in love and that this time he had found the idealist he sought. Certainly the sentiments he expressed seemed to make him ideal. Candidly he told Billy of his heartbreaks and how he had forever foresworn all love. Then he promised to be true to him if he would be his. He believed him.

Billy was an expert lover, the first to come close to matching Randall's intuitive pleasuring skills. His fingers sought out the most sensitive regions of Randall's body and caressed them before pressing harder and taking a more masculine hold. He breathed warmly into his kisses, strategically placing the occasional nibble or bite in some extra-ticklish area. He was the first to aggressively toy with Randall's anal sphincter before boring it with his great erection, fingering it, and even touching it exquisitely with the pointed end of his tongue. Randall had fairly squealed with delight before being penetrated, and for the first time since his deflowering, he came volcanically solely under the onslaught of Billy's fucking.

The next morning, feeling expansive, at breakfast Billy planned an elaborate party for the following Saturday night, to be in Randall's "honor." He enumerated the string of notables who would be present. Randall left him, walking on air. Surely the gods were being good today.

CHAPTER
17

Randall by this time had absorbed the New York customs and indeed no longer looked on himself as anything other than a New Yorker.

To while away the afternoon, Randall lunched at the Waldorf-Astoria, then went to a haberdasher's for a gift for Billy Pickup and also something for himself.

Billy had bidden Randall to bring Henri along. The party was to begin at eleven-thirty, after theater, and of course would last all night. Randall knew that most of Billy's crowd would attend the Empire, where a musical comedy was the attraction. Several of the cast would be at the party. He and Henri attended the Empire too. Randall was surprised to see how many of his New York acquaintances were present. He had not realized how much his circle had widened since he and Henri had taken to frequenting the resorts of a more Bohemian character.

In the foremost row he saw Billy Pickup. He hoped he would come to the lobby during the entr'acte, so that he might present Henri. Randall

observed that Billy kept his opera glass pointed
almost constantly at—one member of the cast. He
was surprised, perhaps a little jealous. When the
intermission arrived, Billy did not come to the foyer;
instead he went backstage. He knew what that
meant. He spoke of it to Henri who sagaciously
remarked: "You'll end up taking whatever comes
your way, enjoying it for the moment, and doing as
the rest of us do. Surely you realize by this time that
these affairs can lead to no lasting bond. Why, these
infatuations are so intense they burn themselves out
to a finish almost as soon as curiosity is satisfied.
Take your love where—and how—you find it. Enjoy!
Pass on! Then you'll never be lonesome or unhappy.
Be in love with love. You may as well realize that the
failure to hold a lover is as much due to the inherent
defect in yourself as to the unfaithful tendency of
your sweetheart. Be like me—a oncer. Love often
and not too hard; don't take your emotions too seriously; then they'll not get the best of you."

It did not shock him. He was changing in his attitude toward life.

The play swept on to a glorious finale and even
then they did not succeed in joining Billy Pickup.

The party was to be held in the studio of Mr. (and
Miss) Painter in East 69th Street. Randall hurried, as
he did not wish to be late. Billy had not yet arrived.
The artist Painter, then beginning to be known for his
murals, was acting host. Already there was a more
than lively crowd, all drinking, singing and dancing,
and doing other things too that suited their fancy.

Painter welcomed Randall with, "I suppose you
are Randy Etrange. Billy told me to expect you with
your friend."

Henri was presented and then Painter with a wave
of his hand announced: "A new friend of Billy's.

Make yourselves acquainted!" That was the end of all formalities. Then he turned to Randall and said, "You will attend my costume party next week, won't you? Everybody in our set who is worth knowing will be there. The sky's the limit. You can wear much, or nothing. Several of my models will be there too. Promise me you'll come." Then he whispered in Randall's ear: "You came early."

Someone was playing, one of the old-fashioned things, a waltz, or a two-step, or a turkey trot, whatever it was the style to dance then. Everyone danced, with frequent breaks for drinks and that followed almost invariably by the choice of a new partner. The reigning Earl of the season, quite the most betitled human object that England had sent out heiress-hunting for some time, danced frequently with Randall.

"My god!" Randall said to Henri afterwards, "What use can a real woman find for a thing like that?"

"They can use their titles, can't they?" Henri laughed.

In the midst of the hubbub, Billy arrived, as one of the girls expressed it, "dragging in something lovely"—a handsome young Irishman, a member of the fire department. The fireman seemed a bit abashed at finding himself in this hilarious crowd, of such a different level from the people with whom he usually associated.

Billy rushed up to Randall with "So glad you came," kissed him and then passed on, forgetting both him and the fireman. His ideas of the duties of a host were rather unusual. He seemed preoccupied and left each guest to make the best of things and amuse himself. With the arrival of the theatrical contingent the reason for the preoccupation became evident—the star of the company had arrived. Much later in the evening Billy came back to Randall and said: "You are going to stay after the party, aren't you?"

Randall, not to be outdone, answered boldly: "Why, of course. What did you expect I came to the party for?"

Off dashed Billy. That was settled. He must look out for his newest conquest, "See that someone does not grab it away from him," said the worldly-wise Henri.

Certainly to be promiscuous was the keynote here. Randall shrugged his shoulders as he confided to Henri, "I'm in it now, so here goes."

A slender, dark young Jew from California, just out of college, claimed him for the next dance, which seemed to resolve itself into a grappling contest. Randall complimented him on the power of his biceps and he begged to see him soon. This type was new, different. Their flirtation was jovial and not anonymous, as were all those men in Boston. He liked him, and thrilled to the touch of his lean body, knowing now that he did not have to love him either. They kissed hungrily, and though Randall felt no actual reciprocation of his passion, neither did he feel any repulsion, but rather a pleasant sense of excitement. He wished to monopolize him. He feared ennui. A little of such intensity went far.

Then a French singer, an unusual blond, claimed him for a dance. At once he told Randall that he loved him, protesting that it was love at first sight. Randall took the Frenchman's declaration lightly; it was only after meeting him many times afterwards and learning that his indifference had wounded the man that Randall realized that he had been quite sincere. Then he felt a kind of gratitude, perhaps a bit of pity which is akin to love. The poor chap had left his beloved Paris and accepted an engagement in New York to forget the disappointment of his first love gone wrong. He too was learning.

The young fireman sought Randall. The party was just as novel to him, and they got on famously. He told Randall of his life in the Fire Department and insisted that he visit the "Hook and Ladder" and meet some of the boys. After a drink together he began to be affectionate; rubbing Randall's shoulders, petting his hair, slapping his rump. They kissed hard, and the fireman's stubbled beard burned his tender cheeks red. He enjoyed him; his speech, his mannerisms; all so different.

"Let's have another drink," the fireman invited, "and then let's go out on the balcony. I want some lovin'."

But Randall did not want "some lovin'" just yet, and pretended to be interested in the piano playing of a young lawyer. The lawyer asked him if he played too. So he sat down on the piano bench beside him and made a medley of parts of Chopin waltzes suitable for dance rhythm. The lawyer followed with his right hand an octave higher, leaving his left free to massage Randall at the fork of his trousers. Billy Pickup saw them, even as a seething erection threatened to burst through Randall's pants. "Having a good time?" he called out. "Remember what you promised me!"

The lawyer seemed not to mind. "You'll give me a chance too, sometime, won't you?" he asked.

Randall was in the mood to promise anything, even if not to fulfill all the promises made. "Oh, I'll try you out," he answered. That seemed to satisfy for the time being.

Thus he passed from one to another. Love was

taken lightly, and Randall felt new freedom in his body's function and movement. He adored being so desired by so many, and for once enjoyed the effect his visage played upon the men of the crowd. It was nearing time to go. He rejoined Henri who asked, "Are you converted to my way a thinking yet?"

"Perhaps a little bit."

"Remember the French saying, 'One only loves.'"

"Implying?"

"That the other accepts. It's this way in life: you love me; I love somebody else; somebody else loves another; another loves still another, and so it goes on ad infinitum. Therefore, why take your loves so seriously? Why, even in marriage you don't suppose a woman takes the man she loves, do you? No, she marries the man she can get. If she happens to love him too, so much the better. Be adaptable. Take what you can get."

It was nearing four. Some had left. Randall had not seen Billy for the past hour. He and Henri went after their wraps. On a divan a couple were writhing, their lips glued together, their great red cocks jutting from open flies. On the way out they passed one of the bedrooms. The door was open. There were such noises! A peep within revealed the forms of three well-built men upon one another in a sweaty, fleshy mass. Transfixed, Randall entered the darkness and stepped up to the most handsome of the trio, who in turn spotted him and moved to undo his trousers. The cock within had moved to a complete stand in seconds, and with the delicious licking then being applied, it would come brief moments later. Randall shrieked so loudly with sheer pleasure that both his "sucker" and Henri Voyeur could do nothing but look on and laugh.

He called to Henri, "Let's escape."

On the way home they laughed gaily. "Did you enjoy it?" Henri asked.

"Of course, in a way. It was exciting. I'm going to meet the Jewish man again and the fireman too, sometime. We're invited to Painter's party next week, a costume affair; let's go."

Randall's Boston experience had been his initiation into and this evening his confirmation in promiscuity.

CHAPTER
18

The next Saturday night, Randall and Henri attended Painter's costume party. Randall determined to follow the artist's advice and wear either much, or nothing. He chose to wear nothing—or practically nothing. To be sure, his skin was protected by a coat of copper-bronze paint and he had a magnificent headdress of eagle plumes and a scanty bunch of feathers suspended from his waist by a deerskin belt. He was beautiful.

The guests were much the same as at Billy's party. Painter was entranced. He piloted Randall about the rooms constantly calling attention to his lovely backside, insisting that he must pose for him. He promised. Why not?

Randall knew he wanted him; but there was no appeal. He was handsome, but his posture was too slouching, his features too soft, and there was a weakness to his face, more evident when he smiled than at any time. His voice too lacked the deep mellow timbre which he was learning to demand. To Henri he confessed, "I can't see him as a lover. As a jolly comrade, yes, but nothing else. How can I circumvent what I know he will demand?"

"That's easy enough," replied Henri. "Tell him you are afraid you have caught a disease. That will stop him if nothing else will."

Randall laughed. "Then I would be out of society entirely, wouldn't I?"

The funniest and also the most pathetic member of the evening party was a scion of the famous Rhinelander family, not yet noted for its miscegenation. Randall observed a fat old woman whose corset stays must have scourged her for her sins. The woman's entire mode was exaggerated. Her face had been "enameled." The profuseness of her makeup but accentuated her wrinkles. Her hair was dyed that usual dark brown sticky-looking mess so many aging dames affect. No doubt their impaired vision prevents them from seeing the imperfections of their artifices.

The funny old creature was made more ludicrous by a combination of brown ostrich feathers, tipped with orange, sweeping over her head and floating down her fat back, the whole contraption held in place by a diamond-studded band which encircled her head. Her gown was intensely decolleté and of a vivid robin's-egg-blue velvet. She carried a bejeweled lorgnette and with that would indicate her prospective conquests.

Her method was simple. She sidled up to the host and demanded, "Present that young man to me," pointing with her lorgnette.

Then began her almost unvaried siren's song: "I've been watching you all the evening. I am sure you are someone unusual, and I wish to know you well"—this with a coquettish smirk. "I'm very fond of young men and know just what you like. I want you

110

to come and see me. I have excellent wines and cigars. And, tee-hee, when you play with me you are safe, for I have influence with the police department."

Then she would draw out a tiny pencil and a notebook, open to a blank page and require her "prospect" to enter his name, address and telephone number. The scheme evidently worked for her. She was always surrounded by a group of that blondish half-feminine type which is forever dancing along the edge of society. She was known to be immensely rich and though niggardly in making repairs to the tenements which she rented to the poor, she was notorious for her lavishness with her lovely young men.

Henri laughed as he said, "You see why it's necessary that some have great wealth, Randy?"

The husky young fireman, who had been present at Pickup's party too, volunteered, "God! She can't touch me. She looks like the plague. Me for you, Randy, any time you want. I give myself away. I don't have to be bought like a flossy dame in a fancy house."

"Thanks. I may wish to take advantage of your offer some day," he answered.

Miss Savoy, the notorious impersonator, came sailing by, in grand drag. "She" gave an appraising glance at Randall, then rushed up, bursting forth in her quick excited manner, "Oh, you sweet, innocent-looking thing! I adore you. You're quite the most beautiful person here. Have you yet committed the unforgivable sin? If not, you must let me teach you!"

"What is it?" asked Randall.

"Well, there are really two of them, one for men and one for women. But I know them both. Dearie, I'm certainly glad you are poor and have no clothes to wear. It makes you show off your beautiful body.

111

Now me, I have to dress extravagantly and be the village cutup to get any attention. Nevertheless, I get it, dearie, all I want. Your mother—" (referring to himself) "—is here to tell you that. Come around and see me when you've nothing else to do." Miss Savoy passed on.

Painter's three models came in wearing veils, pink, light blue and delicate green. But still Randall continued to be the belle of the ball.

An anomalous-looking masculine woman, Miss Bull-Mawgan, and her inseparable friend, Elsie Dike, dropped in, "Just to look at the scenery," said La Bull-Mawgan in her deep masculine type of voice. Really, she had her eye on the models. But Elsie always kept close to her friend for fear that some of the money would be spent on another one. Though it was an evening party, both wore mannish riding clothes. La Bull-Mawgan stepped up to Randall— "Really, my dear, I can't tell whether you are a boy or a girl. I wish I knew."

"Well, don't call me either; just call me *it*," hinted Randall delicately.

"But it does make such a difference, you know," said La Bull-Mawgan. "I'll find out from Painter. He'll tell me." She passed on, followed by her Elsie.

Just then the policeman on the beat entered. He had been apprised of the entertainment by Robert, Painter's butler, and dropped in to have a bit of the liquid cheer which was being so freely served. Randall had often seen him on the avenue and been struck with his magnificent masculine beauty. Of course he was Irish, or of Irish descent. What wonderful lovers they are, those Irish. Connoisseurs say that they are the best, but mercenary. He called to Randall: "Hello, little one, come and help me drink this!"

He smiled and showed perfect, even teeth. His eyes were blue-gray, set off by dark lashes and brows; his hair almost black; his skin smooth, fair, tinted pink, with blotches of red on the cheeks, along the jaws and at the edges of his ears. His hair had a wave like an artificial marcel. His height, his erectness, his deep voice all made an irresistible appeal to Randall. He was infatuated! He knew he could not resist him, and in fact no longer wished to try. Evidently this patrolman appealed to him for the time being. He would take what the gods so kindly offered at the moment, and went to him. Randall permitted him to make the advances, for they prefer it that way, and quickly finding the air hot and oppressive this lovely man in blue piloted him to the back stairway. Luckily, no one else had discovered it. He opened his overcoat and shared it with Randall, cuddling against his warm body, feeling the beauty of his tense muscles. "Do you like me, kid?" he asked.

Intuition prompted Randall to reply in his idiom, "You bet yer life I do."

"Do yuh want me?"

In answer Randall wrapped his arms about him and rested his head against his chest. "My first man in uniform," he thought as he slipped open the buttons of the officer's blue blouse. The fragrance of this firm and burly body thrilled him. He could feel the leather of the cop's belt holster creak as they moved, and he kissed his mouth as if he were a young girl upon her first date with the man of her dreams.

But tenderness was cast away after only their first few moments together. Fresh passion filling the police officer with unbridled lust, he grabbed the globes of Randall's nude buttocks with rough hands and pulled the smaller, leaner man's beautiful body upon his own. Lifting Randall into the air from beneath the shoulders, he licked and chewed upon his well-formed breast, teasing each teat with his tongue and teeth. Randall loved being held and manipulated in such a way, and covered his man in blue with pecking kisses. Then suddenly, Randall was turned around, such that his hindquarters faced the officer. What flimsy flap of cloth was left over the crack was torn violently away, and Randall was invaded with the fleshy muzzle of this Irishman's personal weapon.

"Hey, Randy!" grunted the cop. "You're a nice 'un, that's fer shure." And he kept at Randall's backside over and over till he discharged his meaty gun deep within his bowels. It stood to reason that Randall should have to play the woman's role to such a he-man. No police officer would get caught dead giving up such an intimate area, either in public or private.

He felt no remorse. Before they returned to the others the cop said, "What about lending me five dollars!"

Randall was more discreet than penurious. Beneath his deerskin belt he had a wad; he made the loan. Shortly after, he and Henri left.

Randall met the cop again on the avenue the next week, and was greeted coldly: "Don't hang around. I got a regular girl; works for Miss Gool. Goin' to get spliced nex' week. Fix you up with a couple friends of mine. What say? There comes the boss! Beat it!"

He walked away wondering what this cop's friends would be like.

In telling Henri of it later he said: "Do you suppose one cop is just as good as another?"

Randall had not even been hurt by the policeman's bluntness.

He began to speculate as to whether he was a typical masochist.

At last Randall had reached the stage where he could laugh not only at others but at himself too—the most saving accomplishment one can possess.

CHAPTER
19

Randall was very busy for months, working hard during the day and attending classes evenings and at odd hours. Once a week, when Saturday came, he permitted himself relaxation. Almost as regularly he brought to a conclusion some flirtation started during the week. Since he did not drink or smoke to any extent, he found that about the only exhausting experience was loss of sleep. So he formed the habit, advised by Henri, of "flopping" at five of a Saturday, sleeping till either eight or nine, relying on food later in the night to make up for the lost dinner. He tried out various types of men. But more and more he found himself drawn toward the athletic type. He told Henri—"They are amenable, these athletes—very!"

Also Randall attended many boxing bouts and thus became acquainted with delightful young pugs from all walks of life. Too, he became acquainted with many college men, sometimes by introduction, quite as often by the simple ruse of asking the direction to some nearby place. As the spring advanced he attended the

Saturday afternoon baseball games. Quite often, learning at which hotels the players were stopping, he would dine there with some of his friends. In a city like New York a professional outdoor athlete can be recognized almost invariably. The baseball players in particular have a very tanned skin, unusually clear bright eyes, very erect carriage, expensive clothing, and a short snappy jerky gait that betrays their quickness of action. All of their movements are swift. Randall tried turning his head with the same speed with which the ball players move. The jerk which resulted made him dizzy and gave him a headache.

Randall's earliest experience had been with men of the intellectual type, muscularly soft; of too soft speech. Now he began to judge his men by two outstanding characteristics: the tones of their voices and the cleanliness of their teeth. With the years, Randall acquired greater charm. He spoke little, only sufficient to keep a man talking about himself, his favorite pursuits, his hopes and ambitions. Randall's wide knowledge of business, his keen appreciation of the true values of life (outside of his questionable love game), his college experiences, all made him desired and respected by these men. They were proud to be loved by him. They would end their description of Randall, "He's been brought out— good and proper—but he's worth knowing."

In summer many of Randall's conquests were made at the bathing beaches. In a swimming suit his own remarkably symmetrical build was shown to perfection. His muscles of steel, beneath skin of velvet, showed to their fullest advantage. Like all of his kind, he looked younger than his years—innocently young. One of his ruses on the beach was to get in the way of a ball, be struck and then, "poor kid," be properly pitied.

Frequently he would swim out to the life savers, look at them and smile. Often as not the life saver is a young Greek god taking this means to save up money to attend college in the fall. They do not make overmuch. An invitation to dine and go to a show after a day's work means just so much more ahead. They start out meaning to be companionable; they end by becoming violent lovers, temporarily, at least. Randall found that the more virile the man, the more readily he succumbed to his open advances.

Sometimes Randall would cross a street where a lovely young policeman was stationed. A simple query as to the location of some nearby place would be the entering wedge. Then he would ask "By the way, what do you smoke? I'll bring you a cigar on my way back." The fictitious errand accomplished, he would return. The next day, or a few days later, he would again pass his way; this time he would have the cigar ready. They were now old friends. Each day would make them better acquainted. By the end of a week, a trip to a theater, or to some summer resort, would be arranged. In telling one of his boon companions of some of his adventures, the less-practiced one remarked, "But I should be so afraid of policemen. How do you broach the subject to them?"

"I don't," answered Randall, "they broach it to me."

"And I suppose you use the language of flowers?"

"Yes, dearie, scarlet pansies!"

Randall Etrange had become a oncer—that is, he was through with a man after one experience.

One Sunday, having spent the afternoon at one of the beaches together, Henri suggested that Randall accompany him to a restaurant in what was beginning to be popularly called "Greenwich Village." Randall had never heard of the eating place before.

Henri described it as "an Italian dump where not the foods, but the people, are what you go to enjoy," and added provokingly, "Wait till you see for yourself."

First they stopped in the basement of the old Brevoort, where at that time one of the gayest and most interesting crowds gathered nightly. From there they went to Tenth Street and west almost to noisy Sixth Avenue. They descended into a basement on the south side of the street, passed through the kitchen and emerged into what had been a backyard but had been converted into a galleried garden. They chose seats on the balcony, close to the railing, where they could both see and, if desired, also be seen. Randall remarked, "It seems very ordinary."

"Wait till they drink some Italian red," said Henri, "then you'll get more than an earful. No one has come here yet and gone away saying that he did not get more than his money's worth."

A fat, pudgy, old, gray, grinning man raised his glass to drink to Randall. He smiled over the brim of his own glass. "Just to keep in practice of being naughty," he informed Henri. Then the old man motioned for them to join his table. Randall shook his head no. A friend of the old man called out to him, "Oh, behave, Jack, be yourself! Can't you see it's fish?"

Billy Pickup entered. Randall went below to have a word with him. As he passed a table at the foot of the stairs, one of the two sitting there nudged the other and spoke audibly, indicating Randall. "Ain't it grand?"

"Grand?" said the other, "It's most marvelously gorgeous. I'd like to make it." He feigned not to hear.

Randall had recently finished a course in abnormal psychology. In this restaurant he saw, with the exception of the actually psychotic, practically every type he had studied about. There were bulldikers with their sweeties; fairies with their sailors or marines or rough trade; tantes (aunties) with their good-looking clerks or chorus molls, and all singing, gesticulating, calling back and forth, in a medley of artificial forced gaiety. An effeminate young man shrieked in an assumed falsetto—"I see a mouse; let me get up on a chair. Protect me, protect me! I demand, I *must* have protection."

"Ah, sit down, you're rockin' the boat. You've mixed your drinks!" a young sailor cautioned.

Another, when opportunity came as the racket subsided temporarily, minced: "Gawd knows my name is pure. Your calumnies are unwarranted. You are slanderous. Don't you insinuate anything about me. I don't have to be insinuated about. My life is an open book. I'm a broad-minded woman. The world sees me as I am. Whoops! I should worry!"

Evidently some sailor had befouled a reputation, for Randall heard someone shriek in falsetto— "Sailor boy, if you don't take back those indecent words, I'll bring my longshoreman over here and he'll almost choke you to death. He's big enough. He's done it to me several times. At first I thought I'd never get over it."

The bulldikers, with few exceptions, were more quiet. But there was one blonde, "Dolly" they called her, not more than eighteen, pink cheeked, exquisite, extremely neat in collar and tie, a mannish coat, and a short tight skirt. As she removed a boy's hat she revealed beautiful hair combed straight back like a college man's. Randall was attracted to this miss. The blonde was sufficiently inebriated to be talkative. She walked up to Randall and began, "Listen, dearie, this is no place for you. Go back where you belong. I know high-grade people when I see them. Used to be one of them too. You don't belong here. This life has got me; don't let it get you!"

Here sailors came with their "boy friends", hoping they would meet some unattached girl and run away with her, meantime having their food and a drink and not paying for it. There was a continual din, a coming and going, a visiting back and forth between tables which would not be permitted in an uptown place. There was the most open lovemaking between people who should not have given themselves away in public.

Acquaintances met, rushed madly up to each other, embraced, kissed. One gushed, "Sweetheart," another, "Dearie." A verbose queenly one burst forth to her sister, "You're looking most marvelously grand. I declare the way you keep your youth and beauty is a source of wonder all along Broadway. You must give me the secret too. Of all things, I must be young."

A marine, overhearing the last sentence called out, "Young, I don't want 'em young, I want 'em experienced."

"And with money too, don't forget the price!" suggested the boy friend who was with the marine.

An absurd old man went to the piano and begged someone to play his accompaniment. The sole song in his repertory was "When You and I Were Young, Maggie." His appearance was greeted with hoots and screams of "Maggie! Maggie! Maggie!" some in hoarse male voice, some in truly feminine voice, but by far the most in shrieking falsetto. He sang and at the end of the lines where "Maggie" occurs, there were bellows and screams as everyone "Maggied." He finished with eclat; the applause was thunderous. Then, when this part of his exhibition was completed, he quietly went over into a corner to get drunk. "He works in a livery stable," a queen volunteered.

After a lull, with time between for drinks, a fat Jewish boy, with a high-pitched voice, delivered a patter song, with exaggerated rolling of eyes, shimmying movement of shoulders, swaying of hips, wriggling and overdone femininity, as he sang, "I cannot make my eyes behave, nor my lips either."

Here one heard *fruit, banana, meat, fish, tomato, cream,* dozens of everyday words used with double meaning. With their voices pitched high and in imitation of the effusive type of woman, the guests declaimed with the utmost exaggeration possible what they had to say, each and all trying at the same time to be the center of interest. They burlesqued all life. This they designated "camping," and to "camp" brilliantly fixed one's social status.

It sounded very amusing on first hearing.

Another time, yielding to his curiosity, Randall again visited the place. He found that most of the remarks which at first he found funny, were repeated over and over, borrowed, loaned and never repaid, till he was reduced to boredom.

Henri summed it up. "Be liberal! Perhaps it's natural to them; what is natural to them may not be natural to another. Imagine them married. What would their offspring be? Probably even more erratic. Perhaps they are fulfilling their destiny by not marrying. Did you ever consider that? I often think that people who do not wish to have children should not be criticized, for probably there is some basic instinct which prompts them not to be parents. Perhaps they are really not fit to have children."

Henri and Randall ended by discussing marriage in all its phases, polygamy, polyandry, monogamy, and Henri advanced the idea that "This is a hell of a civilization which does not permit each type to live its life as it sees fit."

They discussed illegitimacy, and Randall laughingly quoted, "There are no illegitimate children; only illegitimate parents." Then he went on to describe the lamentations of his last lover, a mutual acquaintance, who had been adopted when a child, and so did not feel sure who his parents were, and was wont to intone tragically, "To think that perhaps I am the child of some couple's night of pleasure."

"As if," said Randall, "we were not all the result of some couple's night of pleasure, whether we are born in or out of wedlock. And thank God they got at least that amount of pleasure out of life."

CHAPTER
20

By this time, Randall had become addicted to cruising, as it is vulgarly called, deliberately walking the streets for the purpose of flirtation, and the ultimate culmination of flirtation.

He narrowed his choice down to one type: the tall, hugely muscled, fair-skinned man with abundantly wavy, lustrous hair, bold blue eyes, and healthy glowing skin. The so-called Irish eye, deep blue, with long, black, curling lashes and dark well-formed brows, would set his heart to beating madly.

In this classification fell most of the professional athletes, many pugilists, many young skilled mechanics, and by far the greater number of the American physically perfect.

Sometimes, after his evening classes, he would saunter down Broadway and pick up "something nice" for a half-hour's diversion. He was always well-stocked with funds these days, and sometimes, when in a great hurry, not wishing to spend time on entertaining, would say, flashing a bill: "I have not time to invite you to eat or to have a drink. Would you be offended if I offered to make it possible for you to seek a pleasant evening's entertainment on your own when we are through?" Even if he did not make such an offer, as often as not the prostitute that is in most men would lead his choice to ask, "What much is there in it for me?" A bargain would be struck, and a heated exchange of physical prowess would follow. More often than not, it would be the cocky street boy who would wind up gasping for breath and nearly swooning under Randall's expert suckings and caressings. Most times there would be some run-down hotel room in which to stage these voluptuous indulgences, but sometimes Randall would feel the hunger of his urges so sharply as to receive a strange man's affections in the dark of a Broadway back alley.

Henri reproached him one evening: "Oh Randy, you are absolutely brazen."

"No," he gave back answer, "just matter of fact. Substitute the word *adroit* and you may be right."

"I wish I had your nerve."

"Nerve? It does not take nerve to say the correct thing sweetly and flatteringly at the right moment."

"Illustrate, please!"

"Last night you saw that man give me the glad eye?"

"Yes, and you reciprocated with an agreeable smile."

"Just so!"

"What did you say when I left you?"

"First I'll tell you what I did not say. I did not ask the time, nor say it was a pleasant evening, nor 'What do you take me for,' but I did say 'Certainly it is pleasant for one as lonesome as I am to receive such pointed attention in a city as big as New York.' Now, I could have said that much with perfect propriety to a plain clothes man. Did that commit me to anything?"

"Then what did he say?"

"He said, 'You looked at me first!' And I smiled—
very, very, *very* sweetly—and answered, 'But who,
getting one glance at you, could help studying you.
Surely you must realize that you are an uncommonly
well-built and fine-looking man.' And he said, 'Not
so bad to look at yourself.' Now that certainly was
making progress. So I queried—'"Not so bad to look
at"?' and then I added, 'But I am very bad to be with;
very, very, *very,* bad to be with. I'm a very, very, *very,*
naughty person—sometimes.' And you know, Henri
Voyeur, how I can lisp that word *very!* I used my
voice, my eyes, my hands and my facial muscles to
express myself. And then he asked 'Just how bad can
you be?' I answered him with another question, boldly putting it up to him, 'Just how bad would you want
me to be?' 'The sky's the limit with me,' said he. I
thought he was a peddler, so I questioned him further: 'The sky's the limit with you, and for how
much?' 'I don't sell anything,' he retorted as if
offended. 'Neither do I,' I hastened to assert. We
bantered back and forth and I managed to keep him
laughing. It is almost axiomatic that if you can make
a man laugh with you, and not at you, you can make
him do almost anything else with you that you wish;
but be sure it is a genuine laugh, for if it's imitation,
that man is dirt! Anyhow, he turned out to be a gorgeous lover, and oncer that I am, I could almost bring
myself to the point—"

"Yes, the point, of course!"

"I don't mean what you mean, but have it your
way! I could almost bring myself to the point of rein-
dulging him, were I not to see him too soon. But that
is impossible. He does not live here, but lives away
down in Texas, and he wants me to visit him there
sometime. Evidently he's rich. Really, he is a friend

worth remembering. He insisted on giving me this ring as a memento."

"Did he have to insist very hard?"

"Oh, be your age!"

"You have all the luck."

"If I do, it's because I'm discriminating. When it's necessary I can be coldly indifferent. There are types that need that too."

Henri changed the subject. "Come on! There's just time to step into Café Martin and see if it's lively."

Alas! Café Martin is no more. It occupied almost a whole block and extended on 27th Street from Broadway to Fifth Avenue. The Broadway side held the cafe, and the Fifth Avenue side the restaurant. That night the orchestra was demonstrating a "novelty." The three pieces had been augmented by Caruso, not in person, but canned Caruso. The effect was not bad. The voice was loud and the rasp of the phonograph was covered by the instrumental accompaniment. Radio music was only being dreamed of then.

Henri and Randall had no sooner stepped through the doors than they received signals from table after table to come over and be guests. It was at Café Martin that the catch phrase, "You must come over," originated. Queer, too, how many of these people were strangers, and in other surroundings would not have been so free and easy. But such was the atmosphere. In those days of legalized traffic in the demon rum, and his little brothers and sisters, cousins, uncles, aunts and grandparents, an evening's entertainment could be comparatively inexpensive.

Henri and Randall joined a group of Wall Street people; the men were talking of trade; the women of housekeeping—the price of meat or fish and how they made their beds; how much they paid a truckman, or a plumber or bricklayer, and how much went to the iceman.

At an adjoining table was a group of near-boys and girls, camping madly. It was agreed by the circumspect and censorious who were present, that the conduct of the people at the adjoining table was unseemly for such a place. That was before the circumspect and censorious had consumed their whiskey-sodas, their pousse-cafés, and other concoctions that delighted them. After the drinks, the rules of etiquette were completely reversed, so much so that eventually the whole crowd was "bounced," if one might apply such a vulgar term to any happening in so elegant a place as Café Martin was. Anyway, they finally "whoops-my-deared" themselves out of the place. Before that happened one of them remarked, "I'd like to have a party with that, wouldn't you, Sammie?" pointing at Randall. "I wonder if I could make it?"

Randall shook his head a violent no.

Then he addressed Randall directly. "Why not?"

"Firstly, because I like my companions to be entirely sober; secondly because there's no appeal."

The reigning Earl of the season came in, looking rather seedy. He had not yet married into millions. Randall admired him for his clever wit. He was an original; reserved in public, but behind closed doors 'twas another story; there he was the most brilliant and scintillant, always the life of the party. Indeed, it was from the Earl that the world-famous Prince learned toe-dancing and how to "strut his stuff."

The entire assemblage was gay. One very emotional young lady, a real woman, wishing to satisfy her exhibitionism, called aloud, for all to hear, "I simply have to dance." She climbed atop one of the tables and danced, a very brief dance, lasting only the time it took the maître d' to walk from the other end of the room.

At Martin's the window shades pulled up from below, not down from above. This revealed a tantalizing glimpse to those outside. Always groups of the pleasure-bound could be seen standing on tiptoe trying to look over the shades and see if there was anything tempting within—no use spending pennies if there was not. The clever ones carried books under their arms to stand on so that they might better see over the shades and spot their prey. The hoi-polloi dubbed them the intellectuals.

The cafe was the gathering place of all the high-grade kept women, wild society woman, dissipated men, ladies of the night, fairies, pimps and "its" of that generation, probably the teachers of today's crop of gay youth that seems to have assimilated everything at a tender age.

In those days, even the women of the demimonde, and their male analogues, comported themselves in public as well as today's so-called respectable young men and women.

By twelve the fun had become fast and furious. Miss Savoy and the famous Mr. (and Miss) Painter were there and laid a wager as to which one could entice the most good-looking people to drink with the party. Randall had taken the seedy Earl into the dark of the café's back room, and taught him a thing or two about hygiene before giving him a marvelous "rimming", which he had recently learned from one of his "tricks." Henri, far more discreet, toyed with himself deep within the folds of his trousers as he looked upon a pair of infinitely handsome young country boys as they were pinched and fondled by their "lady" escorts for the evening. Finally, Savoy and the Painters had became so drunk and reckless that they commissioned some of their companions to go out on Broadway with the order, "Drag in anything nice you see."

Never was there another such evening at the place. It marked the high tide of the Café Martin.

CHAPTER
21

Randall was lucky. Another turn in the market made him independent. He resigned his position and matriculated at one of the universities to finish the pre-medical course which he had previously outlined. It left him much free time, and it is to be feared that some of it he did not use as judiciously as he should have done.

More money of course made him more popular. It always does! He met many handsome young men at college, who, as he said, "needed to be brought out," or "needed to make their bow to society." He treated them well—Saturday luncheons at the prominent hotels; theater parties; dances afterwards, wherever the most enjoyable music could be had. He was somewhat older than these boys, but looked younger. He had the advantage of experience, for which they admired him quite as much as his physical attributes.

Now, college boys are always much sought after by the society buds. One of Randall's chief amusements of a Saturday afternoon and evening was to pit his wiles against the social position of the young set that always crowds about such places as are on the lists approved by the "matrons." The boys would desert any of the buds at any time to do Randall's bidding, that is, so long as he was interested in them.

Many a society marriage quickly followed a jilting by Randall, the "sweet young things" catching the youths on the rebound, as it were. It is often that way—far more often then women generally imagine.

In college Randall was as successful socially as he had been with the Broadway set, though it required a change of method.

"Do something for Alma Mater," was the slogan. He responded nobly and did everything in sight, and if it was not in sight he ferreted it out.

One of the biologists, commenting on him said, "He certainly lives up to his name. He's quite the queerest thing I've ever had in my classes. Learn? He absorbs subjects; but he never asks me a question that is not connected with reproduction. I half believe he does it to embarrass me. He has some theory of his own about glands, too. His own interpretation of sexual variation from the normal is that it is conditioned by functional disturbances of various endocrine glands. At that, he may be right."

What Randall learned about him was even more amusing than what he suspected about Randall.

The biologist was still a halfway Presbyterian, despite his education, and still had many of the inhibitions of that good Christian sect. He liked to draw, and would hire a model, ostensibly to pose for him; he would sit in one corner of the room, watch the handsome, athletically built young man slowly remove his clothes and take a pose. Then he would sigh spasmodically, his hands shoved deeply into his pockets, the better to tease himself into a contained frenzy while watching the youth's rippling muscles and shy disposition, and bring himself to crisis there in front of the poor creature.

"That's all, you can robe yourself," he would then say. And these men he did not secure through the usual agencies, "as these would be too perfect in feature, and too effeminate in build"; instead he would sally out onto a certain stretch of Broadway late at night and pick those up who would take on a "rougher-edged, more he-man type of appearance." Yet he was wont to boast that he had never been immoral.

The French professor told Randall what the biologist had said about him, and the philosophy professor told Randall what a Broadway woman had said to him about the biologist. The criticism of the biologist was the nearest Randall ever came to scandal, at that college.

Of course Randall played the part of the leading lady in the college show of that year, and he lived the part. No wonder! Also he made most of the compact, densely muscled men of the polo team; the tall, lean men of the basketball team; and each of the heavily muscled, soft-edged men of the baseball team. The huge and stocky men of the football team he left for others. He had not time to do everything.

Withal, Randall had a gay life that year. He was making the most of it to fortify himself against the four years of medical school, with its nerve-racking, soul-torturing duties.

CHAPTER
22

As soon as the college examinations were finished, Randall and Henri Voyeur and another friend, Percy Chichi, set out on a summer tour to include the Pacific Coast and as much as possible of that which lay between it and New York.

"My grand cruise," Randall styled it.

They visited Atlantic City in time to attend the famous Iceman's Ball, noted far and wide for the fashionable drags displayed. Now, in Atlantic City, the icemen are all colored and quite as likely to be ladies as men. Nevertheless, all the *famosi* of Philadelphia, and many of those from New York—white, lily-white indeed—attend the function, which is more or less of a panic, of course.

Then they stopped at Philadelphia, and Vine-Streeted to their hearts' content.

They had an evening in Baltimore before going on to assault the social bastions of Washington, and Randall pointed out the hallowed spot where he had been led astray.

At the capital they spent the greater part of a

romantic moonlit night in the ever beautiful Lafayette Park. Five different times Randall took a drive, and never walked back.

In Chicago they did the famous bathing resorts. But they tarried only a little while, for they were anxious, as Henri said, "to get out to the wide open spaces" and to this Percy Chichi added, "Where men are men and women are double-breasted."

In Colorado they stopped at a cattle ranch and were guests at the bunkhouse. Here Randall could be useful and, as always, pitched right in and did everything possible, while Henri became amorous with the cook, and Percy Chichi, who was good at plain sewing, fussed with the cowboys' clothes.

One cowboy Randall found well nigh irresistible. He led him on till the cowpoke was so madly in love with him that he threatened to shoot anyone else who even tried to borrow him for an evening, let alone take him completely away. With his rugged, chiseled features and powerful body all clothed in faded and dusty denims, he had captured Randall's eye from the start. Though the man had been shy at first, it would not be long before Randall had him alone performing some favor or other for the defenseless city slicker.

As a lover the cowboy was as astonishing as any man Randall had taken since he himself was taken by the likes of Teddy and Mr. Fisher. The cowboy had treated him as his "lady" and kissed and caressed him with all the passion and romance of a courting gunslinger. He squeezed and sucked Randall's nipples as if they were "perfect little titties," and he called Randall's twitching anal sphincter his "hot little pussy chute," or "daddy's little squeeze box." He made Randall straddle him and ride him as he would a bronco horse, and his repeated smackings and slappings of Randall's thighs and buttocks drove Randall to crisis, forcing him to shoot jets of come several times each night.

Of course Randall would become bored with such a usual situation. He wished to go on to Frisco, to the gayer life there.

The cowboy, tall, tanned, handsome, strong and virile, was so infatuated that he could not endure the thought of separation from Randall. Over and over when they were alone he would say, "I wish it was possible for us to marry. God! Wouldn't that be great?"

"That would be just too great for anything," Randall assured him. "It would lead to the murder of two people at least, that of myself and of the first man other than you that I looked at."

"But you wouldn't want to look at any other man!"

"No, not till you had worn yourself out; which wouldn't be long at your present rate. Then I'd be looking for something more peppy while you were sleeping and afterwards you'd swing the gun. We'd better thank God that marriage is entirely out of the question."

"Well, love is not," sighed Cowboy. "Crawl right up into my arms, honey, and love me some more." They were off again.

Randall loved the passion of this man of the cattle ranges, but his experience had taught him that satisfaction only could result in a nervous exhaustion that would be displayed by irritability and the end would be dispute, jealousy, recriminations and eventually hatred. He wished to preserve a happy memory of this cowboy and also he wished him to remember

Randall as tenderly. He must leave him while he still longed for his vigorous embraces. But in his present frame of mind the cowboy could not let him go.

Now, when Randall would steal up behind him, put his arms around him and kiss him on the neck, Cowboy still became wildly excited and amorous, such a contrast to the affair with one lover who, toward the last, had so often blurted out venomously, "For God's sake, can't you ever leave me alone? I want to do some work once in a while. How can I think with you pawing me and smearing yourself all over me all the time?"

Better to break Cowboy's heart, and the little that was left of his own, than to spoil their remembrance of each other by eventual hatred.

Besides, he knew he could not be constant. Nor, he realized when he thought it over calmly, did he wish to be. Had it been possible he would have chosen to love Cowboy till he was tired of him, and then come back to him when he was tired of somebody else—a lovely arrangement, for Randall. Well he knew that once Cowboy's insistence began to wane, he would be seeking stolen sweets elsewhere. What had been ideal must remain an ideal!

The last night of his stay they rode far out on the desert. They tethered their horses, as they had brought supper with them. After eating, Cowboy piled one saddle atop the other and spread a blanket on the ground. He lay with his back against the saddles, Randall cuddled in his arms. Together they watched the glory of the sunset fade. As the twilight deepened, Randall snuggled closer. He loosened the collar of his shirt and ran his hand softly over Cowboy's warm chest and felt the steady beating of his heart. He kissed his hands, his brow, his cheeks, his lips, his eyelids, over and over he kissed him everywhere.

Randall's repeated caresses raised Cowboy's passions to a fever pitch. He inserted his tongue into Randall's mouth more deeply than Randall had ever felt before. At once Randall's shirt was torn open, the buttons let fly to the ground. Cowboy's fingers played his ribs, sliding up and down the length of his breast and his belly. Randall moaned, straddling this extraordinary man's denim-clad thighs and rubbing the mound of his crotch with his small, round buttocks.

Soon they were thrashing, their lovemaking kicking up small clouds of dust from the prairie ground. How Randall adored being manhandled, tossed about like a rag doll by this man who smelled of horse and hay. Taken completely and turned about, Randall then was thrown upon the piled saddles such that his sweet behind was pushed high and made vulnerable in the firelight. Cowboy was upon him in seconds, gripping and smacking each buttock with joyous enthusiasm. With each slap Randall's erection grew more livid and powerful upon the hard leather.

When Cowboy could stand no more, he laid his great member downward and fell upon Randall's behind with a single piston thrust. Gripping the horn and the rear of the saddle for support, Cowboy began to fuck Randall's fanny with the type of gusto for which his kind is known. Randall had never known a man before who made love with such unbridled glee. The very idea was enough to unleash a torrent of emotion from him and cause his cock to tremble and burst with ejaculate even upon the rough cowhide. Cowboy himself simply kept pounding away, that is till he could stand no more himself, and then he withdrew his lengthy skewer to fire his seed in a pearlescent arc over Randall's plump butt and onto his tapered, muscular back.

141

They returned to the bunkhouse. Cowboy hastily retired for the night. He would not kiss Randall before the others. He was quite exhausted; but not randy Randall! He was still aquiver, wild with an excitement that would kindle any man, no matter what his pretensions to virtue.

Had the cowboy seen what he did he would have killed him. There were other young men working at the Bar Star Ranch, some almost as vigorous and attractive as Cowboy. Randall lingered at the bunkhouse door. He forgot his intention to preserve an ideal. To use his own words in telling of what he later described as the greatest night of his life, "What I did is just nobody's business." Suffice it to say, he awoke in the predawn light in a great heap of denim shirts and pants, leather chaps, riding boots, and well over a thousand pounds of assorted sweaty, snoring, masculine flesh. Whatever it was, he had done it.

He and Henri and Percy Chichi left the next day, and if the send-off was a hearty one, 'twas because Randall had given the impression to each of his separate dozen lovers that he was the favorite. To them his visit had been a welcome, relief-giving interlude.

Randall wrote to Cowboy often for a time; then gradually his letters were less frequent and far less lengthy, and finally he put in an artistic touch of despair as his wanderings took him further away: "Cowboy, dear sweetheart, it seems that Fate is determined to keep us separated. My memories of you will always remain the sweetest of my life." That was after a silence of a month. He never wrote to him again.

Cowboy missed Randall so. In desperation he married the pretty daughter of a saloon-keeper, and probably that marriage was happier than it otherwise would have been. The wife was accepted as a makeshift, a compromise, as are so many wives—and husbands too. And as such, she was judged and her limitations easily tolerated; for after all, toleration is a fairly good basis for a successful marriage.

CHAPTER
23

In San Francisco the trio, Randall, Henri Voyeur and Percy Chichi, were the guests of the famous Beach-Bitsches.

The Beach-Bitsche family had settled in California so long ago as to be eligible for all of the wonderful societies which there exist for the annihilation of the inferiority complex. Coming from Europe, the family had originally settled in Randall's natal village, Kuntzville, Pa. Then the name was invariably spelled Bütsche. Eventually, the family being prolific, and procreation then being held to be naught but a virtue, they had increased to such an extent that expansion became necessary. Thus one branch settled here, another there. So they had spread and intermarried till they were allied to all of the "best" families of America.

With attempted Anglicization of the name, some had changed it to Beach; some had retained the original spelling, but some, as if to take the curse off the name, modified the patronymic by combining it beautifully by means of the aristocratic hyphen, with the name of the maternal grandparent, or even with any nice name which they fancied. Some Frenchified the name, making it La Bitsche.

There was an elegant Miss Drexel-Bitsche of Philadelphia; also there were the Brown-Bütsches of New Rochelle (very classy indeed), and a whole Bitsche-Fuchs family in New York. But no matter what variations they made of the name, they all still belonged to the same family, and retained the dominant family characteristic.

The California branch had long been represented by the Beach-Bitsche family; the Chicago branch by the Bitsche-Beach family, the St. Louis branch by the Bitsche-Bitsche family, the New Orleans off-shoot by the La Bitsche family, and New York by every possible combination of the name; there were even Levy-Bütsches, Cohen-Bütsches and other Yiddish Bütsches. In California, the elegant and very accomplished Old Aunty Beach-Bitsche was the head. She and the rest of her kin were (quite properly) in no sense ashamed of the name, and clung to it tenaciously.

In more recent years, with great wealth, the family tree has begun to die out at the top, as is usual in all families that are too far removed from the necessity of working, and, incidentally, living regularly. Nevertheless, some one of the Bütsches, hyphenated or otherwise, occasionally gets married and proceeds to multiply, that the breed may not be lost to the world; anyway, there is always someone left to live worthily up to the name.

Old Aunty Beach-Bitsche, a very understanding sort of person, laid out a program for the entertainment of her guests, such as she knew they would like.

First she arranged with Reggie Beach-Bitsche, her nephew, to take her guests on a slumming tour, always the chief objective of visitors from the East. So they explored the Barbary Coast and visited the Bull Pen and the Log Cabin, places which Miss Savoy, in "her" infinite wisdom, had recommended to them as being especially entertaining.

Then they visited Chinatown. A very rich merchant, seeing Randall, became enamored of him at once. Certainly he appealed to Randall. With time something might have come of it, after Randall's fears had been allayed. He accepted his jade, but not his love; he was irrationally afraid of leprosy.

Perhaps one of the most amusing episodes of their visit to California was an evening spent at a party across the Bay. Here were gathered together, at some sort of old home party, all of the famous Bütsches of California. Among those present were Freddie Bütsche and his brothers, Percy and Clarence, each renowned for some special accomplishment. Then too there were some of the O'Neill-Bütsches, Riley-Bütsches, Jones-Bütsches, and other Bütsches without number. Also there were Junior Beach and Marjorie Beach and Sissy Beach, who had dropped what to them had seemed the undesirable part of their hyphenated name. They had been taken severely to task for this by old Aunty Beach-Bitsche, who never lost an opportunity to castigate them for this action and went about roaring, "You dirty whelps, you ought to be ashamed to face the rest of us. I'm proud of being just what I am, a Beach and a Bitsche."

There had just been one of those so-called scandals when someone in San Francisco had done as he or she pleased, had been publicly "exposed," arrested and possibly incarcerated in a dungeon for doing what God (if there is one) had given the impulse to do. Everybody was excited by the injustice.

147

Sissy Beach spoke in a high-pitched voice: "I wish to Gawd there was some place in these U.S.A., where a temp'ramental person could lead an untrammeled life and be and act natural. As it is, the rich can get away with anything, but the poor must live by laws which should never have been perpetrated. Conduct! What right has any individual to be interested in my conduct, be that what it may, so long as I do no harm to him and do not interfere with another's right to life, liberty and the pursuit of happiness."

He thrust between his lips a cigarette holder of exaggerated length (anything Sissy had to do with would be exaggerated), and pulled it back and forth as if to stimulate his imagination.

"What's the matter with Palm Beach?" asked a pretty young thing who had not been out long.

Sissy whooped excitedly, "For the rich, the very rich only, not for the likes of you and me."

"Try Butte, Montana," suggested the ever-practical, old, fat and most sophisticated Bütsche present, indeed none other than Old Aunty Beach-Bitsche.

"And why should one retire to the desert?"

Randall answered that: "I just came from the so-called desert, and the most thrilling episode of my life."

"You tell 'em, dearie," commanded Old Aunty Beach-Bitsche in her affected high-pitched campy voice, and then she added, "I've been for long stretches of time in Paris and Berlin, where freedom is a thing that is lived, not talked about, and I'd stay there were it not that I crave the American type. And so do the Europeans, let me tell you. Why, the greatest thrills of my life have been in the desert mining camps, and out on the cattle ranges."

So followed Randall's story of himself and Cowboy. All listened open-mouthed and yearned.

When he had finished, one of the younger, more imaginative and still idealistic Beach-Bitsches, Miss Kitty, began a wish-fulfillment daydream—

"Wouldn't it be grand if there were an island or something—"

"Or something," contemptuously uttered one of the aunties, then sniffed. "Now, don't get all mixed up with Homer and Tennyson and the Island of Lesbos too. Go on!"

"Let me see," the other continued pensively, "where was I? Oh, yes, wouldn't it be grand, wouldn't it be just perfectly, marvelously gorgeous, if there were an island, or some place, an Island of Bliss—"

"You are sure you mean bliss?"

"Yes, an island or some place where we could all live or go to easily whenever we pleased and do all the things we wish to do without thought of the narrow-mindedness of others."

"You are asking too much. Oh, for the Isle of Crete! You are wishing a return to the good old Pagan times when all honor was paid even to prostitutes."

"No, not asking too much, just asking for natural morality, a thing which varies with each bird, beast and human and for which due allowance is not made in law-making. Do people, for instance, indulge in 'love' for the express purpose of procreation, or do they enjoy the love and incidentally have a child? Until they do the former (which has never been and never will be), they have no right to criticize those who indulge in love for love's sweet sake, and by love, you know what I mean—no matter how a person may love."

"Are you talking of sexual aberration now?" queried Old Aunt Minnie.

"Well, I'd not call anything by such a lewd-sound-

ing name. I'm elegant, I am." She went through the
dainty motion of replacing a stray back curl. "I only
defecate, micturate, deflate, and indulge in emesis
and tussion as occasion may require. Now look those
things up in the dictionary, dearie, and you'll at least
know how to express them, if not to do them, ele-
gantly in public."

"Oh, you slay me!" ejaculated Old Aunt Minnie.

Marjorie Bitsche then contributed her bit to the
conversation—"Pish, tush and shush! She's getting
refined!"

"Getting refined! I've always been. I was born that
way."

"Born that way! You were put into a dirty hole the
same as the rest of us and came out the same way we
did, in a cabbage patch. Much, quite too much of
your assumed elegance is purest affectation. Says the
bard: 'A rose by other name would smell as sweet.'
Without going into too much detail, dearie, let me
assure you" (she pronounced this so meticulously
that it suggested another word) "let me assure you
that a smell by any other name would be just as bad.
You can defecate and micturate all you wish, but that
won't indicate that your intestinal peristalsis and your
kidney functions are any more normal than mine, or
any less offensive, e'en though I describe them in
older and far plainer English. So there!" She gave a
defiant toss of her head.

"Are you razzing me?"

"Suit yourself. And as for being born elegant,
you'd be the one to hold that you were born of an
immaculate conception."

"Well, I was!"

"There she goes. What did I tell you, girls?"

In her precise, prissy way, Miss Beach-Bitsche
explicated: "Not only I, but every other person, dog,

150

fish, bird, animal being that is not reproduced by—"
(here she swallowed hard) "—parthenogenesis, is the
result of an immaculate conception. No matter how
gross, how accidental, or how brutal the sexual
congress may be, any volitional act of the participant
certainly ends with the freeing of the spermatozoa to
swim like eels. If God chooses to bring the ovum and
the spermatozoa together, He does so, and then, and
then only, does actual conception take place." (Again
she tossed her head grandly.) "Far be it from me to
criticize any act of God and hold it is not immaculate.
Quite the reverse!"

"How profound you can be, Kitty. I wonder if
everybody understands you. You've been taking up
with someone learned, I see! Go right on! You'll
soon have us all edified, if not educated."

So Miss Kitty Beach-Bitsche continued. "On our
island, wouldn't it be gorgeous to have the men, the
real he-men, wear uniforms?"

She had struck a responsive note. With that they
all became enthusiastic, as their kind will about anything useless and impractical, and first one and then
another made a suggestion.

Ella Bitsche, who was legal-minded, said: "The only
sins will be theft, blackmail, cheating at cards and murder."

Marjorie, who loved wild episodes, stipulated:
"There will be no breach of promise suits permitted,
for anyone of any sense knows that when one is all
pashed up, he, she or it is not really responsible and
therefore any promise secured at such a time should
not be binding."

Minnie La Bitsche, who loved gaiety, catalogued
the amusements: costume balls, drags, dance halls
where one might dance as and with whom one
pleased regardless of sex or the brand of perfumery

used. Jazz orchestras made up of men or women who really knew how to.

"I like polo players," piped up Maude La Bitsche. "Have some polo players. I like to see their bare arms and their bare necks and chests."

"Chauffeurs and army officers for me," piped up Sissy Beach. "Puttees are my fetish."

Then Old Aunty Beach-Bitsche, the fat, gray sophisticate, added her preference: "Don't forget the women in blue overalls and blue shirts, the plumbers and steamfitters and such. I like 'em rough and strong and sturdy, you know."

"Oh, Aunty Beach-Bitsche, don't! Rough trade of the womanly persuasion, after you're through with it, is such a bore!"

A Miss Jackson-Browning, who had not been present at the beginning of the conversation, asked: "Are you talking of a Turkish heaven?"

"No," Miss Kitty explained, "just talking of freedom as it should be practiced in the U.S., or any other place professing to be a republic. We are planning an island to be peopled with men who are wise and tolerant, women who are understanding, a place where everyone would do as he pleased so long as he did not injure others in doing it; a place where each one's own brand of morals would be respected, conditioned as they so often are by prenatal developments."

Soft-voiced Old Aunt Minnie was the next to state a preference. Aunt Minnie, who loved reciprocity, stipulated, "Don't forget to have some of those luverly graceful chorus boys live on your island too."

"Why, Minnie!" shrieked one, "I didn't know you loved chorus molls. I'll have to get my panties pleated and begin my daily exercise with a lipstick and an eyebrow pencil."

"Now, Kitty, please go on with your enchanting island," Randall besought her.

So Miss Beach-Bitsche continued: "We'd have ladies of the day and ladies of the evening and ladies who are not ladies and gentlemen who are not gentlemen, and a house of all nations where girls from every clime could dwell and appear in our free and easy society in their native costumes, or lack of costumes. We'd have gambling with cards and wheels and numbers and we'd have swimming pools and athletic stadiums and all sorts of sports, including all the famous indoor sports. And we'd have—"

"Now, Kitty, who would finance such an enterprise?"

"Well, the jewelers would be with us and most of the lawyers and doctors, and in fact most of the professional men and women in all walks of life. You don't know your geography if you don't know that. There'd be just millions for it—millions of people, I mean, if you could get them to tell the truth."

"How you do calculate. Some more bitch arithmetic!"

"And now have you finished with all your gorgeously marvelous wishing?"

"I think so," Kitty lisped.

"Well, you left one thing out. How about having a few good fairies on your dream isle to wave their magic wands and give you everything you want?"

The party broke up. The Eastern visitors received numerous invitations. Everyone said, "You must come over." Miss Ella added, "Just let me know when you're coming and I'll bake a cake"; Marjorie lilted, "Do come whenever you can"; Kitty, "Bring your knitting and your plain sewing and I'll teach you a few fancy stitches and some embroidery—California stuff."

153

What followed was a delightful week of California.

The Percival Beach-Bütsches gave a drag the next night under the protection of people higher up. Henri, Randall and Percy Chichi were invited. Randall decided to be brilliant and go as a queen. He had with him a drag—"Something gorgeous, simply devastating," Percy Chichi called it. Henri and Percy had the fun of helping him with his elaborate makeup. Randall gave one final glimpse into a full-length mirror and exclaimed, "I'm sure I don't know myself. No wonder I'm a misunderstood person with little dabs of paint making my ladylike features look like what they ain't."

Arriving at the party, Randall made a triumphant entry. Everywhere he was greeted with exclamations of approval or surprise—"Gorgeous! Marvelous! You slay me! You slay me *completely*." Randall was a long way from the hayfields of Pennsylvania. He had lived up to the prophecies of one of his former doting school teachers: "My dear, you will go far."

A member of congress wished to make love to him. So did a lieutenant of police, even though he explained his real status to them. The male man, the real virile he-man, could not fail to become amorous on seeing Randall disguised as a queen.

"Where is your king?" someone queried.

"I'm a Virgin Queen, like the kind you read about in history," camped Randall.

Two of the younger Beach-Bütsches were there, dressed as gamins, sucking on huge peppermint-flavored candy sticks. When Randall stepped out of character long enough to grab one and draw its sizable girth down into his throat so deeply as to thrill and horrify the crowd, the merriment was hilarious.

So spontaneous was he.

Only one who has camped in the Far West would

know how to appreciate and enjoy such a party to the full.

Dozens of high-grade prostitutes and kept women of the town were at the drag, all determined to honor the Eastern visitors and make the occasion a memorable one. Some lovely women from the Bull Pen had been invited, one of them, the most beautiful of all, a three-way woman who had been educated in Paris and spoke French, Spanish and English.

The prestige of the Bulls and the Dikes was shed over the affair, and these people, along with the Bütsches, prominent as they were, could carry any social function to a glorious success.

Randall and Henri and Percy Chichi must have attended half a dozen balls while there, and then— after the balls!

Always Randall went in his royal disguise. This acting did not fail to stamp his character; forever after his gestures were queenly. He learned not only to play the part but to live the part.

Among the crowd that Randall met was one of the Dikes who went by the nickname of "Bobby" though her real name was Valerie. "Bobby" was wild about baseball and played it like a man. Randall was wild about men and liked to watch them move when playing ball. He and Bobby became great pals, for one could pass along to the other the good things that the other did not care to accommodate.

Bobby was clever; had to be. Her family was rich, but thought to reform Bobby by cutting her allowance. Bobby reacted characteristically and, like so many of her kind, lived off other women, trading on the admiration which she was able to inspire. At that time she was featuring Miss Fish, the very rich and powerful. One afternoon she insisted that Randall lay aside his regal role long enough to call with her on Miss Fish.

155

Miss Fish was in the mood to be entertaining, in her way.

She showed them the recently acquired old paintings and told the price paid: she showed them the wonderful new swimming pool and priced that; "the Fish family bathtub" Bobby dubbed it. She showed them her wonderful organ, which had cost her so much. Everything Miss Fish possessed was either "wonderful" or "quite wonderful."

Miss Fish could never see enough of Bobby, who, of course, was always bored, but had to endure, if she wished to borrow money. Really she had brought Randall along as buffer. It was "Bobby dear, come here, dear, and let me fix your tie, dear." (Bobby of course wore severely tailored clothes, like any other collar-and-tie woman.) "Bobby dear" went there. "Now, Bobby dear, take my hand while I mount the stops. There, dear." He released Bobby and gave her a pat on the shoulder. "I don't know what I'd do without you, dear. You are such a help, dear." Bobby rolled her eyes mischievously at Randall and Randall smiled and nodded his head in understanding.

In commenting on Miss Fish afterwards, Randall said, "Despite all her wealth, she's quite the most ignorant woman I've ever met. Why, she does not even know enough to shave the hair from her axillae and use deodorants, to say nothing of such gentle arts as eyebrow plucking and the use of perfumes. Where and what kind of an education has she picked up? For Gawd's sake, somebody give her a dictionary, and tell her to look up the useful words and the anatomical names for the more discussed parts of the human body. The way she describes things they sound revolting, whereas if she used high-sounding euphemisms, they'd perhaps sound artistic, if not appealing." Miss Fish had reached that stage of life where she enjoyed reminiscing rather than performance, and was given to telling in the utmost detail all about her various escapades and peculiar adulteries; of how she was first seduced, and how many in turn she herself had brought out.

Randall and Bobby on their way home dropped into the tearoom which the Bütsches patronized at that time and where some of their number could be found every afternoon. Here they would linger and rant and rave about their johns, "parties" with this one and "parties" with that one and almost invariably when pressed to give details would draw in their lips tightly and say, "My lips are sealed."

"Yes, now!" camped Randall.

There they ran into Sissy Beach, and nothing would do but that they should promise to go across the bay again that night to attend another party. Before going they went back after Miss Fish, who would not miss anything for the world, especially as the famous Bulls and Dikes were to be there too, and, lucky stroke, they also picked up Henri Voyeur and Percy Chichi; for the party, which started out to be a grand dinner, ended in a panic. However, the first part of the evening passed off gaily enough.

Among those present were Miss Ella Bitsche and several of her sisters, all of whom were obsessed with the desire to look like Oscar Wilde. It's more than possible that they did, for physiological and psychological peculiarities seem to be reflected in the visage. For instance, the goitrous, the hydrocephalic, the acromegalic, the kiphotic, each bears a resemblance to its own kind. Miss Ella used to carry in her pocket a photograph of the great poet. She wore her hair cut the same fashion. She was fond of decking herself out à la Wilde and reading "Reading Gaol," for the benefit of anyone who had the patience to listen. Usually auditors were scarce, for each desired to strut his own stuff and be the center of amazement, if not of amusement. Miss Bitsche's recitations were quite likely to be interrupted by "Oh! Shut your trap, Ella! I want to show the new queen's walk," or "You Wilde woman, don't you ever get tired of your own voice?"

To these and like comments Miss Bitsche would invariable reply—"You have no Art" and the answer usually was "You don't know the half of it, dearie; just try me and see."

In the midst of a little spat between the Bitsche sisters, the "hostess" announced dinner. He did not call it dinner, but coming into the drawing room performed a curtsy in the manner of a queen's lady in waiting and intoned: "The feast is spread," then led the way into the dining hall. Pridefully he explained, "I have not only a feast for the eye, but something substantial to satisfy the taste of any and every one."

He displayed a heterogeneous mixture: "Fish, all kinds of seafood, meat, chicken, cheese, tomatoes, fruit, bananas, nuts, anything you want," he camped, "and if you don't see what you want, ask for it, or go out and drag it in. Now, don't go away and say that you didn't have a good time."

And there were good things to drink too—and *eau de vie*.

Some tough sailors whom some gay thing had cruised and dragged into the party, a semi-pro pinch-hitter and a local pug of course drank too much (seeing the drinks were free), and preliminary to passing into coma, reached the stage of self-importance that could only be gratified by being disagreeable, overbearing and destructive. They made openly sneering remarks about their lovely "hostess" and his boy and girl friends. The pug wished to put the gloves on with Bobby Dike, who was angry enough to accept the challenge, but specified that the bout should be without gloves and that Queensberry rules should be ignored; that the bout should end only with a knockout and that any implement within arm's reach might be used, and he added, "You can forget I am a woman, or even anything remotely resembling a woman."

At this point Miss Fish screamed, "Oh! I'm so nervous! I'm so nervous I must leave at once. I cannot afford notoriety. I have so much to lose."

"Yes," said one Bitsche, "you've millions to lose, by the time you die, and you're always afraid of having to pay hush money!"

Henri and Randall saved the situation; they knew their stuff, and knew how to handle rough trade when it became too rough.

Henri took Bobby by the arm and persuaded her to walk out on the verandah with him where he had something to tell her.

Randall stepped over to the "tough guys" and guffawed, "She's funny! Why, it makes me laugh to think of her tackling anybody as big as you. It would be like a kitten trying to claw a lion" (just in time he had thought to change *dog* to *lion*). "Now, let's have some more drinks. Aunty Beach-Bitsche, break out some more liquor."

Randall poured out a stiff one for each of the men and suggested bottoms up, and then another and another. He pretended to drink too. One passed out at once. The others became less noisy and more fisheyed. In fifteen minutes the toughs were all in a state of coma.

Then the dirty work began, the Bütsches' revenge.

Randall obtained assurance that these men did not know their way to the houseboat. Then one by one the inebriates were carried bodily farther down the dock and laid on an old scow, but first the belongings of one set was transferred to the pockets of the sailors. Then the scow was towed out a little way from the dock and set afloat.

The court records the next day told the story and the newspaper headlines announced "Drunken Sailors Battle Drunken Civilians After Robbing Them and Stealing a Scow."

When it was all over, Old Aunty Beach-Bitsche lapsed into very uncouth vernacular and exclaimed, "Well, I've had my bellyful of rough trade."

Sissy Beach could not refrain from being cattish. "I'll say you have!"

"Oh, you slay me! You traduce me," wailed hoary-headed old Aunty Beach-Bitsche.

CHAPTER
24

They had had a wonderful time in California. Randall's last vacation was finished. Ahead of him lay four years of hard work in the medical school, with summers spent clerking in hospitals, and all that to be followed by the grind of two years of internship. He enrolled in one of the very excellent Philadelphia medical schools.

His work began in mid-September. He was fascinated by the subjects. Each day satisfied his craving to know some of the secrets of life. His very effeminacy was an asset in the work. He could cut, snip and dissect more deftly than his more masculine fellow students. He studied in a different way from the others. They memorized. He correlated, if need be, using drawings and writing as an aid to memory. Almost incessantly he was at work, not diverted by sports or social climbing. Of course his fellow students despised him—at first.

One thing Randall permitted himself: Saturday night outings. These he would often spend either in Philadelphia's Chinatown or at the famous Baden-

Baden on Vine Street. Occasionally he attended the weekend costume balls, where he usually walked off with the prize. At intervals he would flit to Washington or New York, but the reward in pleasure did not seem to be commensurate with the expense and trouble of such extensive traveling. Philadelphia has more than plenty!

Of course Christmas week in New York was different; but even ever-fascinating New York was discarded by Randall on New Year's Day for Philadelphia's great offering, the Mummer's Parade. In this he always made it a point to take part, appearing as a queen, the role he played so well. And how regal he could be! Completely so. The word "queen" is old Anglo-Saxon for woman. Certainly it should be as easy for one as another to play the part. After all, there's much truth in the saying that the Colonel's lady and Julie O'Grady are sisters between—no, under their skins. Randall loved to flirt with the real he-men who lined the route, to return quip for quip and jibe for jibe.

In those days prohibition was not. There were drinking places everywhere, ranging from sawdusty saloons to gilded hotel bars, and though Randall did not care much for drinking, he did like the flattering attention of men in general and especially of he-men in particular, those he selected from the crowds who paid him court. Then the place to find men, real he-men, was in the drinking places. Now they are widely scattered throughout the country on drunken fishing and hunting parties, willing as ever but so much more difficult to locate.

Men viewed the Mummer's Parade with the very object of paying court. For one of the flirtatious disposition, as Randall had become, this was a gala occasion. There was trade everywhere. Of course there was always the usual sprinkling of dirt, but the clever ones, with their sharpened sensibilities, their so-called intuition, were almost mind-readers.

And the trade, both rough and otherwise, adored Randall, for he could always amuse them—make them laugh, man's great craving. Indeed, some of the rough trade was not so rough after all, and could be very gentle between the sheets. Randall was of the type they all liked to cuddle, and he enjoyed all the petting they were able to bestow, if their bodies and mouths were clean and they had a clean body odor. He averred that a real healthy, clean he-man has a definite sex odor that is agreeable. Certainly he'd had experience enough to know, if anyone would. So, using his eyes, ears, olfactory senses and judgment, Randall picked and chose. He was showered with needless gifts. Men were forever wishing to give him this, that and the other things.

Once, when Miss Jacqueline Bitsche, then a novice, complained to him that men were so expensive, Randall laughed and told her—"One piece of trade," as he dubbed a lover, "should be good for luncheon, another for tickets to the matinee, another for dinner, and still another for theater in the evening." Certainly Philadelphia always offered entertainment when Randall wanted it.

So passed the first year, made up of much hard work alternated with a few spots of high play.

The medical class discussed him much. Of course, most of them continued to despise him. To begin with, he was above them in native intelligence, and also too good in his studies; then too, he was not "one of them" and they did not understand him, and true to human nature, what they did not quite understand they either feared or hated. The truth is each was secretly willing to try for his favors. Always they were imagining the very exquisiteness of sensation that might be enjoyed. Their imaginations disturbed them and made them uncomfortable. So, in fighting their desires, they also fought Randall. The conventional are ever intolerant of those who live as they please. Jealousy of a freedom of spirit which they cannot attain drives them on to seek to destroy such a freedom. So, after talking the subject over in a secret meeting of those who thought it their duty "to uphold the honor of the school," one of their number was delegated to lead Randall on, to seduce him and compromise him.

One called Hemans had been selected. Night after night he called on Randall, ostensibly to study with him. In truth Randall taught him much. The man did not appeal to him though, and his intuitions guided him aright, for one evening, a chap named Mason Linberg, a very handsome fellow who ran with the crowd, dropped into Randall's room. They were alone. That the walls might not hear he spoke almost in a whisper. "Sweet Randy, you know I admire some of your characteristics very much, especially your scholarship. I have had a more liberal environment than the majority of these poor students. Therefore, I do not judge you, or others. Whatever your private life may be is no concern of mine. I'm here to warn you. The other fellows are trying to frame you, and I think that bumptious Hemans has been chosen to lead you on. Just be careful."

"Thanks, Linberg," said Randall, "and since you are liberal minded, let me give you the reward you deserve." He stepped over to him, put his arms about him and looked into his lovely blue eyes. He kissed him—very gently—then slipped down to unhitch his pants. What fell forward was a beautifully tremendous penis, well on its way to full arousal, belying young Mason's reddening face.

"Why, Mason!" said Randall. "I do believe you have never been taken so. Is this true?"

"No, Randy," responded Linberg. "I must confess I could have never dreamed this, though I am greatly embarrassed for wanting it nonetheless."

"Then I shall make it special for you, and we will never mention it again. It shall be our little secret, forever," promised Randall. And with that Randall gently took Mason's tremendous member between his lips, then pushed it slowly, teasingly, ever farther into his mouth.

Mason's cock filled Randall's mouth comfortably, and his throat widened to compensate for the girth of its throbbing head. The young student gasped, preparing to let fly with his sperm into his new friend's esophagus. But Randall perceived this before it came, and expertly pressed the heavy base of Mason's priapus to successfully stifle the crisis.

For an endless span of time thereafter, Randall sweetly sucked and gobbled Mason's pulsing cock. He did this until the young man's hands were in his hair, and he was begging for release. Grinning with an almost diabolical glee, Randall finally acquiesced, and sped his actions to a glorious frenzy. Mason groaned and fairly howled with pleasure as he was brought to that state of no return. When he came his knees buckled from under him and he collapsed in a dead faint before the last of his sperm had even spilt. Though they both had a hearty laugh thereafter, Randall took their little secret to his grave.

Hemans continued his visits. When he thought friendship had progressed to such a stage that it might be diverted into passion, he put his arms about Randall. "Don't do that, it makes me uncomfortable," said Randall. A few minutes later he tried again, at the same time trying to pull Randall's head down into the crotch of his pants. "Don't do that! Please don't do that!" said Randall more sharply!

"Don't you like me, Randall?"

"Yes, at a distance, but to me you smell like fish." Hemans did not comprehend that.

"I smell the same as you do, like the dissecting room."

"That was a figure of speech," explained Randall.

But he would not be repulsed and began again trying to force him—to pet.

"What are you after, you son-of-a-bitch?" yelled Randall.

In those pre-war days son-of-a-bitch had not become the term of endearment and praise it now is and was considered deadly insult.

Hemans muttered: "I'll never speak to you again."

"Don't! I'll be satisfied," Randall assured him.

In revenge, Hemans lied to his fellow students and told them he had proven that Randall was all they had suspected.

He was called before one of those sanctimonious gatherings so dear to the collegiate, "a student committee."

"We do not consider you desirable," they told him gloatingly.

Randall arose in his wrath and borrowed language he had heard some of his rough trade use with good effect. For at least once in his life his voice took on an almost masculine tone—"See here, I don't give a damn what you or your associates and friends think of me. I have the number of every one of you—you kettleful of stinking fish. But you haven't so much as *that* on me!" (He touched the tip of his little finger.)

"Hemans says otherwise," the "chairman" announced like a judge giving sentence.

"Is Shemans here to face me? Bring it here and let it say to my face the lies it has told you," demanded Randall.

So the uncomfortable Hemans was brought in. Randall flew to the attack, not waiting for any of the procedure so beloved of men "sitting in session," the ritual which the class of 1912 wished to follow.

"You damned son-of-a-bitch, what have you been telling these people?" he shouted furiously. "Now admit that you haven't a thing on me; admit that you lied. If you don't, I'll choke the truth out of you."

Hemans flushed painfully. Finally he spoke: "I told you fellows what I thought was the best thing to tell you to get rid of this person."

"And it was a lie!" screamed Randall. "Tell them!"

"Well, it was not quite exactly the truth," he admitted.

"There's your answer," sneered Randall. "Some day I'll prove to you that I have more guts than any of you self-styled men." He wiggled his hips (or was it dragged his fanny?) out of the room.

Little Randall cared. He realized full well that behind their hatred, fostered by those who had reared them, was jealousy of his freedom from the responsibility that cumbered their own lives, the responsibility that they wished on themselves, the upkeep of a home, the protection of children and all the problems of marriage and family life. If he had only married, and played less openly, they might have forgiven him; but he knew well the futility of marrying to reform, to change one's nature.

That ended the chief collegiate episode of his first year in medicine.

CHAPTER
25

The second year of Randall's medical course had begun.

Came a Saturday in late September, balmy and pleasant as the Philadelphia fair days are apt to be. Randall was downtown and stepped into a tearoom adjacent to the City Hall. The place was crowded with rather rough-looking stuff, but over in one corner he spied his good friend, Linberg. He motioned to him and at the door said, "Come on! Let's beat it from this place. It's simply full of dirt."

Out onto Market Street they sauntered. Randall recognized a subtle change in Mason Linberg. "What has happened to you, Mason?" he asked. "You impress me as being more mature, more experienced, different somehow from what you were a year ago."

"I am different," he replied. "I spent the whole summer at Atlantic City; had a good job in a hotel." Then he went into details of all the opportunities that such a position offered in the way of enlightenment and social development and ended: "I've been brought out socially, as it were!"

"Oh! You haven't yet been brought out," Randall told him, laughing.

"Well, I'm here to learn. I put myself in your hands."

"Be sure you stay there," Randall warned him. Then he continued, "It is Saturday night and we shall celebrate. I have more pennies this year, lucky in some deals which my old banking friend in New York saw to. First, we'll pick up a bodyguard, preferably one soldier and one marine, or one sailor. They are easier to manage than if we take two of the same kind—not well enough acquainted to connive."

A passerby spoke to Randall, who did not return the salutation. Mason called his attentions to the fact. Randall explained, "I never speak to tearoom or t.b. acquaintances on the street! Neither does anyone else who is socially experienced."

They continued to cruise Market Street. Down near the Reading Terminal, Randall saw Whitey, seaman first-class, a tall, broad-shouldered blond with flaxen hair, a chap with whom he had been out on former occasions, but whose flesh he had never sampled. "Isn't he marvelous?" he asked Linberg. "Do you wish to take him on?" Mason did not object.

Whitey had been standing at the corner of 12th and Market gloating at the "skirts" as they passed by. Payday was still in the offing. Therefore free amusement for the evening appealed to him.

A little farther on a lone marine was standing. "That looks good to me," said Randall. "I'm going to cruise it. Do you know him, Whitey?"

"Not very well," answered Whitey. "But I guess he's O.K. If he ain't, well, it's just too bad, for I'm here, little one, ain't I?"

As they approached, Randall looked directly at the marine and smiled slightly. He brightened and grinned broadly.

"Want to join our party, soldier-of-the-sea?" queried Randall.

"Sure! Whither away?"

"Willow Grove, first. After that, any place you say, but we're going to end at Baden-Baden, on Vine Street. That satisfactory?"

"O.K. with me! All set? Let's shove off. Can't get goin' too soon to suit me. Got anything to drink with you?"

"No, but we have the wherewithal."

They settled themselves in a Willow Grove car and as Randall paid the fare (for 'tis ever the "woman" who pays and pays and pays), he peeled off two five-dollar bills from his roll, with: "Here, sailor-boy, here's your spending money," and "Here's yours, gorgeous," to the marine.

"Thanks," the marine had the grace to answer. "You're good."

"You don't know the half of it, dearie," camped Randall. "I know how to spend money like a drunken sailor. Whitey taught me, didn't you, Whitey?"

"Taught you! That's to make the porpoises laugh. Little anybody can teach you. I think you were born wise. Say, Randy, did I tell you about the last ship's dance? One of your sisters, Little Egypt, the coochee-coochee who follows the fairs, well, Little Egypt come over in a drag all gold and pearls and diamonds. What a wow! Prettiest thing there. She got too many drinks under her belt. She said he lost her self-control. I'll say she did. About a dozen kids got her back of the coal bunkers and started to use her somethin' fierce. I happened along in my dungarees and she threw her-self at me. There was a pretty mix-up of grease paint and machine grease and she says, 'Fer God's sake, save me, Whitey!' So I say to them guys, 'Hey, youse, this is my kid. Beat it!' And say, did they beat it? I guess yes. The only thing Little Egypt lost was her wig."

"Mason, you have nothing to fear from this boy," Randall assured his friend, "He's a square shooter. Aren't you, Whitey?"

"Ah, live and let live is my motto. Little Egypt is all right—in her way. Maybe it ain't my way; maybe it ain't your way; but she don't harm nobody. If you don't like her ways, keep away from her. If you want to go with her, that's your business, and if she wants to go with you, that's her business."

At Willow Grove they dined and listened to the music, tried all the feats of strength and tests of skill, and won a lot of dolls and blankets and canes they did not want and gave to some boys at the gate. It was about ten when they left and returned to Philadelphia to a small imitation of Atlantic City, a colored cabaret in Susquehanna Street. One of the entertainers, a slim, pretty mulatto girl, sang, then went from group to group repeating her chorus, writhing her body suggestively, the spotlight accompanying her on her rounds of silver-gathering.

Arrived at Randall's table she acted more amorously than ever, even bringing a chair back into play, rubbing certain parts of her body against it. As the voluptuous girl moved on, Randall leaned over, pretending to smell the contaminated portion of the chair, then straightened up with a wrinkled nose and a wry expression as if the odor was vile, and shook his head in unfavorable judgment. His pantomime was greeted with howls of delight. Of course, the action was not refined, but there was no need for refinement in that place, and Randall was adaptable. Besides, he wished to make everybody laugh.

Randall danced with Whitey; he danced with the marine; he danced with every strange good-looking thing in the place, moving with them in their sensuous swayings, back and forth, up and down, twisting and driving movements, becoming more and more amorous as the night went on, for everyone who knows anything is aware that the dance is just a form of uncompleted sexual indulgence, just like hugging, kissing, or any other petting, though the dance, bringing into play the senses of hearing and of rhythm, in addition to sight, touch and smell, is the most potent combination of sex stimulation that exists, outside of certain drugs.

Finally Whitey, always outspoken and to the point, said, "Come on, Randy, let's get out of this. I want action."

So they left, Randall walking close in the embrace of the adorable Whitey, Linberg and the marine following.

Whitey was eager. They took the shortest route possible to Baden-Baden, where their evening's entertainment would include much flirtation and more rollicking. But it was only after this that Randall was enabled to reach one of his long-time personal goals: the bedding of this exquisite seaman Whitey, at long last. Since he was half-drunk and with a personal fire hose bloated with desire, this would not prove a difficult fantasy to fulfill!

First Randall played coy, teasing Whitey about his golden, almost cornsilk-colored hair and his fair, almost ghostly complexion. Then he admired Whitey's powerful, broad build, asking him questions about his big arms and his expansive chest. Randall ran his fingers down the seaman's body, tracing the grooves of his muscles and the places where the flesh had either folded or molded over bone and sinew. Before long, Whitey could not have cared if Randall were an old shoe—he would fuck it!

Sunday morning Randall awoke to the pleasant sound of church bells ringing. He felt gloriously happy. He ran downstairs to the bath. At the door he stopped. He heard the marine and then Whitey's great booming voice. The marine spoke in a high-pitched Southern drawl—"Five dollahs! That Randy's got mo' money. They both got good watches too. Let's roll 'em. They're nothin' but a pair of damn—"

"You dirty pimp," Whitey broke out. "An' I thought you was a decent he-man. Randy's my friend. He's treated us swell. I've a notion to crack your Goddam skull. Now you beat it out of here and don't you even look back. If I so much as hear another peep out of you, I'll be a dentist to your pretty teeth, and I won't use forceps, neither. Now beat it!" He did.

As Whitey came out into the hall, Randall asked with an innocent air: "Where's the Marine? Isn't he going to have breakfast with us?"

"He ain't goin' to have breakfast with us, now, nor never! He's dirt! If you ever hear of him tryin' to make trouble anywheres, let me know and if you even so much as see him standin' still on the street, tell me. I'll see he keeps movin' fast."

Thus grew up the tradition, perhaps wrongly, that "marines is dirt."

Despite the marine's defection, they made a merry breakfast party, such as can so often be seen of a Sunday morning in that older part of Philadelphia. There were Randall and Whitey and Linberg and four or five more gay young things that fluttered as they walked along.

The party passed the Tenth Street Fire House and gave their friends there a friendly wave of the hand and were good-naturedly razzed in return. One chubby-faced fat fireman put his hands on his hips, wiggled and let out a "whoops-my-dear!" Another called,

"Ella, you're losing your hair pins," and still another, "Kitty, you should wear your veil when you're on the streets."

"Come on and have breakfast with us," Randall invited generously.

"We cahn't, doncher knaow. Duty b'foaw pleshaw." The tallest one, Gripes, spoke mockingly.

Randall tossed him two dollars with a gay, "Go get yourselves a can of beer then. That'll shut your traps."

They passed on to howls of, "You must come over! Oh, you must come over."

All of Randall's set knew these firemen. In warm weather the fellows usually sat on benches in front of the firehouse and camped madly with anyone who, as one of the Beaches expressed it, "was too obvious." A swaying, short-stepped walk, or clothing that was especially indicative, would call forth comment interspersed with all the familiar war cries designed to put the poor things *hors de combat.*

That morning, Randall's crowd was in luck. The firebell rang and soon the truck, loaded with men, swung into the street. As they passed the gay girls screamed, "Fireman, save my child, yours and mine."

Randall and his party continued on their way to the vicinage of Camac Street, where they broke fast at a cellar that catered especially to the "temp'ramentals," a place presided over by one of the more humble members of the Dike family, a place where one almost needed to learn a new language to understand and take part in the conversation. This Dike, unlike the usually lugubrious members of that large and conspicuous family, sometimes described as notorious, sometimes as famous, sometimes as infamous, this Dike was very gay, jolly and happy-go-lucky. "Billee" Dike did not make a great amount of money, but she made a living and was at all times surrounded by congenial companions of all sexes. The typical attitude of most of the members of the Dike family is that they are nature's tragedy; that of Randall and his friends that they are nature's joke and that it is their duty to turn life into a roaring farce. Now, who is right?

As Randall and his satellites entered, one girl was weeping on Billee's shoulder, telling how she was heartbroken because Ruby had stood her up and given to that "awful thing" the seal ring which Norma had given to Carter, and Carter had given to Bobby and Bobby had given to her, and it wasn't fair because Ruby had promised never to take the ring off her finger.

The lady, Miss Mae Bull, continued telling Miss Dike the story and at the end repeated: "I simply can't be happy again till I've been stewed."

"Well, don't get stewed here," cautioned Miss Dike. "I don't want the place to get a bad name. Remember, a good name is more to be desired than great riches."

"By whom?" screamed someone in Randall's party. "Not by me. I'll take the pennies every time."

"You would," said Miss Dike witheringly. "You're that kind. And after you got the pennies, you'd spend them foolishly on some grand thing that didn't give a damn for you. I know you. You're like our old friend Aunty Bütsche-O'Brien, the original Aunty Bütsche-O'Brien, who, it is said, went through the family fortune and spent her declining days (though Gawd knows she never declined anything) in the poor house."

"Oh, Billee, hurry up and put on the teapot and the waffle iron," begged Randall. "I'm hungry."

"Didn't you get anything to eat last night, dearie?"

lilted Miss Dike. "Where'd you go? What did you get?"

"Ask Whitey," replied Randall. "He was with me. He can tell."

Appealed to, Whitey answered oracularly, "Bygones is bygones. I never tell nothin'."

"That's why I trust him and love him so," said Randall.

"Love him how?"

"Love him so—" He made a movement as if to demonstrate.

"Well, don't love him so, or love him so-so here. This is a respectable house."

"Who said so? Oh, yes, I remember the alderman told that to the judge the last time you were arrested for—"

"Never mind what I was arrested for. Just remember the charges were not proven," defended Miss Dike. "You must recall that people were very excited at that time and were going to make us all pure—by law."

"Pure?" someone yelled. "Gawd knows my name is pure. You're completely pure too, ain't you, Billee?"

"Yes, but I'd like to be otherwise, if I only knew how. They say you have to be double jointed and I simply can't qualify."

All this while Miss Dike was boiling coffee, bringing out dishes, stirring batter, ably helped by everyone in the place. In one corner of the dining room someone was crooning the Habañera from *Carmen*, while "Gypsy," a somewhat nondescript sort of person who had her moments, was strutting her stuff—a Spanish dance, garbaged with two rings of onion over her ears for earrings, a stalk of celery between her teeth for a rose, and a red tablecloth for a Spanish shawl. One "gifted" person drummed softly with table cutlery, spoons and dishes, and another used two pot lids for cymbals.

The cop on the beat passed by; then, attracted by the sounds of merriment, came back and stepped in. (They are always getting in where there's anything good.) He was a handsome young person who had worked his way up in life, having started as an elevator boy. He then became a local lightweight boxer, later a successful beach patrolman, and finally he was a cop. Later on he won a beauty contest and went to Hollywood and became internationally famous—a lovely rise!

Everybody was delighted to have him present, and before he left the very best of them laid themselves out to give him a good time.

"How you're cutting up?" he greeted them. "That's right; we're only young once."

"Young?" gurgled an old aunty who happened to be present. "You flatter me! Just for that I'm going to entertain you. I'm going to recite." She suited action to word, hopped nimbly up on a bench and began:

The West, the West, I love the West.
Next to the East, I love it best.
The hoptoads hop, the birds do sing,
And I'm too glad for anything.
I shot a prairie dog today.
Oh, mercy me! Hooray! Hooray!

There was sufficient applause to hearten her. She announced in her grand queenly manner, "The next time you come I'll recite 'The Bastard King of England.' That's a long one. You'll all like that! Mine is the unexpurgated edition. It tells exactly how he did what to her and she did which to him." Then she called to the cop: "Now you can come sit on my lap and make love to me."

"Later on," he answered.

"How much later?"

"When the wife goes to Atlantic City."

"And that will be?"

"In two weeks, and you must come over. Got to make a pull now."

They loaded him with gifts. One thrust a package of cigarettes into his hand; another put half a dozen cigars in his cap; another gave him a box of candy for the privilege of touching his club; and still another gave him a package of cravats for having been permitted the honor of holding his gun.

Randall handed him the inevitable two dollars, "just for being a good fellow," and he went away—happy.

One had been thrilled; another stunned; another frightened by proximity to the law; another had been "recognized"; and the old aunty had been completely overjoyed.

There were about thirty people in the basement. The number was augmented by the arrival of a dozen university freshmen who were getting their first taste of freedom and the wisdom of the ages. They were pretty young boys, evidently from very good families, and they showed great adaptability in fitting themselves into the fun and frolic. It was anything for a laugh!

One, taking off his coat, said: "I'm so hot I could fry an egg."

The subject of eggs having been poached, one boy demonstrated how big his mouth was by closing it on an egg without breakage. Then there broke out a perfect orgy of mouth measuring, each one trying to demonstrate how much he could get into his mouth—if necessary. The quarter of a waffle was set as a standard.

"I bet on Sissy Beach," one of them wagered.

"My Gawd! Is there a Sissy Beach here in Philadelphia too?" someone asked.

"Wait till you see," was the answer.

One boy, who evidently knew Miss Dike well, had disappeared upstairs. At the moment of the question he returned, but he had undergone a transformation. His suit had been exchanged for a street costume of Miss Dike's. His face had been made up and he wore a huge picture hat, the vogue at the time. Truth to tell, women's garb suited him better than men's, and he was destined later to win stellar honors as the leading "lady" of the Varsity Show; that almost goes without saying. In repose his mouth was not so large; in fact it was beautifully formed and curved and would have been a suitable adornment for almost any feminine face. But the most unusual feature of that most unusual mouth was its extensibility. Wagers were laid. Randall bet for him, for he had seen him perform some place or other.

With a sense of artistic balance, Miss Dike wickedly insisted that but a single rule to this game was to be changed: "To hell with mere waffles and all of this innuendo! Let us see some real he-men take the place of breakfast foods. Bring on some of our finest members. Only by this means can we truly know for certain our champion!"

A young and strapping bystander was quickly fetched and made to strip before the crowd. A few well-placed applications of bacon grease had him standing a full nine inches from base to head, and the audience roared with decadent approval. The first contestant tried and choked as the fat head of the poor man's cock touched his pharynx. The second one, in a drunken attempt to mark his record, bit down hard, causing the proud hunk to yelp with pain. "Oh, he's a biter," shouted Miss Bull. Of course the old aunty fluttered over to administer first aid.

The contest went on. Another one made the mistake of holding his breath. A small blob of early emission slipped down his throat and he exploded, a great wad of saliva hitting the old aunty on the nose. In queenly manner she rose to the occasion—"At my age, any attention is a compliment. Thanks." Then the field was open to Sissy.

He sat on the edge of the table, one foot crossed over the other, one hand lying palm upward in the other relaxed on his lap. He smiled a superb, growing, elastic smile before bending gracefully over to slip the entire length of the young man's aching shaft into his mouth, nuzzling the hair of his belly before withdrawing it. The hopelessly enflamed stud was then grabbed by a few lusting admirers and made to be relieved mere instants later.

Of course, there was a hubbub the like of which only such a crowd could make. Loud were the cries, *"Sissy! Sissy! Sissy!"* followed by a typical freshman yell:

Rah! Rah! Rah!
Don't tell Pa.
Sissy beat 'em.
Ha! Ha! Ha!
Sissy! Sissy! Sissy!

—followed by *"Speech! Speech! Speech!"*

Then Sissy lisped, "This is my debut in Philadelphia society and I thank you for the very hearty welcome you have accorded me. If I have made you happy, I am very pleased to have made you

181

happy. And in the future, if I can do anything else to make you happy, I shall be very pleased to do any and every thing to make you happy. And let us remember on this calm Sabbath morn, that where two or three happy ones are gathered together, there also shall others be made happy, and if we continue to do everything, and promote happiness, after a while there will be so much doing to make people happy, that perfect happiness will be diffused throughout the whole world and at last everybody will be made happy. Ladies, gentlemen, and others, I thank you." He then ran nimbly up the stairway.

Whitey spoke feelingly, "That kid can have just anything I got just any old time."

Then the very Russian Miss Stupintek made her grand entry, in gorgeous Sunday morning drag. She was fond of declaiming that she had been the favorite of a Grand Duke when just turned eighteen, but the Duchess had found out about the affair and created such a scandal that the Stupintek had to choose between flight and Siberia.

"Zhoos t'ink," she would grieve. "Almos' vas I de same like a Dooshess."

So in the free and easy and generous society of Philadelphia's best, she was accorded the honors, which she had earned, and was dubbed, "La Duchesse Stupintek." She knew too how to carry herself with an air that was even more than queenly.

In Philadelphia, Miss Stupintek trimmed hats for a living and complained bitterly whenever a needle pricked her flesh—"'Ere I vork. In Rooshye, I do odder t'ings."

Pressed for further explanation she would shrug her shoulders, roll her eyes, and with pouting lips murmur, "Oh, odder t'ings." Then as if enlightening sufficiently, "T'ings I lof to do."

To hear her say "lof" would almost set the imagination running wild. To see her say it would also give an adequate understanding of the thorough training which that Russian tongue had undergone. When she sounded the "I," the underside of her tongue caressed the inner border of her too crimson upper lip, and as she finished the word *love,* the tip of her tongue darted out of her mouth as if in invitation.

She said little; but she did much!

When la Stupintek did deign to speak, everyone listened, for the few words she spoke were always pregnant with meaning. She created either a riot or a panic wherever she went. Evenings she never appeared except in grand drag à la duchesse, with yards and yards of costly lace or velvet trailing along behind her.

It was La Stupintek who, in later years when war was declared against Germany, announced bravely: "Now I go to Shairmannee. I fight at ze Shairman. I swear I kill die Krone Prints; but eet weel take mahnts and mahnts and mahnts." After that she was called "Dee Kroneprintsessen."

This was Randall's opportunity. Long she had wished to know "La Duchesse" and study her.

The feast was over. Nothing more remained to be done but to go to church. There was a flutter of departure and the usual little squabble as to who should pay.

"Here, let me pay," spoke up Whitey. "I got some dough. I had all kinds of a good time. Now lemme do my share." Nobly he broke out the five dollars which Randall had given him the night before and settled the bill for their portion of the crowd.

Then the Catholics went their way to "worship" at St. Sappho's and the Protestants to "worship" at St. Messalina's.

183

Randall was not in the least religious. He had dismissed all that years ago as "just so much superstition."

"Going to church?" asked Linberg.

"Why, certainly," he answered. "It's the only safe place to kneel nowadays."

So he attended with his crowd at St. Messalina's, and went through the motions.

Linberg asked him afterwards, "And what did you pray for, Randy, you old infidel?"

He pursed his lips, assumed an old-maidish look and answered, "I prayed the same as I always pray. 'Dear Gawd, send me a nice piece of trade; and when I die, let me die in the arms of a lover.'" Little he recked that his prayer would be answered.

The rest of that year was made up of hard work, mostly, interspersed with an occasional repetition of a Saturday night such as their first one. More and more of his fellow students were "stepping out," some spending freely the money which their parents sent them, and some, the poorer ones, profiting financially by their excursions into the downtown night life.

Linberg and Randall and a few of the others would now dish the dirt at times, exchanging bits of current new slang, repeating brilliant remarks they had heard, telling the gossip of the very amusing social set in which they moved.

CHAPTER
26

June came. Randall and Linberg worked through the vacation as substitute interns in one of the better New York hospitals, "a perfectly grand place."

Of course it was a joy to Randall to have the privilege of initiating Linberg into the pleasures of New York night life—that city whose chief charm is its vastness and the opportunity such size offers for promiscuity. Normal home lovers flee its contaminations and hurry to the suburbs as fast as overcrowded conveyances will take them. This daily efflux speaks much for the innate chastity of the poor wage slaves who daily are obliged to invade Manhattan to earn their sustenance. One could moralize indefinitely on this—if one were so inclined.

First Randall introduced Linberg to Riverside Drive, after dusk, naturally. The Drive was crowded with gobs.

"Oh, the fleet's in, the fleet's in," joyously caroled Randall, as what gay man wouldn't who'd had a Whitey? "Whitey's a C.P.O. now. I wonder what he

185

brought me from Panama? I wonder! I wonder! I wonder!" he lilted.

"Just stop wondering," a voice sounded in his ear. He turned quickly, looking up into glorious deep blue, black-fringed eyes.

"Who are you?" he asked, and then added, "I don't know you!"

"Well, there's no harm getting acquainted, is there?" the handsome sailor asked.

"There!" Randall turned quickly to Linberg, "didn't I tell you I always make friends wherever I go? Come on, sailor man, speak your little piece. You're lonesome; you're unacquainted; you have no friends in New York; you don't know where to go; you want a cigarette; you want a light; you have only a nickel to get back to the Yard. Now, you tell the rest."

"You told the most of it, except I got a six months' roll and you're the person I've picked to help spend it. I like you, kid! Get me? I like you! Were you ever in the Navy?"

"Quite the contrary," camped Randall.

Randall did look very young that night. Before coming out he had rouged and touched up his sensuous lips, oh, so carefully.

"But my friend here," he said. "I can't leave him; he's new to New York."

"Oh, he can come along as ballast!"

They started. The sailor spent his money freely—theater, supper, cabs, and afterwards, well, it was Randall's night off, so what was the difference. He whispered to Linberg before they parted, "I believe I'm in love again. If I'm murdered you'll know where to look for me."

But that evening was to prove erotic beyond what Randall dreamed. As he and the blue-eyed seaman were about to make plans to relieve the barely disguised tension that had been throbbing deep within them all evening, the sailor called out, "Ahoy there, matey!"

Before them stood another bronzed, muscular man of the sea, almost as handsome as the one Randall was with. Apparently he knew Randall's new-found friend. "Whatcha got there, buddy?"

"Somethin' fine! Want some?—that is, if it's OK with you," he added hastily, with a broad grin at Randall.

Randall spoke not a word, but the mixture of delight and amazement on his face said a mouthful.

A West Side hotel chamber, barren save for an ancient post-bed, set the stage for Randall's latest challenge—the taking on of a pair of seamen. What their names were made no difference to Randall, ballast or otherwise, so long as they both bore dense, meaty muscles and washboard stomachs, thick biceps and gigantic cocks. It also helped a great deal that their balls were filled to the brim with oceans of sperm just waiting for release. Less than halfway through their frolic, Randall simply gave up in his attempt to orchestrate these animals, and allowed them to maul him between themselves as wolves would a choice stretch of fresh meat. So eager were they at one point that they thrust their members at once into Randall's mouth. Eyes fairly bulging, Randall widened his jaws to the cause, then gulped down what seemed to be pints of pearly fluid. Glutted with come, Randall lay back as the sailor men finished him off, licking and sucking his raging erection until it felt as if his penis had split asunder, unleashing a torrent of hot come.

The second sailor left as quickly as he had appeared, but Randall's friend remained through the night. They brought each other off so many times they lost count.

Before he parted from him the next morning, the gob took Randall's address, promising to call him up again at night. He thrust gifts upon him—a beautiful jade ring he had picked up in Panama; bottles of expensive perfume; silk pajamas; embroidered hand-kerchiefs; all the pretty things sailors bring back to their sweethearts. But Randall never saw him again.

A few days later he said to Mason with a sigh, "Something must have happened to him," and ever afterward he spoke of him as his "royal lover," for he had told Randall over and over again as he caressed him intimately (and Randall caressed right back again), "You are one queen! You are some queen!"

Parted from his sailor, he hurried back to the hos-pital. He and Linberg made the urinalyses and the work had to be done quickly. Later in the day they took histories, which they loved to do as it gave them an opportunity to probe into the lives of others and learn much, very much, that was amusing. And how they did probe!

Both were trying to make a good impression on the chief of their service in the hope of getting appointments as interns after their college courses were finished. Before a week rolled around, Linberg jokingly announced to Randall, "The chief has his eye on you and I think his regard is favorable. I think he's trying to make you!"

"My Gawd! So soon? What must an innocent girl *do* under such circumstances?" camped Randall. "And I thought I had been behaving discreetly."

Linberg was right. A few days later Randall was invited by the chief to dine at the Plaza. He was not one to turn a friend down and quickly answered, "I would be delighted to join you, doctor, but I have promised Mason Linberg, the friend who came up here with me, to go out with him tonight. He does not know the town yet."

"Can't you bring him along?"

"That would be splendid. You will find Mason very entertaining. He plays piano well and sings enchantingly and," he added significantly, "he's just as broad-minded as I am." *I'll let that sink in,* he thought.

Then the good doctor went on to explain, needlessly, that his wife and family were away and that he became very lonesome of evenings; that his usual club friends were out of town and that Randall and Mason would be conferring a great favor on him; anyway, he went on with a lot of useless explaining.

The truth was that he was one of those people who had learned too late in life what was the matter with him and that marriage could never hold him. He was glad to be rid of his family, and secretly wished he had none.

The invitation meant much to Linberg, as he had little spending money. Randall, as usual, had plenty. So they had their "little hunk of supper" at the Plaza. And afterwards there was a roof garden show and nice drinks at an exclusive café. Then the ride home in the chief's automobile—still more or less of a novelty, though it brought to Randall bittersweet memory of his carefree rides with Teddy. How long ago that seemed!

That evening was but the beginning of a pleasant summer for them with the chief's extra car and a chauffeur at their disposal all the time. The chief ceased to be lonesome and assured them that their youth (though Randall's was somewhat spurious) and enthusiasm had given him a new outlook on life, a "rejuvenation" he called it.

The chief was very, very wealthy and could offer them all that was best in New York. These treats impressed Mason. They were "old stuff" to Randall, though he enjoyed flitting about.

So the happy summer passed. They promised the chief they would be especially attentive to the course in obstetrics and venereal diseases, and he in turn promised that they should intern under him.

When they were alone one day and the chief had Randall cuddling in his arms, he said: "I'm so glad I've found you."

"I'm so glad you've found yourself," was Randall's rejoinder.

When it was time to return to Philadelphia, the chief drove them over in his car, stopping at Princeton, en route, to visit an old college chum (and exhibit his charming young friends too, probably). The friend talked long and broadly on psychology. Physically he was a repulsive specimen, but he had compensated for that by cultivating his mind. Randall summed him up exactly—"He's a very wise person."

Late in the afternoon they continued on their way, detouring through the pleasant pastoral parts of Pennsylvania. They even had the good doctor camp along the wayside.

The chief, not having had to earn his money, was generous with it. Before leaving Philadelphia, he took an outline of their courses, then equipped them with the very expensive books necessary for their next year's work, bought each of them a microscope, gave them season tickets for concerts and theatrical amusements, paid Mason's tuition and room rent for the year and insisted on giving both of them charge accounts at tailors' and department stores. That man was grateful for his happiness.

All of these gifts were a great help to Mason. Of course Randall was not rich, but he had plenty of money. He demurred at accepting such favors from the chief, but in the end accepted, as it seemed to make the old dear so happy.

Randall, in speaking of the dear doctor, later said to Mason, "There is no person more to be pitied than the one who finds out what he really wants too late in life; that is, after marriage."

CHAPTER
27

The third year of Randall's medical work started with a rush. There were new subjects to learn and old ones to review. Good student that he was, yet he found the work taxing. Sometimes he found himself becoming irritable. Then he would whisper to Mason, "Virtue has its own reward. Watch me be good for a while," and his Saturday night sprees would be limited to the theater, the opera or a concert. Mason plugged away with equal assiduity. Now they could only spare a part of Christmas week or part of a night before a holiday for gadding. Of course, the chief came over on an average of once a month, and they taught him how to cruise. Usually he brought his family with him, but as Randall was in medicine and always Mason came along too, the surgeon could "get away with things" under the very nose of his wife.

The high spot of that year was probably the course of lectures in psychiatry, and the course in neurology, taught by the same professor. Psychiatry of itself did not attract them so much, for they had more or less a fatalistic feeling toward the patients, believing that the treatment of mental disease is a thankless task and should have started with the ancestors. But they enjoyed the lectures by reason of the antics which the professor indulged in when demonstrating the symptoms of various types of disease. His powers of mimicry could hardly be excelled. Tremors, palsies, twitches, limps, deformities, all of these he could simulate so convincingly as to make them recognizable when seen in a patient. The lecture he seemed most to enjoy giving was on certain phases of psychopathia. He loved to talk of the androgynous. He knew his subject well; that part of it Randall said he knew all too well. Randall verified all of his statements when he visited Berlin just before the World War began. Then he wrote to Mason, after visiting the corner of Unter der Linden and Friedrichstrasse at night, that if indeed there is a third sex, there it could be found, and that Professor Jimmie Stay had not exaggerated.

The professor would describe all sorts of aberrant types, their prominent, wild eyes, their too thick or too narrow chests or hips and their too thin or too heavy leg muscles; he would illustrate the swagger of the feminine type and the mincing short-stepped swaying gait of the masculine, the fluttering, so called; he would tell of their nocturnal amusements and occupations, and when he had finished he had so enthused his entire class that they were ready to go downtown and start a laboratory course at once. In speaking of his Berlin experiences he always ended his remarks, "But they never approached me. They seemed to sense in some way that I was not one of them." And here Randall whispered to Mason, "Poof! Poof! Some more of that protective coloration!"

After the course was over Randall confided to Mason, "If there's one thing I despise it is a person who pretends he is something he is not. Imagine that one posing as a real he-man."

"Posing is the only way to be respected and disreputable at the same time," answered Mason.

CHAPTER
28

The third summer vacation Randall and Mason spent "jerking babies." By preference they went out together. They were sent to poor families all over New York City, mostly to Italian and black families, occasionally to an Irish, German or Jewish family.

Bobby Dike, in from California, was taking something in summer school at the same time. She was reconciled to her family again and had money; besides, she'd come into an inheritance. She possessed a new car and she insisted on using it for their benefit. Bobby preferred to go about town with men. She whistled, smoked and drank like a man. She was that kind. At the wheel, in her sport togs, she passed for one. When she went with Randall and Mason on their cases, she stood by, ready to help, pretending to be a nurse. She had at one time started a nursing course, but like everything else on which Bobby embarked, it was never finished.

But Bobby liked to regard the drama. Papa, Mama, Grandma, and at least two children usually filled the two ill-ventilated rooms. Mama probably would be found rolling about on the soiled bed groaning, *"Mamma mia! Mamma mia!"* or *"Howly Mary! Howly Mary!"* or *"Lawdy, Lawdy, Lawdy!"* or simply, *"Oi, Oi, Oi!"* depending on the nationality. At intervals the women would all yell in their respective tongues, "Never again, never again!" Papa would be scared speechless. The children would cry. Grandma would joke and jest with the patient, telling her it was nothing; that she had had her fun and that as soon as this was over she would forget the pain and be ready to start all over again, for "'tis a pain that's soon forgotten." And it looks as if Grandma is right.

Sometimes it would be an "unwed mother"; this always moved Randall to camp to Mason his own version of that dear old nursery rhyme—"There was an old woman who lived in a shoe, who had so many children because she didn't know what to do."

On their return to New York they had seen the chief, of course, but he was not so attentive as the previous summer. Absence had not made the heart grow fonder, but had provided opportunity for interest to wander to a younger and newer acquaintance.

CHAPTER
29

Their fourth year in the medical school flew by as if on wings. They now did practically everything that a regular practitioner of medicine would do, though they lacked much of the assurance that the successful practitioner cultivates.

Of course the nurses in the hospital connected with the medical school tried to marry the handsome Mason, and of course they detested Randall for his very obvious influence over him.

Now, as often as not, Mason and Randall were joined by the other members of their class when they went downtown for their gay Saturday nights. At last these boys away from home had discovered that the world is not the sexless, friendless place they had been taught it was, and before the end of that year most of them had been had. Randall took great pleasure in watching many of his classmates—so straight-suited and staid until now—have the clothing veritably stripped from their youthful, muscular bodies, and their virgin cocks sucked by Philadelphia's finest queers.

The brooding influence of city life had "wised them up," and at least they had become pleasantly tolerant of others, all except the one who was destined to become a medical missionary, incidentally quite the poorest student in the class and also quite the most gullible. Even some of the professors were, to speak poetically, "occasionally lifting the veil." One day when Randall asked one of them if he would kindly spray his tonsils for him, he camped gaily about the subject, and, later on did indeed spray the inside of his mouth with a cream far more soothing to Randall than liquored medication!

They were graduated. Mason and Randall, now joint possessors of a Ford car, hurried away to New York and to their hospital appointments. They were interns and as such had to live in the hospital. But they had their own lives to live too and to that end began looking for a flat.

They decided that the flat must be in a part of town where they could do much as they pleased; that it must not be in too refined a locality or their speed might be cramped.

Finally they found a "walkup flat" on the third floor of an old-fashioned building that housed three other apartments. Above them were four students. Well and good! Below them were two very elegant-looking young ladies, who became friendly with them at once, even before they had leased their flat. Later they found that these good girls were kept by several rich men (though each man thought that he was the sole lover of the girl he was interested in) and that, being practical and wishing to put something away for old age, they chose a cheap apartment instead of having an expensive place. Besides, their lovers preferred to visit in a part of the city where there was no chance of recognition. On the ground floor lived what the kept women called "the only respectable person in the place," a Mrs. Backhaus, a woman of probably fifty years. "So long as you don't make a noise and let her get anything on you, it's all right," one of the kept women assured Mason and Randall.

Said the other, "She's always trying to catch the students when they rush dames upstairs. We help them circumvent her by having the girls call on us first. Nothing like a little cooperation! I hope we will be friends, if you decide to take the flat." Kept women anywhere are always more or less lonely, and long for friendships founded on something other than necessity. So long as their own shortcomings are overlooked, they are usually quite willing to overlook the shortcomings of others, though there are some who, hoping to pose as respectable women, criticize every and any thing they can in others. Often kept women are amusing company, as Randall and Mason found out.

CHAPTER 30

Miss Painter was giving a reception, an afternoon drag. Mason and Randall had been invited. Old Aunty Beach-Bitsche, of San Francisco, was visiting New York, and the reception was in her honor. Randall had been asked to be in the receiving line. That required an entirely new and elegant drag. His place was to be next to Miss Savoy, the impersonator, noted for "her" low comedy, sometimes too low. Randall was indeed glad, for this promised great fun. He was familiar with the story of Miss Savoy's defense of her personal reputation. Miss Savoy had been variously described and one dramatic critic had told her to her face what he did not dare to write as a columnist—"Miss Savoy, you are a dirty-mouthed slut!" To this Miss Savoy had calmly answered, "The very idea! Why, how you slay me! A dirty thing never came out of my mouth. My language is perfectly pure, innocent. What others make of it—well, if someone chooses to distort the innocent into evil, such a one is evil himself—evil incarnate, incarnate, mind you." She swallowed obviously as if she had rid himself of the statement with an effort.

Socially, Miss Savoy had more good connections than any woman in New York. She was the offspring of excruciating Helen McHaggart, the celebrated beauty. Helen McHaggart had in turn been unfaithful to both of her common-law husbands and all of their male friends too. She was noted for her wit and could make anybody laugh at anything, everything, or nothing. Miss Savoy kept up the family traditions. Through the beautiful Helen, Miss Savoy was related to the Bulls, the Dikes, the Godowns, the Pickups, the Mawgans, the Carters, the Munros, and other famous people. She was indeed original. She was college bred but only allowed that to be perceptible at times. Still, she had an education and was a person of parts. At college, asked to fill out one of those intimate, too intimate, questionnaires, when she came to the question, "What sports are you interested in," she answered, "I am a sexual athlete. Naturally, I am interested in all indoor sports." Only association with Miss Savoy could give an adequate idea of her complex personality. She created a stir wherever she went, and more, she kept it going.

Miss Savoy's speaking voice was a marvel. Formerly she had sung, and once, when taking the high note of a love song sung to the tune of Gounod's *Ave Maria* (properly, she insisted), her voice broke and ever after she spoke in a foghorn contralto; she said it was change of life.

Then too, among the important guests was to be Señorita Perra. Her movements were the poetry of motion, and where her American sisters fluttered, she undulated, rather than walked. She was renowned for her beauty and her *savoir faire*. When someone mentioned her manners to Miss Savoy, that whimsical person gave utterance to some gossip—"They do say her bedroom manners are marvelous." But Miss Savoy was likely to say anything, anywhere, either in private or on the stage. It was this which made her a theatrical star and also caused her to be sought after by all "society." Her social leadership was undisputed. When she had toured South America and Spain she had made it a point to become acquainted with all of the Perras, representing as they do the epitome of culture in both of the Spanish portions of the world. She was wont to pay them tribute thus: "Why, till I learned Spanish ways, I didn't know a thing, dearie."

The promised presence of both the Señorita and Miss Savoy added to Randall's and Mason's eagerness to attend the reception.

Thus, they were looking forward to an amusing afternoon. Before they attended the affair, Randall advised Mason, "Be sure to stand near and you'll hear more than an earful when Miss Savoy begins to spout. So far you've only met her when she was on her good behavior."

It was a brilliant occasion in East 69th Street. None outshone Mason and Randall. Mason's tall figure was one to enhance the value of the finest New York tailoring. Randall wore a blond wig, just suited to his natural coloring, and a blue velvet drag from Louise Brown & Co., with a picture hat that framed his beautiful face and accentuated his now strikingly feminine loveliness. His ermine-bordered coat gave the necessary regal touch. With the bearing of a queen he swept through the corridors of the fashionable apartment house, while all society looked on and gasped in surprised envy.

As at all such receptions there was much twittering conversation. One overhearing the greetings accorded would have decided that the crowd was made up of New York's most punctilious and polite. It was always Miss This and Miss That. Occasionally an "Ella" or a "Kitty" would slip out, but that did not necessarily mean that was the proper baptismal name of the person addressed, or even that the person was of the sex that the name connoted; rather it was oftenest used in good-humored derision; thus they often used "Miss" also. Not only real girls but men that were not real he-men were often referred to as "Miss So-and-so." A necktie of peculiar flaming hue worn by any man would bring forth comment—"See! Miss So-and-so is all dressed up in drag this morning." A man with a boutonniere would be described, "Miss So-and-so is wearing a corsage bouquet."

As for their surnames, many of them preferred to travel incognito and assume names that seemed best to suit their personalities, or even to hide their identities, as is so common in good New York society. A chance resemblance to any famous woman, especially an actress, often provided the requisite *nom de guerre*.

Some gave free vent to their fancy, and half the time the name chosen might even be that of the opposite sex, indicating probably the temperament and inclinations of the person, if not the actual sex, which after all, may have been more or less problematical. So at this reception the titles applied more to disposition than to sex.

The other side of their personality, the less conventional, they were wont to speak of as a different person—for instance, Miss Savoy commonly spoke of himself as "your mother"; Miss Kitty Fuchs of himself as "your sister"; Miss Beach of himself as "Your Aunt Ella." This Miss Beach had been born Vasilacopoulos, but when he went into society he changed it to the good English name of Beach.

At these receptions the camping was always brilliant.

Randall took his position in the receiving line beside Miss Savoy, who graciously whispered: "My Gawd, you are queenly. Nobody would suspect you of being what you are."

Then the other guests began to arrive. Robert, the butler, announced in his voice that had first been trained at a railway station—

"Miss Kitty Fuchs!"

"Indeed! Miss Kitty! But how delightful! I've been longing to see you," almost shrieked Miss Savoy.

"I'm so glad you approve," minced Miss Kitty.

"Well, it's nobody's business but your own, and besides, the butler should not tell," chirruped Miss Savoy.

"That's the lady's name," explained Mason who was standing near.

"Well, he shouldn't have such a puzzling name," defended Miss Savoy. "My mistake," she went on, stifling her laughter with her lacy handkerchief, then regaining some degree of self-control continued, "I beseech you, Miss Kitty, I beseech you to exonerate me." If Miss Savoy committed any social lapse, and 'tis to be feared she committed many, she would hasten to seek exoneration. To ask pardon or excuse, she held, was common, and Miss Savoy would not be common, no, not for the world.

"Miss Kuntz!" bellowed the butler.

"Plural! Oh, you marvelous woman," burst forth Miss Savoy. "I've heard so much about you and your wonderful ways. I've been hoping to meet you, too."

"Miss Tom and Mister Tom."

"I am perplexed. Which is Mister and which is

Miss?" asked Miss Savoy. "I can't tell which from t'other."

"Mister and Miss Fish!"

"Again I am bothered," said Miss Savoy. "Noun or verb?"

"Verb, of course, stupid," explained Randall.

"Active or passive?" chortled Miss Savoy.

"Mr. and Mrs. Morrison Godown!"

"Both?" almost shrieked Miss Savoy. "Mrs. Godown, are you anomalous? No offense. Please exonerate me. That's a new word I've just learned and I'm using it for practice."

"Miss Stepp."

"My Gawd! What a tragedy," giggled Miss Savoy, and everybody else.

"Miss Fall—of Idaho!"

Miss Savoy could not resist—"Well, dearie, don't fall too low; you may regret it. I'm always careful about that myself—a certain degree of discretion."

"Miss Ella Fitzhugh!"

"Hugh only?" questioned Miss Savoy, and then added, "I don't believe it."

"Miss Billee Browning!"

"What? Billee too? Oh, my Gawd!" Then turning to her hostess, Miss Savoy suggested, "Dearie, you'll only have to give the society reporter a list of the names of those present to let the public know just what kind of a party it was."

Then there was a collation and a lovely "co-ed" (a typical homo-mollis) from Springfield College sang a lovely song in one of those lovely sissy tenors which in recent years someone has kindly dignified as crooning.

This was followed by gay music and gayer dancing and much intense loving, and finally conversation, and the subject was man, the real he-man.

It began with Old Aunty Beach-Bitsche, who opined, "There are no real men, any more, no real he-men."

"Before we can discuss that properly," said Miss Savoy in her most erudite manner, "we must define the term. Just what is meant by a he-man?"

Miss Minnie Beach, who had been described as so romantic he could idealize a sewer, closed his eyes as if entranced and murmured poetically—"A real he-man is Gawd's most glorious work."

"That's not complete enough," said Miss Fuchs dipping his oar into the conversational flow. "I suppose after all a real he-man is a male who can propagate."

"There's more to it than that," corrected Miss Savoy.

"Let's solve it by elimination," ventured Miss Browning, who had a degree from a famous Massachusetts university.

"That's mathematics," shrilled Miss Savoy. "Leave out all bitch arithmetic."

Miss Astor made some useful suggestions in his high-pitched voice, rippling along at a furious rate—"A real he-man does not care to juggle a frying pan, whether at home or camping in the wilds. He does not teach school, either, and he does not name his son Junior as if it takes two of 'em in the same family to make one good whole man." He cast his eyes toward heaven, then continued rapidly as if he had found the inspiration he had been seeking, "No honest-to-God man is a minister, a nurse, a physician, a musician, a painter, a poet, any kind of an author, a chef, a butler, a house servant, a waiter, a tutor, an actor, a stage dancer, a college professor, a shopkeeper, a hairdresser, a barber—"

"You can't run on like that forever," broke in Miss

Savoy. "Give somebody else a chance to express an opinion. But are there any other occupations to which he has an aversion?"

"Dozens of them," added the well-informed Miss Astor. "Millinery, dressmaking, all the occupations in which women and Frenchmen delight, also book-keeping, clerking in shops of all sorts, especially jewelry stores, all the refined occupations, hundreds of the jobs city life has brought into being."

"There seems to be an abundance of intermediates to fill them," said Miss Savoy as if weighing the evidence. Then she turned to Mason. "Now, doctor dear, speaking as a professional man, tell us something about real he-men."

"A real he-man never needs to be circumcised. Also a real he-man can always leak without turning on the water faucet," said Mason who had had one drink too many and hence lapsed into vulgarity.

That set off Old Aunty Beach-Bitsche who rocked back and forth in glee as she added her bit: "A real he-man can fill out his pants properly."

Then Mason added some more, "Even with age a real he-man does not take on fat and look like an old woman in the face."

Quoth Miss Browning, "Up our way they think hair makes the man; but I have seen bearded ladies."

Randall offered as his contribution, "I have observed that a real he-man has no inhibitions."

"A real he-man never becomes bald!"

"A real he-man is never knock-kneed!"

"A real he-man is never a smarty!" in chorus piped up Miss Browning and Miss Fish and Miss Godown, each trying to be heard above the other.

"No real he-man is ever rich," said Miss Hoover, "and I ought to know something about it. Only those who possess the woman's instinct of greed save and seek to acquire unnecessary wealth. That's the reason so many rich men's sons are—well, what they are. Poor things, they inherit the paternal taint in an intensified form. No rich man should ever take the chance of being a parent, with all the disappointment that inevitably follows. If a he-man has anything he spends it all liberally. But that doesn't mean that a liberal spender is necessarily a he-man; there may be other motives, conscious or unconscious."

The hostess spoke up. "You have given us food for thought, Miss Hoover. Now somebody else give us some useful information."

Miss Stepp started to sing, "Remember, this year's trade is next year's—" but someone interrupted, "Oh! Shut up! Don't destroy all illusions!"

Miss Fall, who was always raving about odors, pleasant or otherwise, and who always put one perfume on her tongue, another behind each ear, another on the back of her neck and in her hair and still another on her breasts, her hands, her knees or any other places where she thought they might be most useful, then contributed a very important observation: "He likes to be clean and not smell bad: but he does not care anything about style so long as he's not conspicuous."

"You can put me down as holding that real he-men always have long fingers and long noses," said Miss Pickup.

Miss Godown broke forth, "He can be told by the way he speaks. He talks briefly and to the point. He is not argumentative like lawyers. He never soliloquizes. He never hems and haws, nor does he precede his remarks with useless exclamations of *well* and *now,* and he never stutters." She paused a moment, gave a careless wave of her hand, and added, "Et cetera."

"What are the signs of lost manhood?" asked almost-innocent Miss Stepp.

"Are you sure you mean signs of its having been lost, or indications of its never having been possessed?"

Miss Stepp did not answer, but continued to question—"Don't you think you can tell real he-men by the way they run after women all the time?"

"My Gawd, dearie, no! Half of that running after women is an attempt to reinforce their very imperfect feeling of mannishness." It was Miss Savoy speaking again with the voice of authority. "No real he-man ever runs after anything. But whatever comes his way, he's ready for it (I said whatever!), and then he forgets it after it's all over. A real he-man will take all the petting you will give, and enjoy the sensation, but he won't bother to pet back again. Why, a real he-man would never even bother to get married if some woman did not keep on pestering him and making a nuisance of herself until he did it. And believe me, no real he-man can ever remain faithful to one woman, unless that one woman keeps all the others herded away from him." It was easy to see which way Miss Savoy's mind ran—in a rut.

The Dikes, the Bulls and Miss Bull-Mawgan, who had strolled in late, looked bored. Nevertheless, La Bull-Mawgan who knew men (and women), if she knew anything at all, gave her definition—"A real he-man is a human male who never gets nervous." She paused as if for thought, but seemed to be unable to get her wits together sufficiently to continue further (Bobby Dike had come into the room).

Here the ever elegant Mrs. Slatterly, who seemed to know a thing or two, broke into the conversation. "But why all this furor about a real he-man? I think they're nicer if they are a bit effeminate; then they can be induced to do things that a real he-man could never be persuaded to attempt."

"Well, you're the one who ought to know!" said Miss Savoy.

Miss Browning, who detested silence, broke forth again: "Once I thought I had a real he-man. I found out he was fish. It makes me sick to think of him."

"Control yourself, dearie," Miss Hoyt hastened to warn. "Too late now!"

"Mason has an idea that the hormones are responsible for real he-men," volunteered Randall.

"Oh, the hormones! The hormones!" camped Miss Savoy with delight. "Go on, Mason and talk about the hormones and the adorable glands. You always sound so convincing. I love to hear you."

"Reserving all my ideas for publication," said Mason, who did not wish to be bothered further. He was over in a corner swapping spit with something nice he had a crush on. They had no time for anything but sex stunts, and Randall had privately been surprised with how brave and wonderfully blatant Mason's behavior could become. Even now, the handsome young man's beautiful cock could be spied as it was caressed and squeezed by his latest beau. His kisses brought a brief and heartfelt pang to Randall's heart. It had been their oath, one decided upon long ago, that Mason's was a love Randall would never pursue. *Alas,* thought Randall.

He had been holding a spoonful of sugar over his cup of tea while he gazed. It was an opportunity for the ever observing Miss Savoy, who called out to him—"Randy, is that invert sugar?"

Randall turned the spoon upside down, dumping the sugar into the tea, stirred vigorously, sipped it and replied, "It is now, dearie! But why question the fact?"

Then Randall contributed some of his personal observations: "Real he-men do not have big fat buttocks, or big breasts or fat arms or big thick calves; those things belong to the female or the male intermediate. To tell the truth, dearies, the real honest-to-Gawd grand glorious he-man is just about as common as his opposite."

"And what do you mean by that?" asked Mrs. Godown, who feigned ignorance.

"Now, Kitty, don't you know what a fairy is, a real live fairy, not the story book kind?" asked Miss Savoy.

"Whoops-my-dear, I should say I do."

"Then, speaking plainly," said Randall, "what I wished to impress upon you is that the real he-men are just about as common in the population as fairies are."

"Well, then, how do women ever get—along?"

"They put up with the makeshifts, grab the best thing they can get, not the thing they really want."

"But how can they produce a breed of real he-men if they can't breed with real he-men?"

"The truth is, they don't, dearie."

"You make me wonder about my father."

"Yes, and your grandfather too!"

"I should think women would love real he-men so!"

"Well, with all the drivel that has been written about love throughout the ages, have you ever heard of a fair damsel or a fine dame falling in love with a eunuch? I ask you?"

Miss Savoy, who had been listening attentively, then said, "To put it succinctly, a real he-man must be possessed of marvelous sexual attributes."

Then Mrs. Slatterly, who wished to justify her yen for flossy gentlemen, became profound and declared,

"The basis of civilization is founded on the gradual repression of the too masculine type. Why, if every male of the species were a real he-man there would be a personal war just as soon as two of them met. They'd kill each other off. It is good for them to have some attraction for each other instead of too much repulsion."

"Is Reggie over there a real he-man?" asked Mrs. Godown in her most innocent manner and just as if she didn't know.

Reggie spoke up in a high-pitched voice. "If I had been brought up differently, I might not be as I am. Please leave me out of the discussion."

Then Oswald broke forth bitterly—"Huh! Look at me. I was brought up right, exactly as the doctors and psychologists specified. I was a he-man once. Yet look what happened. After having grippe, complicated by pneumonia, and then meningitis, I was a different person; there was some inner change. What in hell has so-called morals to do with my life anyway?"

"But you are digressing, Oswald!" said the hostess. "Have a sense of humor. Remember Gawd must have his little jokes on the human species."

"I feel bitter, bitter against the half-men who make our laws. Come on; let's legislate against the tides too."

"Be practical," suggested Miss Bull-Mawgan. "The only recourse is to see that every ecclesiastical student is properly seduced, and thus liberalized. The pulpit, after all, makes the laws of this country."

A chap from Philadelphia named Queen spoke up. "Well, dearie, I was a seminarian once and I'm here to tell you that the theological schools are not without their liberalizing propagandists. That's where I was brought out pretty. What do you think, Mary Savoy, is it the bringing up that makes us as we are?"

"No, indeed!" answered the almost omniscient Miss Savoy. "Oswald is right; the outward is but the expression of the inward. I think we've exhausted the subject, all but the laboratory course. Now that we know what a real he-man is like, let's all go out and look for some."

People began leaving. There was the usual laughter and shrill callings back and forth, the exchange of "brilliant" remarks as the party broke up.

The reception, which started with such elegance, ended in a typical panic, as so often affairs in society do.

Arriving home, Randall said to Mason "Now you can feel that you've made your bow to 'society.'"

Said Mason, "Our hostess is most elegant and seems to try to be important socially. Does she succeed?"

"I'll say she does," answered Randall, "and so do all of our crowd."

CHAPTER
31

At Christmas, Mason and Randall "threw a party," a grand affair. They sent out cards to all of their friends in New York and Philadelphia—La Duchesse Stupintek, "Tillie the Toiler," Miss Savoy, "Bertha the Sewing Machine Girl," Miss Mae Bull, Miss Elsie Dike, La Bull-Mawgan, Miss Kuntz, the Beaches and the Fishes, the usual gay crowd; also to dear Old Aunty Beach-Bitsche from California, who had continued to remain in New York after the Horse Show and other of the major social events. Among those invited were many stage people and many supposed doubles of famous actresses who assumed the names of the stars they imitated, or, more likely, caricatured—"Carter," "Miss Anna Held," and "Lillian Russell," to mention only a few of the notables who were impersonated.

There was a Christmas tree.

The Beaches appeared, dragging their usual gorgeous laces and velvets regally behind them. The "noted actresses" came in all the borrowed finery they could command.

Randall was gayer than ever, the reaction to a difficult life-saving emergency operation he had performed on a tenement house brat during the afternoon. He said to Mason at dinner, "It was glorious to see that purple-faced little child come back to life. And I don't mind telling you that after it was all over and the mother was weeping, I broke down and shed tears, too. Now they look on me as a tender-hearted angel. Well, I suppose I am to them. I left them a fifty-dollar bill. I couldn't bear their misery."

The weather was cold and snowy, conducive to that elevation of spirit that comes when one steps from the inclement out-of-doors into a festive interior. The tree was borne down by gifts, and for every guest there was a present of at least one cake of soap of a much advertised floating brand, wholly suited to the personalities of the recipients—just in case they did not have one in their homes. Then they provided Dutch Cleanser "to brighten up their prospects," lovely rubber goods appropriate to the sex of the individual, gorgeously colored douchebags and beautiful pessaries; medicaments with specific directions for their use for specific diseases; atomizers for throat spraying; half a dozen nice diapers for a lady who, it was rumored, would need them unless she got out of her predicament (which she did later on, unless the whole thing was a fabrication); canned tomatoes; tinned fish and other things with directions to make use of them when they could not get anything else.

Too, there were other presents of a more expensive type—a beautiful prayer book for "Bertha the Sewing Machine Girl," who, though he was known to be a clandestine prostitute, was, nevertheless, very religious (he had been one of the Petits-Jesus); a splendid necklace for "Tillie the Toiler" (so dubbed because he worked so hard—at anything he did);

exquisite perfumes for those who were ladies, or at least thought they were ladies; handkerchiefs for everybody, with the price tag left on—just under 70 cents—but Randall insisted he was too busy to take the tags off. "Besides," he said, "I'll leave them on so they'll know I'm not cheating."

The two kept women who lived on the floor below were bidden, and when one of the college boys stuck his head out to hear what all the pow-wow was about, he and his crowd too were invited, and accepted with alacrity.

The first arrivals came quietly immediately after theater, but as the night advanced there was more and more hilarity and noise. By two o'clock the three establishments were thrown into one. They were all keeping open house, traipsing back and forth, clattering up and down stairs, whooping, singing, shouting and making a jolly noise just suited to such an occasion and to that type of people.

About half past two, the respectable Mrs. Backhaus, who lived on the ground floor, came out into the lower hall in wrapper, bedroom slippers and curlpapers, and shouted angrily up the stairs—"I want to know what this noise is all about! Don't you know that this is a respectable house and that respectable people should be in bed and asleep?"

Mason, liquored up a bit, called down— "Oh, we're willing to go to bed, come along!"

At that Mrs. Backhaus screamed, "I warn you, one and all, I warn you, that if these carryings-on do not stop, I shall call the police."

By that time Randall was in the lower hall. The only respectable woman in the house looked him up and down, at first not recognizing him under his wig and drag, but when she did, broke forth, "You, you dissolute people; you are responsible for this. I'll find out all about you before this is over. I'll look up your employers and tell them just what kind of people you are."

"Oh, go on and tell them, you old blatherskite," retorted Randall. "And when you've finished, remember that to the pure all things are pure, and that includes us. Besides, I know a few things about you, too," he continued, making up his story as he went along—"You're the woman whose first child does not belong to her husband, though he thinks it does. I've heard all about you!"

"I'll have you arrested!"

"Me? Arrested! And you want me to tell in court all I have heard about you?"

Now, no woman who has lived all of her life in New York City is so stainless that there is not some weak place in the armor of her respectability, and this woman was no exception. She feared what Randall might really know. But she was the kind who wished to have the last word.

"I wish my husband was here!"

"I wish he were, too," caroled Randall. "I'd take him right away from you. You know I could!"

"You're a bold, bad person." Mrs. Backhaus, the respectable, turned toward her door.

"You don't know the half of it," laughed Randall.

"And I don't want to either!"

"You wouldn't understand it if you did!" Then Randall had an inspiration. Up the stairway he flew. To the Christmas tree he hurried, telling them all, "I'm going to take a Christmas present to dear Mrs. Backhaus." He selected the largest douchebag remaining, then quickly slid down the banisters to the ground floor, knocked at the lady's door, and as Mrs. Backhaus opened it, said, "Merry Christmas. Here's a pretty douchebag for you," then pranced away toward the stairway, narrowly avoiding the douchebag which dear Mrs. Backhaus hurled after him.

"Now I'm going to call the police," the irate woman declared.

"I hope they'll send the reserves. They'll be fresh. We can use them," Randall gave back answer.

They had not long to wait. Soon a big, good-looking officer arrived. Randall came down to meet him. Mrs. Backhaus, her door ajar, was peeking out to see all that could be seen. As soon as the officer came in from the street she began—"Officer, arrest that person and all of that crowd upstairs. Not only are they disturbing the peace but I have every reason to believe they are grossly immoral people." And to Randall she said, "You ought to be ashamed of yourself acting this way on Christmas Eve."

"Officer," said Randall, "she ought to be ashamed of herself. I gave her a Christmas present, a perfectly lovely douchebag and she threw it at me. Now, is that a Christian spirit?"

"What kind of a place is this you're runnin'?" asked the officer like a magistrate hearing the evidence.

"Come right on upstairs and I'll show you," said Randall as he took his arm. At the landing he turned and stuck out his tongue at Mrs. Backhaus.

On the second floor Randall explained to the officer: "Now, these ladies in this apartment really have reason to feel aggrieved. We woke them up out of their beauty sleep. You know it was their beauty sleep. See how beautiful they are! Well, they are not complaining about the rumpus, but have joined in the festivities as becomes good Christians. It's Christmas and we should all celebrate. Don't you think so, officer? Now come up to my apartment."

The officer was ushered in and looked about in admiration.

"My, what a swell place you got," he said, "and this is what yuh call home?"

"Yes, and you must make yourself at home, too, thoroughly so. See our tree! Just take anything off it you wish. There's some queer soap, always useful, even though amusing. Did you get any presents yet? No? Oh, you poor thing! Mason! Go get twenty-five dollars out of my gold mesh bag and bring it here to the officer." (Randall had no gold mesh bag, but he did have the twenty-five dollars.) "Officer, do have some champagne. Cigars? Cigarettes? Help yourself."

"Thanks, don't care if I do," said the officer politely as he stuffed his pockets full of all they would hold, then downed a glass of champagne as if it were so much water.

Randall knew his stuff. "Have some more champagne, officer?"

"Thanks, don't care if I do." He drank as most people would drink when possessed of a terrible thirst. And so Randall plied him with the delightful and deceptive liquid.

"Now, officer, I want you to meet all the celebrities, since you'll have to give a report on us and our guests. This is 'Bertha the Sewing Machine Girl.' Bertha, do your fancy curtsy. This is 'Tillie the Toiler.' This is Old Aunty Beach-Bitsche all the way from California. And these are all the stage celebrities, or at least they pretend they are. Most of them are chorus molls, but, oh! so talented and accomplished." Randall rolled his eyes expressively, then continued. "Mason, fix up a nice box for the officer and put in a bottle of champagne, too, for evidence that we were giving a respectable party. And somebody open another bottle now. Have some more champagne, officer?"

"Not so fast! Not so fast! I'm almost full up now. Where's the—" he whispered to Randall.

"Third door down the hall, officer. But you need not be afraid to speak right out loud here. We call things by their right names, don't we girls—a spade's a spade." He appealed to those surrounding them.

The modest officer retired but soon returned.

"Come here, dear," Randall called to him, and then to some of the girls and chorus molls standing about, "Now show the officers what you can do."

Beach, the one from Philadelphia nicknamed "Sissy," was there that season doing an impersonation of Eric-Erica, the museum wonder, one-half of whose body was feminine, and the other half masculine. Sissy's left side had been shaven of all hair. A false but very real-looking mammary gland had been attached to the left side of the chest. The makeup of the left side was of delicate pink and white; that of the right of deep tan and red. The left eyebrow had been replaced by a delicate penciled line. Bracelets and rings adorned the left hand and arm. The left foot was encased in a dainty silk slipper. On the right foot, Sissy wore an athletic shoe; on the right hand a boxing glove.

Like a good showman, Mason made the introduction:

"Ladies and gentlemen, we have before us Eric-Erica, the most renowned and most marvelous anatomical puzzle known to modern medicine." He slipped a Spanish shawl from the left shoulder. "As you will see, one side is feminine." Here Sissy assumed the attitude of a Venus de Milo. "On the other side"—he removed half of a coat—"we have a masculine form.

"Eric-Erica will now tell you of her or his peculiar nature, one-half feminine, the other half masculine."

"And the midline neuter," Miss Kitty Fuchs volunteered. There were titters. Then the supposed Eric-Erica recited a little piece, turning the feminine side first to the audience and speaking in a feminine treble out of the left corner of the mouth:

"Ladies and gentleman, I was born as you see me—part male, part female. Shortly after my birth, the most distinguished savants of the world were called in to observe me and decide to which sex I belong. One doctor held to one thing; another to another. The advisability of operative procedures was carefully considered, pro and con, and there was much learned discussion as to whether, by the excision of certain projecting parts, one set of organs could be caused to atrophy and the other set, thus set free, to develop independently. But my mother, a deeply religious woman, said, 'What Gawd hath joined together, let no man put asunder.' In reality, I am twins in one body. In the embryo we choose our sex, and I, well, I just chose to be something different. Now, some of you might consider this a great disadvantage. The truth is, that it gives me a wonderful choice—of interests. I am a person of one hand and one heart and one body, but also a person of two sexes. I can marry either a man or a woman. Were I so to choose, I could gratify either sex. Modesty, strongly reinforced by the prejudices of the general public, prevents me from exposing the more intimate parts of my body. But if there is a physician in the audience, or any body of scientific men present who wish to verify all of my claims, for the very small consideration of five dollars I will submit to an intimate medical examination—this only in the interests of science, however.

"In one phase of the moon, I have a predilection for the feminine role; in another phase a desire to act the opposite part. For those who may be especially interested, I may state that in the full of the moon I am entirely feminine in my reactions and at that time undergo the usual ordeal that any normal female is subject to; I refer to the physiological hemorrhage. As you will see, the left side is feminine. Were a person of the opposite sex to touch this exquisite dainty skin, I would shiver with delight. The officer may touch me." He swatted the rounded buttock.

"See!" exclaimed Sissy shimmying deliciously, then went on with the rigmarole—"You will observe the wonderful development of my left breast. From this I lactate. Officer, when your wife gives birth to twins the next time, I know it will be twins, you're such a strong rugged man, I'll let you use this side for a wet nurse. You will observe the delicate turning of the shapely lower limb. With this I can do ballet steps, and coincidentally execute an Irish jig with the masculine right foot. With my dainty left hand I do not only plain sewing but most delicate embroidery and also play the scale on the flute, my favorite instrument."

Then Sissy turned and continued in a hoarse husky masculine voice, "This side is that of a he-man. I box! I fight! I play baseball! I chop wood like Theodore Roosevelt. Look at that chest! There's no tit there. Look at that leg! See that muscle! That's kicked many a ball to goal. An' I'm here to take on any man for a bout, provided he'll strap one arm to his side. I'll do the same. I couldn't trust my ladylike partner on the left not to scratch or gouge an eye. Ladies and gentlemen, we thank you, myself, and the little sister that is in me."

The officer stood up—"The rest of yuh can stay

free but that's the one I'm goin' to take back to the station house for me arrest."

All the ladies and near-ladies spoke up: "Sissy, you have all the luck. What a gorgeous time you'll have." And when the time came, Sissy went willingly enough with the officer and had the time of his young life, and returned the next day—unscathed.

The party went gaily on. "Tillie the Toiler" did his couch dance, shaking his grass skirt right in the face of the policeman.

Wells, the triple voiced, sang in bass, contralto and soprano—"I need thee every hour," completely mystifying the officer as to his actual personality. Sometimes Wells was a little bit mystified himself about that too, as who wouldn't be, under the circumstances.

Then everyone urged Randall to give his imitation of a tenement house woman having a baby, but he refused to bother to take off his elaborate drag and perform.

After that everybody danced, each one claiming the right to break and have one turn with the officer. Finally he and Randall retired to one of the rooms to talk things over in a friendly way—for Randall knew that this could well be the last man in uniform he could have before completing his collegiate examinations and being shipped to some God-unknown locale for graduate work.

Of course, he was not disappointed. This policeman was more handsome than any he had ever had. For this conquest he used all his charms to pull this officer completely out of uniform, and he donned the scoffed blouse, cap and leathered holster before mounting this Aztec god. Perhaps this officer had spent some seed already today, for it took him longer than Randall thought usual to be brought to thrilling climax. But Randall had more than one trick up his sleeve—or, it should be said, up his rectum. Muscles long practiced in taking and gripping shafts of all sizes and shapes took hold of this man's cock and wrapped and rolled over it until he could stand no more. "It appears you are under arrest," Randall grinned wickedly with a tip of the patrolman's cap.

"Yes!" cried the cop. "Oh yes!" After sufficient time, he left, declaring to Randall that he'd never had such a good time in his life.

He was loaded with gifts under one arm and little "Sissy" Beach under the other, loudly asseverating, "It took me four years to graduate from college. How long will it take me to graduate from jail, officer?"

"We'll keep you there always," the cop answered jocosely.

"Oh, goody, goody, goody, what loads and loads of nice reckless people I'll meet," shrilled Sissy.

At the foot of the stairs, Virtue, as typified by the not too tarnished Mrs. Backhaus, was waiting.

The officer assured her—"Lady, I give 'em all hell. I beat up the sassy one and I gave a black eye to the big fresh one that goes round wishin' douchebags on her respectable neighbors. This one under me arm is the ringleader, and this one goes to the Island, just to put the fear of God into people who don't know how to be respectable." Mrs. Backhaus retired to her apartment, shut and locked the door. The officer turned to the gay crowd on the stairway gave them a solemn wink and went his way.

But the party was not yet over. There was a loud noise in the hall below; many shrieks and much masculine guffawing. The ebullient Miss Savoy had arrived! Arrived, indeed, accompanied by what she styled the guardians of her moral rectitude: four handsome young men, one a rich man's chauffeur, another a lightweight boxer, a third a member of the beach patrol and the fourth a metal construction worker. So much hubbub could not fail to arouse the inquiring instinct of respectable Mrs. Backhaus, who, in curl papers and flannel wrapper, again sped into the hall. Randall and Miss Kitty Fuchs hurried down to meet them.

Miss Savoy made a picture, indeed: tall, slender, garbed in richest black, her red wig topped by a picture hat, her slender waist corseted till there was doubtless room only for her backbone and one lone intestine to pass through the narrowest part of the garment, a picture indeed as she advanced with both arms outstretched exclaiming—"Randy's mother, I am sure. Merry Christmas, Mother, how are you and all the brood?"

The only real refined lady in the house glared, sweeping Miss Savoy in contemptuous judgment. "Your place is upstairs, but it ought to be on the streets," she announced severely.

"Oh, me! A woman of the streets," camped Miss Savoy in her voice that suggested any and every little old thing. "You flatter me! I've never done it yet, but now that you encourage me I shall go right out and try as soon as I have attended the party. Come on, sweetheart, do you want to go upstairs?" Her inflection suggested more than her mere words.

Then she raised her skirts unnecessarily high, revealing thin legs, much lace trimmed white petticoat, and bright green silk drawers, as she said "to bring out the color of my red hair."

Percy Bütsche suggested, "You must be a contortionist."

"You don't know the half of it, dearie," answered Miss Savoy.

Then Miss Fuchs accused Miss Savoy—"You are

stealing my thunder, you have borrowed my idea, Miss Savoy, you who pride yourself on being so original. You know well that I have long gone about bragging that I always have my sweetheart wear blue socks to match the color of my eyes. You can't work over my originality and get away with it."

At the second landing Miss Savoy almost stumbled over fat old Aunty Beach-Bitsche, who, seeing indistinctly, in her alcoholized mood fumbled about as they passed and groped wildly.

"What are you trying to do, dearie?" chirruped Miss Savoy.

"I'm trying to get up—"

"Up what? Oh, stay where you are and be comfortable!"

As Miss Savoy's head appeared above the top of the second balustrade, someone caroled joyfully, "Oh, the fairy godmother has come, bringing beautiful gifts with her!"

Miss Savoy advanced, distributing kisses impartially. Almost out of breath she gasped to Randall: "Dearie, look what I brought to your party. Yes, I knew you would be pleased."

And "Miss" Etrange, not to be outdone, urged the others, "Now, girls, make these good-looking young men feel welcome. Mason, will you show them where to put their things?" And Mason did.

Miss Savoy raved over the gifts she received, especially the handkerchiefs, which she insisted were "Lovely! And just the size of pleasure towels."

Randall made the rounds, introducing the actor as the accomplished and notorious Miss Savoy, "A success, of whom you've all seen much and I hope will see more." Then he urged: "Now, Mary, just show them your green drawers."

Then Miss Savoy performed the famous curtsy

which she had learned in one of the cribs of New Orleans—a writhing, a brief whirl which threw her skirts high above her head and allowed a glimpse of the green silk drawers before the skirts had settled about her body again.

Miss Savoy was in her element. She strutted her stuff gaily, knowing well that every innuendo, every double meaning would be appreciated at full worth. "Bertha the Sewing Machine Girl" passed. Bertha had long resisted the temptations of New York and had only recently been brought out. Miss Savoy knew the story and gurgled, in an attempt at gurgling, "Oh, Miss Bertha, how is your virtue?"

"Alas! It bothered me so much I had to get rid of it," gushed that one.

Randall and Mason had not been the least snobbish. Their invitations had been sent out without regard to the social or financial standing of their acquaintances, "brilliance" being the sole criterion for entrance into the charmed circle. Each had at least one entertaining accomplishment. Some sang; some danced exquisitely; some acted; some played—various instruments. Their music ran to sentimental love songs or to the gayest of dance rhythms.

Miss Savoy was versatile. She could talk man-talk, woman-talk, boy-talk, girl-talk, baby-talk and even fairy-talk.

To them and their crowd life was one hilarious riot, as it can be in a city the size of New York.

The party had been a success. True, Mason and Randall were dispossessed the day after Christmas, but then, they cared not. There were other places.

CHAPTER
32

Randall and Mason had almost finished their internships. Randall had become more serious looking. He still possessed the same betraying voice that challenged the interest of all men and caused them to try to lead him on, incidentally leading themselves farther than they did him. If there were any choosing to be done, Randall did it!

Mason, with maturity, had fulfilled his early promise. He was now more handsome than ever, and added to that had assimilated all the arts of love.

The chief, though he had been indifferent to Randall and Mason for some time, now that separation loomed had, perversely enough, resumed his interest in the pair.

Of course, Randall now had his own growing fortune. Good spender that he was, yet he was careful never to go beyond half of his income. His one grief had been that his mother had passed away, the mother for whom he was now in a position to do so much.

With growing means, and with advancement in his profession, Randall's opportunities were enlarged.

He could now have afforded a family, had he wished one—at least the façade of one replete with an adopted child, of course. That almost went without saying, for Randall believed that no one was justified in reproducing a victim for the diseases, troubles, disappointments and unhappiness that are the lot of the average person.

What Mason lacked in personal fortune, the chief made up. It was he, the chief, who decided that Randall and Mason should do postgraduate work in Berlin and Vienna.

So it was arranged that they would be abroad for two full years and at the end of that time return to New York, where Mason would relieve the chief of all gonorrheal and syphilitic patients and Randall take over obstetrical cases.

Randall was tired. The crop of bastard babies that spring had been "something fierce." In those days the men were only a little less virtuous than the women. While Randall was "jerking" little bastard babies, Mason was disinfecting diseased males.

Randall was eagerly looking forward to seeing Europe again. With the banker, years before, he had learned the art of travel. Now he was to enjoy it all again, with the avid Mason.

Their plans were made, and the eve of departure arrived. Randall was waiting up for Mason's return. He was sitting alone in half reverie, thinking of him and his comradeship that meant so much more than love. The sharp ring of the telephone ended these pleasant thoughts.

It was Mason speaking: "Randy, dear, I have a great surprise for you. I'm married!"

"For God's sake, Mason, when and why and to whom?"

"Married half an hour ago to Bobby Dike. Now

you understand—a marriage of convenience. Life will be safer for both of us and as we have a perfect understanding of each other, far more complete than the average couple possesses, we shall be able to do much to add to each other's happiness. Now, what I want of you is this: Get all the Bulls and the Dikes and the Beaches and the Beach-Bitsches and the Bitsche-Beaches and the other members of the family together and come down to the ship. We've arranged to have our reception there—orchestra, dancing, and collation, in fact, a typical Bohemian impromptu."

Mason married! Yes, it was better. The outward appearance of the conventions would be preserved; the inward—oh, well! The less said the better. It was the politic thing for everyone in their set to do. It would not change Randall's relationship to Mason. Besides, Bobby Dike needed protection. Already she had taken part in several escapades which narrowly avoided gross scandal. Mason, despite all his many and very varied love affairs, had been discreet enough to keep always within the bounds of his own social set. But not Bobby! It was characteristic of Mason to play it safe. Even in 1914 blackmail, though not a tenth as common as in these degenerate days, was something to be reckoned with. Now, blackmail is the first concern of too many of the present-day sons and daughters of the foreign born. They are not seduced by love, as Randall had been, but are seduced by the desire, which their parents have inculcated, to prey on others.

Mason well knew how to deal with anything sinister. Yes, Randall was glad. Bobby Dike, now Mrs. Linberg, had always been a good pal. Randall remembered with amusement how they had cruised together when he visited San Francisco, each lending

233

cooperation in landing trade for the other, often exchanging favors. The trip would be more interesting with her. Bobby was unlike the average run of Dike—she was always gay, never afflicted with the familiar morose humors.

Randall spent a good hour telephoning and then went to the ship.

After Randall, Miss Savoy was the next to arrive. She had rushed from the theater without change and was, of course, wearing a remarkable drag. Her greeting to the newlywed couple was characteristic—

"Oh, my dears, let me kiss you—anywhere you wish. And let me wish you joy, or is it give you joy? I'm a woman of experience. If there's anything in the home life you don't know how to do, just tell 'your mother.' I'll show you how to do it. I offer you my felicitations. I wish somebody would marry me—over and over again. I'd like to be married every day of the week." Turning to Bobby—"And Mason dear is going to shelter and provide for you! Some people have all the luck. I don't know which one to congratulate and which one to wish happiness to; the rule I believe is to congratulate the man and wish happiness to the woman—but I'm all confused. Please exonerate me." Then she turned to Mason and gushed on—"Where's the cabin boy? I must have the cabin boy at once. Call the cabin boy."

A steward appeared. Miss Savoy, assuming a vacant idiotic expression, broke forth as she looked him over, "Are you the chambermaid? I've never been on a boat before. At least not when I was sober. I didn't know they had he-chambermaids aboard ship. I suppose you serve both the gentlemen and the ladies? Oh, how gorgeous! I envy you your lot. But I did not summon you here to jest. I just can't keep my back hair from falling down. Will you get me some hairpins?"

The other guests arrived and behaved more or less discreetly when in the brightly lighted saloon, but what they did in the stateroom, well, as Miss Savoy said afterwards, "That's just nobody's business."

Each arrival had something suggestive to offer in the way of a wedding gift. At that time of night it was well nigh impossible to buy gifts, but they all rose to the occasion, stopping at the all-night drugstores, picking up what they could, as Ella expressed to Kitty, "more for the camp of the thing than anything else." And then she continued, "Knowing them as I do, I would not put it past them to have had ante-nuptial experience, nor have I any narrow-minded ideas that they won't indulge in extramarital relationships. The things they won't do—well, ain't Nature grand!"

"Do you think the marriage will take?" asked Kitty.

"What do you mean take?"

"Will they have children? Of course, Bobby Dike could give birth if she wished to, but the question is, will she wish to?"

"Well, I doubt if she ever could give birth even if she wished to. You know as well as I do that she's as queerly constructed in her physical makeup as she is in her—well, in her mental. Look at her too narrow hips. Could a child slip between them? Look at her flat breasts, her manatee walk. If that thing can grow a child, they can be made in a test tube."

"What about the handsome Mason?"

"He's adaptable—I think. But after all, it's a sensible marriage, what all of us in our set should do, to play safe." Miss Kitty Fuchs believed in finishing a subject. Rushing up to the couple she asked, "Are you going to use birth control, or are you going to have children?"

"If there are any children, Mason will have to give birth to them," Mrs. Linberg, née Dike, announced. "If there's one thing I object to it is getting all mussed up giving birth. I've been on several baby-jerking expeditions with Randall and Mason. There's simply got to be a new way invented, for I won't stoop to such vulgarity."

"Vulgarity? Remember some things, dear, are all in the point of view."

Miss Savoy proceeded to uphold Mrs. Linberg's contention: "I don't want to be a parent. One of my friends had a little boy and when he was five years old he died of diabetes; another had a little girl with epileptic fits; and my mother had *me*! Every family has something the matter with it. No, indeed! No children for me!"

About that time Old Aunty Beach-Bitsche came aboard and made her sweet remarks in her usual frank and outspoken way—"Bobby, I envy you. I've always had an unholy yen for Mason myself. And what will all the Bütsches and the chief do now that you are dragging him away to Europe? Over there they'll probably seduce him in some new way we don't know anything about yet, and he'll never come back to us."

"And what might that be?" inquired Miss Savoy, but for once no one listened, for Bobby, the unblushing bride, was speaking. "Aunty Beach-Bitsche, control yourself! I shall lend him out to friends and near relations. We are coming back in two years."

"And I shall have drunk myself to death by that time," wailed old Aunty Beach-Bitsche. "But Mason, we shall be friends to the end."

Another opportunity for Miss Savoy—"Which

end? I didn't know you loved Mason so much, Aunty Beach-Bitsche!"

"Love him? I love every inch of him, from the ends of the hairs of his head to the tips of his toenails. Why, I love his very guts!"

"That's a very vulgar but adequate description of the depths of your passion, Aunty Beach-Bitsche!"

The crowd came thicker and faster and there was less opportunity for extended banter. Dancing commenced. Mason and some of the Beaches disappeared into one of the staterooms and were gone—a long time. Before retiring later that evening, Randall looked upon Mason's nude behind with horror—it was beet red, the victim of an old fashioned European birching delivered by those wicked Beaches as punishment for leaving them to fend for themselves. The treat after the trick, however, declared the grinning Linberg, made the sting of the whipping more than worth withstanding: not a single portion of his body escaped the forlorn mob's farewell kisses. It would take him the rest of the cruise to recover.

When somebody finally commented on the fact of Mason's lengthy absence, Miss Savoy, in a regal manner, rose to the defense of the queen's favorite child. "Well, what are staterooms for?"

The dancers romped, wriggled, squirmed, bounced, jolted, bustled, strutted, glided, bumped and pistoned back and forth for at least two hours. Then there was a lull for food and drinks.

Near morning the reception broke up.

Of course, Miss Savoy was the last to leave, and as she put foot on the gangplank struck a dramatic attitude, calling to those aboard, "Pause one moment! Has everyone on the boat been seduced? Well, if they haven't, it's not my fault. I did my part. I gave them a chance." As she passed along the pier she confided to Miss Kitty Fuchs, "We've given them a ready-made reputation aboard the ship. Everybody will be waiting to meet them; they'll know who and what they are!"

Randall returned to the flat, attended to gathering the odds and ends together, bundled everything into a cab and came back to the ship to await the send-off. By eleven, those in society were there by the dozens to wish them bon voyage—Miss Fuchs, Miss Kuntz, Miss Godown, Miss Fitzhugh, Miss Hoover, Miss Astor and all the prominent ones, the "flagrant ones" some envious Beach called them. They swarmed all over the ship, making the most of the opportunity to see strange things.

A bell sounded and then the cry, "all off who are going off." The ship began to slip from the dock. There was a mixed sound of clanging bells and whistles and shouts of goodbye from the pier and decks. Those on the pier seemed more anxious to attract attention to themselves than to pay heed to their friends aboard ship. There was a hysterical quality to the gaiety—so characteristic of New York.

Loud shouts of "bon voyage" followed. Most of them gave it an English pronunciation, but not Miss Savoy, who shouted *"bon voyage"* and other French messages through a megaphone, some of the messages more discreetly expressed in the foreign tongue than in the native New York idiom. She explained to one of the waiting Beaches, "I want everybody to know I can speak it too."

A bystander (from Boston, of course) was heard to ask, "Who is that vivacious one so fully endowed with vim, vigor and vitality?"

Her companion answered, "That's Miss Savoy, the notorious impersonator."

"Whom is he seeing off?"

"See that queer-looking woman in the mannish clothes and the very handsome young man and well, I don't know what the other one is, whether it's a man or a woman. Let me have your glasses a moment."

CHAPTER
33

Hardly was the ship beyond Sandy Hook than Bobby, née Dike, came running to Mason and Randall, who had been pacing the decks, making campy remarks about such of the other passengers as exhibited any least idiosyncrasy. "Now, Marjorie, we are cruising in every sense of the word," Mason greeted her.

"Yes, and someone else is, too. What do you think! La Bull-Mawgan and that damned bitch, Elsie Dike, are aboard ship, sneaking over to Paris again!"

"Well, what of it? That's their right!"

"But you don't understand! Don't you remember how La Bull-Mawgan rushed me at Miss Painter's party? I'm going to watch them and I'm going to take some of the self-conceit out of La Bull-Mawgan before I get through with her. They've seats at the captain's table and I'm going to get one there too."

"The captain," camped Randall. "I'd love to kiss the captain to find out if it's true that these brave men of the sea have that salty flavor people are always telling about."

Of course the wealth of Bobby Linberg, née Dike, procured seats at the captain's table. Bobby would not have given a tinker's damn to sit there had it not been that Miss Bull-Mawgan and her dear friend were to sit there, too, and Bobby was determined to make it uncomfortable for them both. She could!

At that time, La Bull-Mawgan was at the zenith of her attractiveness and her following was—a multitude. Certainly she was the high priestess of her cult—the woman cult. Wherever she went she was followed by a coterie of ecstatic feminine admirers. She was popularly reported to have initiated more young girls than all the other women in New York together. But that was stretching the truth. Some enemy must have started such a rumor. Afterward, Bobby, in describing the lady, said, "She has nothing on me except brazenness. I can flaunt myself in some places, but not quite in every place as she does. Well, she gets her thrills, and I get mine."

There was not much of importance that happened aboard ship. While Mason and Randall enjoyed cruising, Bobby, true to her instincts, took part in all the sports, the rougher the better, interspersing her games with—oh, well, as La Duchesse Stupintek would say, "odder t'ings." Of course she had little annoying spats with Elsie Dike and of course when Elsie was not about Bobby paid court to Miss Bull-Mawgan.

At the end of the trip, Miss Bull-Mawgan gave a pressing, a very pressing invitation to Bobby: "My dear, I shall be charmed if you will visit me in Paris."

"And does that include my husband?" asked Bobby.

"Why, certainly, if you insist."

"And I suppose you will offer me the usual string of pearls, the grand imitation French kind you are so fond of distributing?" said Bobby, who had grown jealous during the trip.

Miss Bull-Mawgan looked disturbed. "I don't know what you mean; but, if you wish to have a string of pearls, yes!"

"Thanks," said Bobby with mock politeness, and then, "You can go to hell, Miss Bull-Mawgan. I don't want to have anything to do with you. Oh! I'm not such a virtuous kind of person that I think myself any better than you, but—you smell like a disease to me."

La Bull-Mawgan controlled herself with difficulty. Bobby continued—"When I look at you, I think that at birth your mother made a mistake and threw away the baby and raised the placenta." She had given the crowning insult of society. Thus Bobby had revenge on La Bull-Mawgan for a fancied slight. But that is like these women. Bobby had a nasty tongue when she wished to use it.

The Amazonian Miss Bull-Mawgan looked venomous, then gave Bobby a resounding slap in the face. She should not have done that, except to a woman of her own size. Thus was started the famous feud, which was to be patched up and break forth again and again at intervals through the years, and, for that matter, is still going.

It was in such crises that Mason was invaluable. His sense of humor never failed him. As Bobby rushed away, Mason hurried to Miss Bull-Mawgan, who, of course, made the story much worse than it really was and even gave a specific name to the disease she said Bobby had accused her of harboring. "How I sympathize with you, Dr. Linberg," she said cooingly, "but just the same, tell that damned wife of yours if she ever comes to Paris, I'll have two Apaches garrote her."

Mason and Randall had not been idle aboard ship. They had indulged in delightful midnight flirtations and done pretty much what and how they pleased.

CHAPTER
34

The voyage was over. Mason and Randall were congratulating each other on the number of delightful affairs they had consummated aboard ship. Bobby, was lamenting, "Oh, you two show so little discrimination that it's easy for you to have a good time wherever you go."

"We must be common," suggested Mason.

Bobby lifted her eyebrows and smiled, then voiced her own hope: "I'm waiting for Paris. There I shall be happy—many, many times. I'll stay there while you and Randy do your work in Vienna."

They debarked at Boulogne-sur-Mer, Mason and Bobby to hasten to Paris, and Randall to Berlin, which he planned to visit for a while before going on to the postgraduate schools in Vienna.

Randall's early Pennsylvania life now proved of use to him. There he had as a child picked up "Pennsylvania Dutch." At college he had learned German grammar and literature and his ear was "formed," so he had no difficulty in conversing with the Germans.

Once settled in the Adlon, he hastened to possess himself of a copy of *Freundschaft* (Friendship) and also bought a copy of *The Isle* to mail to Bobby. He had a few letters of introduction but also planned to make some informal acquaintances—"by intuition" as he called it.

The local slang amused him much—*"warmer Bruder,* See *Frucht, Tante,"* etc.

Part of his first evening Randall spent in a small resort in Fuchtwangerstrasse. Later he went to a cabaret and still later, past midnight, to the corner of Unter den Linden and Friedrichstrasse to observe the type of night life there offered. Professor Jimmie Stay's description was correct. Here he saw Berlin's night wanderers in all their variety—men who looked like women; women who looked like men; and men and women who sold themselves to anybody and everybody.

He wrote Mason fully and added, "By comparison with what I see here in Berlin, Mason, you are worth 10,000 marks a night. Just for the camp of the thing, I have taken out a special license. At last I have a legal status befitting my station in life. One could quite well copy German methods in many things. Certainly Berlin is one of the most tolerant cities in the world. I like it better than Paris. Why can't so-called Christian American cities emulate her? Miss Savoy's conclusion gives the reason—'Americans do so love to manage everybody's business but their own. Religious people won't permit anybody to be happy if they can help it. To them anything that is enjoyable is a sin. Not content with being miserable themselves, they wish to make everybody else miserable, too.'"

Randall thought he had never seen such beautiful blond young men, but their youth made no physical appeal, for his fetish was for men of 28 to 35. He found that most Germans, once they had passed out of their teens, were likely to become fat, gross and physically repugnant. There were exceptions, of course, and one of these he met quite casually while visiting Potsdam. He was a man of title, tall, slender, blond, even more handsome than Mason Linberg. And he had never had a love affair!

"I am Count Karl von G.," he said simply.

"And I am Randall Etrange, an American visiting Europe for medical study."

The Count was very frank. "I did not know Americans could be so fascinating," he told Randall. "I do not know why I am following you, a person of whom I know absolutely nothing, but to whom I am drawn by some unknown power. We know nothing of each other, yet I trust you."

"For being fascinated, I kiss you," said Randall, "and for trusting me, I kiss you, more and more and more" (suiting action to word). He had to teach him everything about love, the most delightful of all instruction. But, what was more difficult, he had to make the Count believe that it was he who was teaching Randall.

Their friendship ripened rapidly. Together they visited theaters, museums, cabarets, and at the end of a week Randall became a guest at his castle. The Count's father was dead, but his mother, a very beautiful woman of middle age, still lived at the castle. Like so many Americans of mixed ancestry, Randall found himself much more at home with these Germans than he had ever been able to feel with the English or with any other Europeans except the Russians.

Many guests were present at the castle that weekend. One and all seemed to make an intensive study of Randall. His quite open love affair with the young

Count caused no adverse comment, in fact, it was taken as a matter of course. A like situation in America would have led to much gossip, and condemnation, if not actual interference. What did surprise the Germans was that Randall appeared to be well educated. Randall was not much of a pianist these days, because medicine took so much of his time, but the castle had an excellent organ and the technique of playing that instrument still seemed natural to him. In more recent years he had made a practice of reading music daily. Thus he was able to help entertain these music-loving people. Then too, his horsemanship was good and he could hunt with them, though he cared neither for riding nor for hunting, unless Karl was with him. His ease in conversing with them also pleased, an accomplishment so unusual in English-speaking people. Too, he was able to discuss all of the newer psychology—a subject then beginning to be popularized.

True, Randall was unusual, but not more unusual than are many young Americans. His former life, that is the part that had to do with his personal advancement, seemed to these Europeans a story of fascinating adventure, rather than the account of hard work, which it really had been.

They pressed him with questions respecting his ambitions for the future. Knowing that these sincere and broad-minded people would not be shocked, he told them that he wished to do research work in venereal disease and, if possible, to find a cure for gonorrhea, that so-called "social disease," which has been fastened on mankind as a penalty for enjoying love. He told them of the work he had already done and of the theories he had formulated. This was fortunate, for the Count knew well a physician in Berlin who would be glad to put a corner of his laboratory at Randall's disposal.

Randall decided to defer his visit to Vienna when the Countess pressed him to remain another week.

Each morning, Randall and handsome Karl rode through the woodland paths of the estate. Sometimes they broke fast in the woods; other times they would go out on the great lake and fish all day. Everywhere they went, there was excuse for love-making. A typically wonderful scene would require that they stand arm in arm before the grandeur of the German countryside and view its beauties till they were so saturated with it that a new desire for love was aroused within them. Then they would embrace joyfully and kiss tenderly, the while murmuring sweet words of devotion, as they disrobed and exposed their warm flesh to the cool twilight breeze. How Karl adored to make love out of doors! His land afforded them privacy for miles, and when he put his throbbing, thick-helmed cock into Randall's hole, he would cry out as if he wished the world to reckon with his passion. He would milk Randall to come gloriously, and then he would feed upon the warm semen, cleaning its every drop from his lover's belly. They sought to draw nearer and nearer to each other, to become one time and again. So the lovely summer days passed.

Evenings, after dinner, there were the usual gatherings of all the guests in the huge reception hall. Acting was natural to Randall. The most finished actors are not those who appear on the stage, but those who must play perfectly several uncongenial roles in real life. Sometimes Randall would amuse them with impersonations, always with the help of Karl, fashioning fantastic drags from material usually reserved for other purposes: bedsheets, pillow cases and bath slippers turned him into a "white sister," regretful of having left "the world" before he knew what it was all about; lace curtains and a bouquet

turned him into a bride who had experienced love
before she had met her husband and was concocting
schemes for further deceiving him. He was in turn a
black woman nursing her half-white child; a New
York society woman attempting an English accent,
than which there is nothing funnier; and a
Krankenschwester (nurse) who was in despair because
the doctor she had loved too well was to marry an
heiress, and the unborn child had not been disposed
of. Most amusing to them of all, he was a Pennsylvania Dutch girl stamping through the mud to feed
the chickens and pigs and, incidentally, to be loved by
a yokel behind a haystack.

Near the end of the week a new guest arrived, the
middle-aged and very distinguished Count von M., a
man accustomed to having his way in most things,
and especially in love.

Randall had been amusing the guests with his
impersonations. When the Count von M. saw him, he
experienced one of those sudden flare-ups of ardor
for which he was noted. Randall had heard much of
the man, who had an international reputation, and
though he did not reciprocate his feeling in the least,
he found it was pleasant to receive the attentions of
such a renowned person; he encouraged him. For the
time being he forgot Karl.

Dancing began. He danced thrice with the Count
von M. As his partner was about to engage him for
the fourth time, a servant stepped up announcing
that Count Karl wished to see Randall at once in his
apartments. He excused himself and hurried after the
servant, whom he dismissed at the door of Count
Karl's sitting room. Randall knocked, calling, "Karl,
may I enter?"

"Yes," he answered in a strange harsh voice.

Karl was standing, gazing into the fire, his back to

the door, but as he stepped within he wheeled about, a pistol in his hand. His face was flushed and wild-looking. He shouted, "How can you torture me so? You do not love me. I am going to kill myself here, now."

"Not love you? What can I do to prove to you that I love you, Karl?" asked Randall appealingly.

Karl let the pistol fall to the floor and stretched out his arms, "Oh, come to me, *Liebchen,* come to me and tell me you love me."

Randall went to his arms and smoothed his hair and patted his cheeks; tenderly he gave him his lips again and again. "That is my answer, naughty boy. Now, don't be jealous any more. The Count von M. is such a noted man that I thought it an honor to you as well as to me to dance with him. I do not love him. I do not even admire him."

"But he wins everyone," Count Karl continued. "He would ruin you."

"No, Karl, he could not ruin me. I am the only person who could do that. But I promise you here and now, Karl, that I shall be all yours, as long as you want me."

"And you will stay in Germany with me? You will give up America?" he asked.

Randall believed more in caresses than in words—the teaching of Miss Savoy. He remembered that whimsical person's advice: "Kiss their sensitive nerve endings," and kissed him a long, lingering, satisfying kiss. Then he explained gently, "Dear Karl, I have my work to do and you have duties of your own as well. My immediate course in life has been arranged. I must remain in Vienna for two years. But our separation shall be only temporary. I shall come to you and you shall come to me. So long as you want me, remember, I am entirely yours."

Then Randall kissed him again and again. Leading him to the bed, he tenderly laid him down and undid his jacket and his puttees. He would boldly show Karl tonight what the "ladies" back in New York would term in slang a "sixty-nine," quelling his lover's angst with a voluptuous new game. How far he had come since he had done this with dear old Teddy that first time! For today Randall was masterful, manipulating Karl's penis to a full and raging stand in seconds, even as his own thickened and rose to full mast.

Randall slipped his cock into Karl's pouting mouth, filling it like an overlarge pacifier, even as he took the Count's shaft into his own. Like an oiled machine, Randall undulated to and fro, pushing his cock down Karl's throat as he pulled Karl's member slowly and evenly from his jaws; then, tipping his lithe and agile body, pulling his cock back, still all the while gobbling Karl back down. This he kept up until at once they both began to pant and gasp as their cocks swelled to capacity. Only then did they simultaneously fire their weighty loads deep into one another's gullets.

"Ah, Karl dear," he murmured, "you satisfy me so completely. But the past has taught me that nothing so sweet can ever last. I warn you, dear, not to believe that Fate will make an exception of us. But I shall never be to blame again for hurting you. Now, if you wish to die, let me die with you, happy!"

Karl laughed hysterically. "Die? Now? No, we shall live—for each other—just you and I, for each other," he repeated over and over, fondling him, kissing his lips, his cheeks, his eyelids.

They were very happy. Sometimes Randall thought of the cowboy and of others. All had something in common physically; all were tall, muscular, blond, vibrant with health. But Karl had the one thing the others lacked: the social and mental attributes of the educated and well bred. At last Randall had found what he had sought, unconsciously, so long.

CHAPTER
35

The following Monday, Randall and Karl returned to Berlin, the former to plunge at once into some research work for which he found better opportunity there than elsewhere, the latter to prepare for the army maneuvers.

Karl's apartment was, of course, at his disposal, and so he left the Adlon. Evenings they dined at various of the famous restaurants and then sought out places where they could dance together.

Randall was doing exceptionally fine work. He found he could hire excellent technicians to assist him. This made progress more rapid, for he was thus able to devote all his time to direction and interpretation. His happy frame of mind made easy his many hours of work.

Count Karl had but recently purchased a new automobile, by that time beginning to be a practical success. They would roll luxuriously about the city in the evening or drive to suburban inns that were renowned for the splendor of their entertainment.

Often as Randall reclined in his arms he would

speak softly and gently: "Beloved, this is heaven if there is such a thing as heaven."

And Randall would assure him, "Karl, my very dear Karl, our love is the sweetest thing in the world. Give me your lips again, dear."

They carried their devotion to the utmost limits. Even when dining they would sip their wine from one glass and share their food morsel by morsel.

"I had never dreamed there could be such happiness as ours," Karl often said. Then Randall would kiss him in answer.

Not a day passed but they would exchange gifts. Count Karl's were of course magnificent, for he was extremely wealthy. He gave Randall many beautiful pieces of jewelry, and Randall gave back lavishly.

Randall wrote to Mason, then in Vienna, telling of his happiness, and Mason, congratulating him, told of a wonderful new love affair of similar intensity which was taking his attention, and also of another one which the amorous and insatiable Bobby had begun in Paris.

So events went on week by week.

Near the end of July, Count Karl returned from Potsdam one evening in a highly excited frame of mind. His regiment was to go to Metz for the maneuvers. There was rumor of activity on the French border. It was even thought that war might ensue. The French were reported to be planning with their allies to attack Germany. To Karl, war-trained as he had been, this contingency seemed an occasion for rejoicing. To Randall, trained to think in terms of peace, the horrors of such an eventuality brought naught but dread. Of course, he had no thought of his own country being so unwise as to become embroiled in a squabble over European jealousies. Then too, he dreaded what Fate might have in store for Karl, and for himself too. But he did not refer to his formerly expressed fear that such perfect love could not last.

Karl insisted: "It will soon be over. If France retires from her arrogant position, I shall be with you—soon. If she does not recede, it will take less than a month to humble her. And I hope that she does not yield. Then we shall conquer her and occupy Paris in a month, and you and I will live there."

CHAPTER
36

Together the Countess von G. and Randall went to see Karl depart. He kissed his mother dutifully. Randall he held a long time in his arms as he passionately kissed his cold lips. Randall was as one stricken with illness. Horror of the possibilities of the future had marked his face. He could not speak; only tears welled from his eyes, in answer to Karl's words.

When the train had departed there was a brief farewell to the Countess; then Randall hastened to his laboratories to try by hard work to submerge his dreads.

Less than a week passed, and the war broke out!

There were too-brief letters from Karl filled with words of love, telling of success and predicting further successes. Then nothing more from him. Anxiously Randall journeyed to the castle now occupied solely by the Countess von G. He found that noble lady grieving, but her sorrow assuaged by pride in a son who had given his life for the Fatherland. The report told briefly that Karl had been killed when a French mine exploded.

Randall condoled her as best he could, but already
the Countess was beginning to feel the distrust which
permeated all of Germany, the distrust of those who
spoke English.

Randall returned sadly to Berlin.

During his absence his laboratories had been dis-
mantled to make room for governmental activities,
the preparation of immune sera and various vaccines.
His copious notes, mostly in abbreviated shorthand,
entirely meaningless to anyone else, had been confis-
cated. At that time what could not be understood
was suspected. Randall volunteered to help them in
their work. His motive was misinterpreted. After all,
they knew nothing about him, and then, too, their
own feeling of self-sufficiency precluded the acceptance of favors from outlanders.

Mason had written from Vienna that he too was
persona non grata.

Randall acted quickly. He journeyed to neutral
territory at once—Switzerland. But he was bored,
without occupation. He had to shake off the frightful
depression following the death of Karl. The newspapers gave little news. He was saved from the pseudo-
patriotic piffle which cumbered the American periodicals during the war. The Swiss papers spoke of the
work of the Red Cross. Randall decided to go to
Paris and offer his services. Perhaps in helping to
assuage the sufferings of others he would forget his
own heartache.

CHAPTER
37

Randall was put to work at once, of course in a sub-servient position. Europeans are slow to grant an American the recognition due to merit. He was put in the medical and surgical wards. His obstetrical training was of little use, for soldiers do not have babies, at least the usual run of them do not, though he did come across one who had the delusion that he had given birth to a dead, rotten, foul-smelling baby composed of feces. He did not have to psychoanalyze that one to find out what was on his mind.

Randall found the young medical men of his own age to be much less well trained than himself. Theories they knew, and they loved to waste time discussing Professor X's view or Professor Y's per-haps opposing conclusion. But for the work in hand they were not so well fitted. Men who would never be skilled, even in minor surgery, were visualizing themselves as masters of neurosurgery.

Randall could speak French after a fashion and of course could read and write it fairly well. However, there were always enough English-speaking patients to take up more than the time he was assigned to them. He was at first delegated to do dressings, work that could have been attended to by a well-trained nurse. Randall took delight in showing the French how much more quick, thorough and effective were the methods he used. Despite the horrors of war, the French still found time to be very jealous of anybody and everything, no matter how trivial. Perhaps that is their dominant trait, thought Randall. Jealousy! Singers, artists of any sort, even the artist of free spending, can enlighten one. Perhaps that is the reason there is always a war looming up in that part of Europe.

One morning Randall was hurrying down the receiving ward to which he was attached. A trainload of patients had been brought in during the night. The ward nurse called, *"Monsieur le docteur, venez ici, s'il vous plait."*

"In a moment," answered Randall. No sooner had he finished speaking than the air was rent with the cry in German, *"Liebchen,* where are you?" Randall stopped. Did he hear aright? The pained cry continued, *"Liebchen,* here am I. I heard you. Come to me."

"Who is calling?" cried Randall in a startled voice. He turned toward the sound.

"Here, here, *Liebchen!"*

The voice was unmistakable—the voice of Karl! He went to the cot and bent over. A helpless, motionless creature lay there, the whole head bound, little of the face showing but distorted lips. A staggering odor of carrion combined with a horrible feculent smell came up from the still-human mass—his beloved Karl. By an effort of the will he overcame his nausea, stooped and gently kissed the swollen lips. He murmured words of love, closing his eyes that he might not see, compelling his imagination to recreate the beloved Karl of the past. He listened to his voice; that alone was unchanged. With eyes closed he could recall him as he had been. Karl was able solely to move his arms. As Randall stood over him whispering the words he loved to hear, he drew him close to his pain-racked, befouled body.

His wounds had been left undressed too long. Two missiles had struck him: one had lacerated his face and blinded him; another had passed through the abdomen and out through the back, not only paralyzing him but leaving a defiling fistula from which half-liquid fecal matter constantly oozed. The only reason he had not been left to die on the field was that his uniform had been practically stripped from him. When the litter bearers came up, calling out in French, he had answered them in their own tongue with an accent which suggested only the Parisian *haute monde*.

Randall obtained the necessary permission to dress his wounds. Poor victim! His pain was agonizing at all times and the apportioned supply of opiates was inadequate to ease his sufferings materially. Intensifying the loathsome situation, there were not dressings to spare to keep him decently clean. Randall at times succeeded in begging or purloining morphine, or, likelier, the more plentiful heroin, but with the least abatement of the effects of the drug, poor Karl would cry out in agony—heart-rending shrieks that horrified all who could hear.

Three dreadful days he lingered. The last night Randall, already worn out from loss of sleep, remained with him, listening to repeated requests to tell him that his vision would return and that operations would cure him and restore them together; listening to vain plans for a life after the war; promising him, not in vain, that he would remain with him.

The effect of the drugs would begin to wear off and finally he would scream, bloodcurdling screams of torture till Randall could beg just a little more sedative. Suddenly he became ominously quiet. Randall realized that his sufferings were almost at an end. He remained conscious till long after midnight, at intervals murmuring words of love for him. Before the break of day he lapsed into unconsciousness, breathing more and more slowly. At the end of a half hour he went out.

Randall kissed the cold blue lips, then gave vent to an anguished cry, perhaps a prayer, "God! Stop it!"

But God did not stop it; none of the Gods stopped it; neither the French God, the German God, the English God, the Protestant God, the Catholic God, nor even the Hebrew God (who was the precursor of them all) stopped the slaughter. Perhaps those who uttered the prayers left some whimsical dido unperformed, such as crossing their fingers, or touching the lips with the left hind foot of a rabbit when they prayed. There were millions praying to French, German, English, Protestant, Catholic, Hebrew, Muslim, Hindu, Buddhist, and God-knows-what Gods, yet it did not avail.

Poor Randall collapsed. When he came to he was in bed. After a moment he regarded his surroundings, then fell into a deep sleep, from which he did not awaken for many hours.

He was well, but tired. His first thought was of his duties and of attending to Karl. Then he remembered. Hurriedly he dressed and returned to the ward. His first inquiry was with regard to the disposal of Karl's body. It was too late! Too much had happened in between. He could learn nothing.

Randall debated whether to try to write to the Countess von G., but finally concluded that no matter how innocently he might word his letter, it would probably be misconstrued, never be sent and cause the ever jealous French to vent their wrath on him. He did nothing except try to forget, applying himself harder then ever to work.

Fortunately, he was transferred to another ward and given added responsibilities. The rapid movement of events caused the recent incidents to appear far distant in perspective. Karl's death seemed as part of an ugly dream. At the end of a month, quite worn out physically, he was ordered to take a week's leave.

Paris was a dull dark place at that time. Randall found a room in a small hotel in the "Quartier," and went to bed, where he remained the greater part of three days.

CHAPTER
38

About three o'clock of the third afternoon Randall dressed with great care and went out. As he entered Rue de l'Odeon, he saw a young English officer standing, looking about rather helplessly. He approached Randall: "Pardon! I say, you look as if you can speak English. You can, can't you?"

Randall smiled and answered, "Sorry, I only speak Americanese. Will that do?"

"Jolly well. You are a good sort, I see that. Do you happen to speak French, too?"

"I understand it and speak well enough for all practical purposes, though my accent leaves much to be desired."

"Then do you mind helping me a bit?"

"Certainly, I'll help you if I can." He went with him to a nearby pharmacy and assisted him in making his purchases, watching carefully to see that he was not cheated. Meanwhile they chatted as if old friends.

The buying attended to, the Englishman asked, "Would you care to dine with me tonight? Do you know of an interesting place, something unusual? Perhaps we can see a bit of the town together."

Randall did not bother to consider. Nothing made any difference any more. He assented without enthusiasm, and this very lack of eagerness impressed the Englishman as evidence of sterling worth.

Randall suggested Page's. Someone had told him it was gay. They found it was more than that—almost as wild as the "Jungle." Madame wished to kiss them both in welcome, but Randall drew back laughing and inquired, "How much extra does that cost?" Madame smiled and waved them forward. They were seated against the wall at a long table with many others. There they could see everything of interest that happened. Much cheap wine, some brandy, and an occasional bottle of champagne were in evidence. A polyglot babble dinned the eardrums. For Page's was the gathering place of all the temperamental set, native, Parisian or visiting.

The Englishman drank quite too much brandy and became proportionately gay; it takes alcohol to make them forget their inhibitions. Suddenly Randall became possessed of a wild mood, in reaction from all the dreary horror he had been through. He shouted and sang and camped quite as madly and effectively as Miss Savoy at her best. Deliberately he made all the common mistakes which English-speaking people fall into when attempting to learn French. The others present pointed him out as *une belle*, the same expression which is used so much in Baltimore and New Orleans.

About eleven they left. His Englishman was handsome; unlike so many of them, he had a lovely clean mouth, beautiful even, healthy white teeth which shone invitingly behind blood-red lips. He was acceptable. Their love-making was unusually quiet for Randall, who had calmed by midnight and found a need for affection. He found himself slipping into his trance of old, that hazy twilight between conscious and unconscious action. He kissed this man, sat upon his enflamed cock, and then allowed him to enter from the rear. Only when the Englishman discovered his passion for being spanked did Randall snap out of it and let loose with one of his patented shrieks of unbridled candor. As his bruised and blushing bottom would dictate the next day, the English did have a penchant for administering salacious punishment!

The next morning Randall left him after breakfast, promising to meet him in the evening.

CHAPTER
39

Now the old urge had been thoroughly aroused. To forget one, Randall enjoyed another. But that was not so easy in Paris at that time, for he was, above all things, fastidious about his "type of men." There must be a certain build, a certain personality, a certain verve. The typical short, ill-formed Frenchman made no appeal to him. He did not admire this type of Parisian, with his short neck, exaggerated nose, badly formed body, made more repulsive by lack of proper, and what to Americans are ordinary, hygienic practices—his vile breath laden with odors of garlic, pyorrhea and putrescent food.

Often the English would attract, until they opened their mouths to speak; then he would look away, and go away, for an Englishman has to be exceptionally well reared before he can be induced to put a brush to his teeth, no matter how well cared for he may otherwise appear.

But Paris was beginning to present many of diverse nationalities. Thus, usually when Randall craved a new love affair, he had it. All of these men, new to Paris, sought variety too, and sought it reck-lessly. Doomed as they were to a chance at the front, they felt that they must crowd what remained of their lives with every experience possible.

Randall returned to hard work, and during his brief leisure played harder than ever. Even air raids he learned to take with the same calm he had felt for American thunderstorms. The days sped, and often as not the nights sped more rapidly.

One evening Randall was dining at le Chalet. Miss Bull-Mawgan was in the crowd. She and Elsie Dike were still in Paris, "doing their bit," they said, pious-ly, but others said they were doing more than that. Certainly they did whatever spectacular war work would yield them the most publicity. Elizabeth Thorndyke, the other of their trio, nicknamed "Clittie" for obvious reasons, had remained in America, using her masculine lion-like voice to harangue others in drives for this, that and the other thing.

There was talk of the United States entering the war. "How foolish!" exclaimed Randall. "We are neutral and shall remain neutral. Why should we become involved in this quarrel and send our own good men to hell?"

Miss Bull-Mawgan, who tried to be really more French than American, thrust out her long jaw and puckered her mouth decisively—"You'll see!" she said. "The big interests want it. America must come in to protect American capital. I know whereof I speak. Besides," she went on sentimentally, "America owes France a debt of gratitude for aid in Colonial days." Miss Bull-Mawgan may have been right. God knows the debt's been more than paid now!

"I hate to think of the useless sacrifice of

America's young men," Randall said pensively. "What is anyone gaining?"

Miss Bull-Mawgan, propagandist that she was, then became accusatory: "You are pro-German, Randy! Everybody knows you had a love affair with a Boche officer—and *what* a love affair! You are just as pro-German as you dare to be. All of you Pennsylvania Dutch are!"

"No, kitty-cat," answered Randall smiling, "I am not pro-German. If I'm pro-anything, I am pro-peace. As for being Pennsylvania Dutch, I happen to have not one drop of Deutsch blood in my veins. My ancestors were French, English, Scotch and Irish and of the four the French is the least dilute. Being born in Pennsylvania does not make one Pennsylvania Dutch, any more than being born in Africa makes a white person a Negro, or being born in Hartford makes one an aristocrat, or, for that matter, a woman!"

"What do you mean, you bitch?" angrily spoke Miss Bull-Mawgan, always spoiling for a fight with someone.

"You understand me well enough, Kitty. You are being so flattered by the French, because of your money, and for purposes of their own, that you're allowing your usual good judgment to be set awry. They'll be wishing some sort of a decoration on you the next thing and you'll be so grand you won't want us to call you by your first name."

"Now, stop being petty, Randy," urged Elsie Dike, who always sided with Miss Bull-Mawgan, possibly because of a real admiration for her, more likely because of the very substantial financial returns which accrued from her studied kowtow.

"Well, Kitty, let's set them all an example of neutrality. Let's stop international politics and be ourselves for a while. Come on and dance with me and make Elsie jealous," suggested Randall gaily.

"You'll have to let me lead," grumbled La Bull-Mawgan in her heavy, rather masculine voice, that voice which expressed her inner urge. She would have been far happier if she had been born a man.

"I am adaptable. I can do either," answered Randall.

So they were off, Randall determined to be gay in spite of war and air raids.

CHAPTER
40

Another year passed. La Bull-Mawgan's prophecy became fact. Randall's reaction was one of stupefaction. His first utterance, knowing his country's politicians and rich men well, was "Now the graft will begin!" There has been ample time to prove whether he was right or wrong.

What a rush there was in America to get into any service! —the useless temperamentals rushing into the auxiliary services, the Y, Casey, and the Red Cross.

The old Catholic Beaches were doing work with Casey, the Protestant Beaches were working with the Y and one of the Beach-Bitsches of Philadelphia—forever after known as "Sally Ann"—was even with the "Army," for the religionists were bound to make the most of this war and vied with each other, quite jealously, in trying to gain publicity—and funds. After all, it's a business, so why shouldn't they?

Soon American troops began to arrive in France. The first detachments were moved about and exhibited everywhere, as much to hearten the discouraged

French and English and to "give them morale" as to strike terror to the Germans and "break their morale." Such useful phrases they used during that war of slogans!

Handsome, tall, blond Western and Southern men began to swarm about Paris. Randall compared them with the other men available. They were enchanting, quite as thrilling to him as they seemed to be to the French girls.

American misses too began to appear. La Bull-Mawgan and her coterie, whom Randall often saw, of course, were overjoyed. Their hopes certainly, and their achievements possibly, were high.

Randall was far happier serving these, his handsome countrymen, than he had been at any time since the death of Count Karl von G.

Tall Oregon and Washington and other Northwestern boys, alert, easy to look at, clean of skin, with shining clean teeth flashing their enchanting smiles! Those were men!

Randall yielded himself eagerly to their embraces, always feeling that any pleasure he might bestow would perhaps be the last the lovely lads would have opportunity to enjoy. Night after night he would slip himself into their arms, caressing them as would a small-town sweetheart bravely prepared to surrender her innocence to her departing soldier boy. Randall minded not that they so desperately sought privacy with him, loving him, kissing him, fucking him violently in secret, lest they be branded queer by the very fellows who would go with Randall on the sly the following eve.

Truly he loved them. That he forgot one in the moment of loving another did not mean that his love was any less sincere. Rather, it indicated that he was capable, again and again, of arousing within himself that necessary spark of infatuation, temporary though it might be, to make a new and strange contact a thing of agonizing joy. How sweetly they smiled as they pounded their beautiful American cocks into his behind! How their eyes sparkled as he sucked them one and all until they exploded with sperm and bliss. Passionate by night, amiable by day, they were all his boys, and he thought nothing of servicing them one and all, in uniform, but especially without.

One day Randall ran across two of the younger Bütsches from California. They laughed uproariously as they "dished the dirt," quoting all of Miss Savoy's wisecracks which they had heard at an entertainment in Brest. They sang Miss Savoy's campy chorus—

Whoops! Whoops! Whoops, my dear!
Can you tell me if he's queer?
Would he learn to do the crawl?
Would he go to balls and all?
Would he dance the can-can-can
For his great big strong he-man?

With all their frivolous attitude toward life, even these two had been capable of their moments of sacrifice and heroism. They told how they had run into each other on the front after a battle.

Said Percy, "We stood there talking so philosophically to each other, and then we began to camp, right out on the battlefield—"

"Ex-battlefield," amended Clarence. "You know well enough where you'd have been if there was any shelling going on, probably sheltered in the captain's arms in a dugout."

"Yes, and you'd crawl into a hole somewhere."

"A hole, of course!"

Then they told Randall how they had volunteered from their little California town, how one of them partially inspired by the other, had written an article for the hometown paper, heading it—"Two Bütsches Go to War." Percy explained, "Of course the wise guys about town intentionally mispronounced our name. We were the first there to volunteer and we made it appear that we were two patriots worthy of emulation."

Clarence added, "And they'll have to be some gifted emulators if they keep pace with us. Going to war has been simply gorgeous. We had leave in New York and looked up Old Aunty Beach-Bitsche. She is doing canteen work and doing everything else that comes her way. We had delicious shivers all the way across to Brest—isn't that a lovely appropriate French name? And since we've been in France we've had a delirious time. Already Percy and I have misbehaved in every way possible we have learned about, neo-French included. Here there are so many delightful ways of getting into mischief. Don't you think so, Randy?"

"My lips are sealed!"

"Now! But wait till the shades of night—"

"Say, Randy, have you met the Prince yet?"

"No, I haven't met the Prince yet and don't want to. I am only interested in men, real he-men. The Prince! The Prince of bitches, I should say. Puts on drag and carries on to the limit—to the *limit,* I said."

"Well, what is this Miss Bull-Mawgan like, the one we hear so much about now?" queried Percy.

"I'd hate to describe her. I might be sued for libel, you know. Besides, we are supposed to be friends—now. She can be very charming and gracious."

"And what is Mason's wife like? I hear she always signs her name 'née Dike'! Just as if everybody wouldn't know without being told."

278

"Well, she's slender as a lath and boyish in appearance, and having the blood of both the Bulls and the Dikes in her, she of course runs true to form. When she puts on a uniform she looks more like a man than a woman. That makes her happy. She's an ambulance driver now. I've even seen her stick a tiny false moustache to her upper lip—affecting the English nearman. She's very elated at present; been wounded. Now she goes about shouting that she's proven himself just as good as any man. She's a panic! Evidently she forgets the physical limitations, or choose to ignore them, or even overcomes them; she's quite ingenious enough to do it if there is a way. She speaks French like a native and often takes Mason and me to task for our lack of interest in perfecting a French accent. We retaliate by telling her we'd be quite as proud of speaking perfect bastard-English, as we would be of speaking perfect French, bastard-Latin. You'll probably meet her and like her. In one way she is different from the rest of the Bulls and Dikes; she is gay, not morose, not a gloom shedder."

Here Clarence broke forth—"Did we tell you about Sissy Beach? When the war broke out, that one was all spilling over with patriotic fervor and rushed to join the Navy. The doctors examined Sissy and found him physically fit, but a mean old pharmacist's mate who had heard Sissy talk gave the doctors the wink and suggested that Sissy had a speech defect. As you know, that one's voice is all defect. The board demanded that Sissy tell why he wished to join the Navy. He started off in his high-pitched coo of 'college leading lady,' telling of his burning patriotism, his eagerness to drown for his country, the duties of all true red-blooded Americans. They let him rant for ten whole minutes. He used every bit of patriotic hokum that the one, two, three and four minute speakers ever invented. Then they turned him down with 'Young man, this man's Navy is no place for you. Why you wouldn't even make a first-class yeomanette.' Sissy broke down and wept—'hot scalding tears,' he described them, and said, 'I think you are the meanest old thing! So there! You deliberately discourage the efforts of a loyal patriot.' Then Sissy floated away—you know that walk—declaiming, 'Well, no one can say that I am not willing to immolate myself on the altar of my country.'"

"What's Sissy doing now?"

"He's become an entertainer; goes to the camps and the Navy Yard and sings and dances and pirouettes and amuses everybody and tells all friends, 'I'm doing my bitterest bit.'"

Said Percy, "Did I tell you that at Brest, Miss Savoy and I got together to dish the dirt?"

"Yes, and she wrote to Mason and me all about it. She still refers to herself as 'Your Aunt Mary' or 'Your mother.' Listen to this!" Randall took a letter from his pocket. "Honest, Your Aunt Mary thought she was pregnant by two Frenchmen, impossible as that may seem, but over here, after visiting Lourdes one comes to believe almost anything possible, especially after seeing two Frenchmen osculate each other. Honest-to-Gawd, dearie, the way they kiss is just nobody's business. Your Aunt Mary is too busy these days to do aught but plain sewing."

Bobby, came along with her newest sweetheart. Randall introduced them and whispered to Percy, "Talk about the scar on her cheek. She loves that. She thinks it's noble."

Bobby was wearing a new, very mannish uniform, quite fitted to her manatee figure, with trousers and puttees like a chauffeur's.

"Why, Mrs. Linberg, I didn't know you were a

woman at first," exclaimed Percy Bütsche. "I mistook you for some fancy sort of Frenchman. That pleases you, I know, for I hear you always wanted to be a man instead of a girl. And that scar! Is that a scar of battle?"

"Yes, sustained in the Argonne. I've done my bit. Let's not talk of it. Give me a cigarette, somebody. I thought some of you Bütsches would be over soon. When the German men see you, they'll throw down their arms and—"

"Surrender themselves to us, I know you mean that."

"You don't have to go to the front right away, do you?"

"We leave in two days."

"I'll give Mason permission to take you to any hole in Paris you wish to visit."

"Oh, joy! The holes of Paris! What may they not be?"

"He'd do it anyway without my permission. But then, you know ours is one of those happy marriages of convenience—absolutely no jealousy; he does as he pleases and I do what I please, and we are loyal and protect each other. If you wish, you may come along with me to La Bull-Mawgan's. She's my friend again, now that we are in war work. There'll be a gay crowd there—everybody, anybody, everything, anything. Since the war, we all hobnob together, demi-monde, haut monde, actors, dancers, and Americans. Believe me, we raise hell having a good time, for we don't know how long we are going to stay here or where we go after we leave here. Be candid! Which do you like, femmes, or the others? I'll arrange anything you want."

They talked in low tones for a while, then, as Bobby, marched off with the two, Randall camped,

"Don't forget your rubber coats, dearies, it may rain—or something!"

Randall had to go back to the hospital to do some thoracotomies.

Percy and Clarence did not come back. Later on Randall met Clarence just back of the lines.

CHAPTER
41

With American boys at the front, Randall could not feel at peace in Paris. If they must suffer, he must suffer too! He resigned from the Red Cross and became a war correspondent, but as there was not much permitted in the way of writing he of course filled in when possible in any hospital work at hand. A few days and he was transferred to work near the front. He had hated to say goodbye to Mason and Bobby. He embraced them, kissing first Bobby and then Mason, and with Mason he put a warmth into his caress such as he was not accustomed to bestow upon him. Bobby turned the situation into a farce beloved of their crowd by half growling, "Randy, you damned bitch, I believe you're getting a yen for my husband!"

With gay laughter they waved goodbye to him at the Gare du Nord.

The first few days in the town near the front were comparatively easy for Randall, really a rest. And when Randall recuperated it meant one thing—he began to look for further excitement, a love affair, or for that matter probably several love affairs. And there were wonderful men of all nations in that town, men engaged in various enterprises.

When Randall looked at a man, the probing scrutiny the man gave him never failed to arouse his interest. He might wonder, "What's the matter with me? Why did he look at me in that critical manner?" Anyway, men always followed him, adroitly engaged him in conversation and tried to please him and merit his good opinion. At least that's the way it worked out.

Randall was now at the height of his beauty—thirty-three years of age and looking ten years younger, as so many of his kind do for some queer reason.

Conquests were easy; he had in turn, and lost, either through their orders to new duty or by his own discard, three captains, ten lieutenants, twenty-five sergeants and a sprinkling of privates that were unusually handsome. One day Randall observed a group of young officers during their off moments reading a book by Krafft-Ebing, which they dubbed their "Bible." Surreptitiously they were seeking sophistication. He suggested, "Now add Havelock Ellis to that and you'll learn something." They all blushed like schoolboys. After all, they were hardly more than that, though classed as "men."

Randall of course spent much of his spare time in an estaminet, at that time the crude center of the social life of the town. Here he would sit and sip champagne, drinking liberally in a quite un-French style. One evening as he was about to step into the pleasant haunt he was restrained by a firm grasp from behind and someone commanded "Guess!"

"Whoops-my-dear, I know that voice—Clarence Bütsche!" Once released, he turned and asked, "What are you doing here?"

"I'm not doing it, only hoping to do it, Randy. And how's your mother?"

"Me? I'm fit for anything, overworked though I have been. Come on in and dish with me—and flirt, too, if you wish. In this place there's plenty doing, as usual."

They entered, arm in arm, firing questions at each other with the speed of machine guns—"Have you heard from dear Old Aunty Beach-Bitsche? Where's Miss Savoy?" and inquiries about the Misses Fitzhugh, Kuntz, Fuchs, Fall and Sissy Beach.

Poor Miss Fuchs, who had the misfortune to be born in Germany, when his parents were making a visit to the Fatherland, was being shadowed all about New York as an enemy alien. He was famished for love. He did not dare to speak to a single enticing stranger. He had been threatened with deportation after the war ended. His speed was seriously crippled. Thus he was miserable indeed.

This, that and the other member of the Bütsche family had joined the Navy, for it is a peculiarity of their family to drift to the coast towns and not dwell inland. They seem attracted to the sea in all its aspects. One or two of the Bütsches were known to have achieved appointments in aviation, with startling results, socially.

Miss Savoy was still in Brest, camping with the soldiers, singing her droll songs, stepping her crazy dances, delivering her patter in her usual mezzo-soprano foghorn voice.

Randall and Clarence took their seats on a bench against the wall—a vantage point. They drew themselves closer together as a femme pushed in beside Clarence and tried to "make him." The "Frenchie" displayed her wares, opening her mouth wide, revealing her pink tongue, rolling her eyes, then she pinched his cheeks and said, "You come wiz me? Hein?" On the other side of Randall a young French officer squeezed in and tried to interest him in an evening's entertainment: "I see you, I love you." Randall nudged Clarence and proceeded to mystify both of the strangers with gibberish—

"Atwhay allshay eway oday ithway ethay itchbay andway eerquay renchmanfay?"

"Ivegay emthay ethay airway!"

"You not American?" asked the "Frenchman."

"Nitchky," answered Randall, shaking his head.

"Eenglish?"

"Nitchky, nit nitchky!"

"Russe?"

"Nitchky nit nitchky," they answered in duo.

Then Randall drew rapidly a small map of the mainland of Alaska and Asia with the Aleutian Islands between, and pointed to them.

"Some Aleuts?" asked the Frenchie.

They both nodded their heads a vigorous yes.

The femme proceeded to maul Clarence, and the Frenchman tried to kiss Randall. As neither appealed, it was remarkably boring. They pushed them away with great vigor.

Suddenly Clarence whispered to Randall, "Look! How is that for a specimen of American-made pulchritude?"

Randall looked toward the doorway, then in a low voice said to Clarence, "My God! I'm lost again. He's so handsome that to regard him gives me a delicious pain. I almost lose my breath. Clarence, I've got to have that. Now cooperate."

The newcomer was a young officer, at least seventy-four inches tall, with a noble head, athletic shoulders and a body that tapered downward like a perfect Greek statue. His hair was thick, dark and wavy. His eyes were large, darkest blue, luminous, and their expression piercing; his nose was properly aquiline;

his lips full, bowed, not too small, and the corners of his mouth had a slight upward trend; his chin was beautifully molded with a teasing suggestion of a dimple; his neck was full, but not too short and bull-like; his skin was what the French term *matte;* and his closely shaven beard shadowed his cheeks, upper lip, chin and neck in that outline which accentuates and improves masculinity. His lips and the tips of his ears were a deep healthy red. He had been a famous athlete in college the past year.

"Get him over here, Clarence. I'm weak," said Randall as he forced his gaze away from the man.

Clarence officiated. "Hello, stranger. Come over here. Here's an extra seat. Shove this way, Randy!"

The man came over. "Have champagne?" asked Clarence.

"Sure, if you've got any to spare," the man answered in a deep resonant voice that would thrill any woman.

"Over long?" asked Clarence.

"Ten days."

"Staying long?" Clarence asked with a laugh.

"That depends. I'm starting on a tour of Germany and it may take some time," he answered in the same bantering spirit.

Then Randall spoke in the voice which so often attracted and held men for some unaccountable reason, "Where are you billeted?"

"Just arrived. Not billeted at all. Thought I'd get the lowdown here, maybe."

"You'll probably draw a haymow over the family dung heap unless you care to accept what I can offer you. You look very tired. I'm rested. You can have my bed and I'll throw some blankets on the floor, or I'll turn in with Clarence here."

"I don't want to drive you out of good quarters."

"Oh, it's not much. Wait till you see the dump. Meantime have a bite and take some more champagne."

They exchanged names. His was Frank. He gave the correct German pronunciation to Clarence Bütsche's names, but Randall's last name was difficult for him.

They talked of things in America and of his college life. Clarence knew better than to intrude his own experiences, and Randall followed Miss Savoy's oft-iterated advice, "Keep 'em talking about themselves and when they run down, ask 'em for advice. They need a listener and they'll grow to feel they need you."

Randall cared absolutely nothing about competitive athletics. What he loved was the physical development of the players. A touchdown was a vague football term to him. Nevertheless he took pains to remember what games he had seen and referred back to them occasionally, expressing regret that something or other had so often kept him from attending the important games of the past.

They discussed the Frenchmen, their greedy extortions, and the lieutenant touched on their gross sexual immorality, comparing it, erroneously, with the "superior" morality of Americans, at which Randall and Clarence Bütsche discreetly rolled their eyes at each other.

"Yes," lisped Randall, "their immorality must be something shameful, but that could not touch you."

"You bet it couldn't. I'm saving myself, keeping myself clean for the return home." He too cherished the belief that the other man, not he, would stop the bullet. "I've seen all of that kind of stuff I want to see and I'm through, for all time," he announced firmly.

Finally Clarence suggested that they turn in. He

escorted Randall and Lieutenant Frank to the little cottage to which Randall had been assigned. "I'll wait below till you two decide what to do," he said, "and day after tomorrow one of you can have my place, for I've got orders."

He had not long to wait for Randall soon thrust his head out of the window and said, "It's all right. See you at breakfast."

Randall's room had a little offset on one side. Here he hung a sheet for a curtain and with blankets made a bed on the floor. He had long since learned to sleep in far more uncomfortable quarters.

The young lieutenant had wrenched a shoulder the day before. Randall volunteered to massage it for him. Frank removed his coat and khaki shirt and Randall examined him carefully. With deepest pleasure he observed the beauty of the upper part of Frank's torso; how big and strong it was; how the broad, flat planes of his pectorals met to jut over the perfectly stacked musculature of his hard abdomen. Then Randall directed him to lie on the bed while he sat on the edge and began a skillful manipulation of each of the muscles, including *petrissage,* of which he and Mason had so often joked in the past. It soothed the wearied man and almost at once he dozed off murmuring, "My God! That's a relief."

Frank's body was sweet and clean smelling, well-fed and as yet unmarked by the ravages of war. As he finished, Randall bent and gently kissed him on the neck, that part where the skin is so soft and sensitive, midway between the angle of the jaw and the hair line at the back of the neck. The lieutenant opened his eyes, startled, then smiled as he murmured, "Oh! It's you. That's all right." He folded his arms about Randall, bringing their faces close enough that Randall could feel his smooth, deep breaths against his cheeks. Then like a contented child the sweet young American sank into a deep sleep.

His clean body odor gave Randall the keenest delight. Though he had become as aroused as he had ever been before, he dared not touch Frank in any other way. Randall's cock was hard and his throat had tightened with desire, but he hesitated to attempt to alter their relationship, and possibly lose him entirely. He had been accepted as a pal, and that he would be.

Gently he disengaged himself.

On his pallet on the floor behind the curtain he lay wakeful a long time, fighting down his erotic compulsion for the first time since he could recall.

They awakened early. There was a brief note of adieu from Clarence Bütsche who had hurried away to battle and make the world safe for plutocracy.

Randall and Lieutenant Frank descended to the tiny living room. Madame found some eggs and provided a tolerable breakfast. The two daughters did their utmost to interest the lieutenant *Americain,* and even Madame, whose husband had too long been far away at the front, was perhaps more ardent than was seemly. But the lieutenant was indifferent. All through his college years he had been surfeited with the attentions of women. To paraphrase a rough leatherneck expression, his attitude had been, "Use 'em and leave 'em." Besides, he was interested in Randall now, who filled completely that need which he felt for companionship.

The days slipped by. Mostly their duty consisted of standing by to await orders. Randall kept to his corner on the floor, declaring that he had so long slept on a hard bed that he felt more comfortable lying with only blankets between him and the boards. But every night he soothed Frank to sleep—even long after the strained muscles had ceased to pain him.

One night, when he thought that he had used therapeutics long enough as an excuse for fondling, he omitted his usual massage of Frank's shoulder. Behind his curtain he prepared for sleep and half clothed, he had slid under his blankets. He blew out the candle and was startled when dear Frank called, "Didn't you forget something!"

"What?" he gasped, his emotion almost overcoming his powers of speech.

"You didn't tuck me in!"

"All right." After pausing a moment to regain self-control, he felt his way across the darkened room.

"That's better," he said as Randall snuggled down beside him, pressing his lips into the soft of his neck, one hand softly caressing his wavy hair. So happy was this young man, so benign and full of innocence. And yet he was so husky and broad shouldered, so muscular and well-fleshed. How Randall wanted to simply devour him, gaze upon his cock and eat it up, push that red and mushroom-headed member deep into the hole of his buttocks and ride him to bliss. But still, those wonderful thoughts would have to remain fantasies, and Randall made no move to change their relation of warm comradeship.

CHAPTER
42

Still they lingered in the little town.

Lieutenant Frank had less and less to do with women in general and hurried away from his former companions to be with Randall. With Randall he was content, content to await any fate. And no one smiled, or looked wise or gossiped as would have been the case back in America. Relations of all sorts, so close to the front, were accepted in those times without comment and without the urge to pry into others' lives and reform all and everything.

Randall made a heroic effort to keep his love for Frank untarnished, and strangely, he was succeeding, and finding the greatest joy of his life in this idealized relationship. Lieutenant Frank, on his part, did not realize how dear Randall had become to him. Now they shared every least thing together, a walk to the canteen, to the post, to the laundry woman, to any little shop to buy what was offered in the way of trinkets for friends. They read together, each holding a corner of the book and taking a turn at reading aloud.

At this time Randall wrote to Mason—

"I have found the ideal of my life." He gave a lengthy description of Lieutenant Frank, and then continued, "Mason, you and the others may ridicule me, but this love is pure, the purest love possible. Frank needs me and I need him. Every night I cuddle in his arms until he relaxes in sleep, then I go to my own corner of the room. I doubt if I would have the strength of character to keep my love for him the pure sentiment it is; that power comes entirely from him. You realize how suggestible I am. I only know that I wish to be whatever he wishes me to be. That would be sufficient."

He wrote fully of the little town, of their life there, and then the note of impending tragedy intruded itself—"Mason, I may never return to you. We must all realize that. My will has been made leaving everything to you to do with as you may please. You and Bobby of course will never have children of your own. Will you, dear, if I never come back, in remembrance of me, adopt a little boy and a little girl orphan? Select talented children (for they suffer so much more than the others if neglected), and give them the advantages which would otherwise be denied them. And when they are grown up, tell them of me, all the good if there is any, and all the bad, for I want no fictitious sainthood.

"Frank will soon be sent to the slaughter, and where he goes I shall go.

"I feel very sad tonight, Mason. Whatever happens, my love will ever attend you and Bobby. I feel it is goodbye, dear—Randy."

Finally came the long-awaited orders to go to the front. Randall, with absolute disbelief in combat, succeeded in getting orders juggled so that he could proceed with Lieutenant Frank's regiment. They were sent to a front where the fighting was known to be hot.

Now Randall had no thought of personal danger. It was always of Lieutenant Frank he was thinking. When they came to the trenches, filthy and vile with blood and excrement, holding the overpowering odor of carrion, they were separated. Randall had to remain behind with the hospital unit as the combatants moved forward. He reverted to his profession, forgetful that he was employed by a newspaper as a columnist.

Not long did they have to wait for their baptism of fire! And then the wounded began coming in to the dressing station; mere boys who had gone forth beautiful were hurried back from the hell, some with arms or legs dangling or missing; some with faces shot away. Some bled to death under Randall's hands. Quickly he worked, patching here and there to stop the flow of blood, deciding which, the more hopeful, should be sent farther back in an attempt to save them; keeping the half-moribund near at hand to see whether they were worth further attempts at salvage. Blood and horror! And the din of battle nearer and nearer. He had almost ceased to feel, only possessed of a mad desire to overpower death. Other than that he felt no emotion except worry for the safety of Lieutenant Frank. Someone not hopelessly wounded had seen him still unscathed, but that was early in the day. Another, a brother officer, brought in late in the afternoon, answered his inquiry: "He was all right an hour ago, but he'll get his yet."

"Get his yet!"

There was a lull. Randall waited in anguish, picturing him brought in dying. Nightfall came on.

There was an order to move the hospital unit further back. Randall hastened. A fresh young medical officer had been brought forward to help. Together they worked furiously and when all was ready Randall suggested, "You follow the litters; I'll remain to dress anything that comes back."

To fall back with Frank still at the front? He could not do it! Madly he started, and in reverse order followed the trail that was coming from the front. The regiment, they told him, lay behind a hill to the left, about half a mile—but a half mile charged with death.

On he went!

A shell hit the road not far in front. That meant the Germans had the range. Quickly he veered to the left, making his way over what had recently been plowed fields. He waded a filthy brook; then began the ascent of the hill which Lieutenant Frank and his company defended. He made his way to the top and entered a trench, stumbling over dead bodies to do so. Automatically, he stooped to examine them. One was still warm, but there was no pulsation of the arteries. He went on.

He recognized the voice of a Polish boy who was in Frank's company, and continued to make his way forward. There was a terrific explosion as a shell broke in front of the trench. In a blaze of light he had a momentary glimpse of Lieutenant Frank, not fifty feet away. He was still uninjured when Randall reached him. He turned quickly, not recognizing the man standing quietly beside him was his pal Randy, and he yelled, "Damn you, soldier, why don't you do your part?"

"Noncombatant, Frank!" cried Randall.

"Hell! Did they have to send you here?" Then he continued to direct his men. He gave the order to move forward. The shells were less numerous but still continued to fall near them as they advanced. Randall continued trudging behind him, obsessed with the idea that he might save his dear friend Frank. There was a shriek overhead, then an explosion, the final shell of attack.

Immediately about them was a cessation of movement!

Randall grasped one of his thighs. He fell to the ground. He knew where to compress the artery. In his kit was one remaining tourniquet. Even at that moment he did not forget to look for Lieutenant Frank. The soldier was still standing, a dark shadow before him. Randall applied the tourniquet swiftly and tightly. Then he dragged himself to his handsome lieutenant. But at that moment, Frank too sank down.

"Are you hurt, Frank?" Randall asked.

"Here," he said, putting Randall's hand on his left arm.

There were still occasional bursts of flame which revealed them upon the battlefield. They sought concealment in a shell hole. There they lay close to each other. It became quieter. With practiced fingers Randall felt Frank's shattered arm. He was bleeding so freely that he must inevitably succumb unless the flow of blood could be stopped. It was Randall's life or his, and loving him as he did there could be but one answer.

Hastily Randall undid the tourniquet from his thigh and transferred it to Frank's arm, charging him, "Pull it tight, Frank, tighter. It will stop your bleeding."

The spurts from his own severed artery weakened him. With one hand he sought to stay the flow of blood, seeking to linger long enough to tell Frank of his love.

Again he lay against him, their heads close, almost touching. The din of battle was ever more distant. With his uninjured right arm Lieutenant Frank held Randall close while he spoke into his ear—

"Frank, I am dying; in a few minutes I shall be gone. I want you to know that I love you more than anything else in the world, more even than my own life. I have not lived a good life, according to the standards of others." He did not spare himself. "Till I met you, I was promiscuous. All my life I have been gay, a lover of men. But I love you now as I have loved no other. Before I go, won't you kiss me, dear; kiss me on the lips?" he whispered, tears of anguish streaming down his pale yet still-beautiful face.

As Frank tenderly kissed Randall's lips, he knew at that moment he loved Randall as he could never love another in all his days.

"Now I am happy. I'm going, Frank," said Randall as he released his pressure on the artery and threw both his arms in weak embrace about his dear Frank's neck.

Thus, Randall Etrange lay dying on the battlefield in France, dying in the arms of the man he loved— the last man he loved.

Indulge yourself in the scorching memoirs of young Eton man-about-town Jack Saul. From his earliest erotic moments with Jerry in the dark of his bedchamber, to his shocking dalliances with the lords and "ladies" of British high (and *very* gay) society, well-endowed Jack's positively *sinful* escapades grow wilder with every chapter! A sensual delight!

016-4   **$4.95**

Meet that remarkably well-set-up young aristocrat, Master Charles Powerscourt: only eighteen, and *quite* innocent…until his arrival at Sir Percival's Royal Academy, where the daily lessons are supplemented with a crash course in pure, sweet sexual heat! Banned for decades, this exuberant account of gay seduction and initiation is too hot to keep secret any longer. Cream and crumpets, anyone?

017-2   **$4.95**

What dark secrets, what fiery passions lay hidden behind strikingly beautiful Lieutenant Imre's emerald eyes? This extraordinary lost classic of fantasy, obsession, gay erotic desire, and romance in a tiny Austro-Hungarian military town on the eve of WWI speaks with a frankness and honesty hardly equalled since its first, fugitive edition in 1908. Finally available in a handsome new edition, *Imre* is a potent and dynamic novel of longing and desire.

019-9 **$4.95**

A hot account of gay love and sex that picks up on the adventures of the four amply-endowed lads last seen in *A Secret Life,* as they lustily explore all the possibilities of homosexual passion. Charlie Powerscourt and his friends cavort on the shores of Devon and in stately Castle Hebworth, then depart for the steamy back streets of Paris, on a quest to unravel the carnal mysteries of "Society X." Growing up has never been so hard!

018-0 **$4.95**

Often attributed to Oscar Wilde, *Teleny* is a strange, compelling novel, set amidst the color and decadence of *fin-de-siècle* Parisian society. A young stud of independent means seeks only a succession of voluptuous and forbidden pleasures, but instead finds love and tragedy when he becomes embroiled in an underground cult devoted to fulfilling the darkest fantasies.

020-2 **$4.95**

He's the most gorgeous man you have ever seen. You yearn for his touch at night, in your empty bed; but you are a man—and he's your co-worker! **BADBOY's** first anthology is a collection of eight sizzling, subtly interconnected stories of man to man on-the-job training by the hottest authors of gay erotica today. Top cops vie for new blood in *Blue Magnets*, pizza boys enjoy a slice of sex in *The Dough Boys*, and many more!

027-X **$4.95**

In the tough, gritty world of the contemporary New York City body-building scene, country boy Tommy joins forces with sexy, streetwise Will Rodriguez in an escalating battle of wits and biceps at the hottest gym in the West Village. A serious, seething account of power and surrender, in a place where young flesh is firm and hard, and those who can't cut it are bound and crushed at the hands of iron-pumping gods.

028-8 **$4.95**

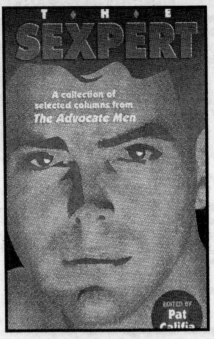

T H E

SEXPERT

A collection of
selected columns from
The Advocate Men

EDITED BY
Pat
Califia

From the pages of the *Advocate Men*—the hottest gay men's magazine in the country—comes *The Sexpert*, the first Badboy nonfiction release.

For many years now, the sophisticated gay man has known that he can turn to one authority for answers to virtually any question on the subject of man-to-man intimacy and sexual performance. From penis size to toy care, bar behavior to AIDS awareness, The Sexpert responds to real concerns with uncanny wisdom and a razor wit.

This collection of The Sexpert's most outrageous and useful columns has been edited by Pat Califia, a former editor of *Advocate Men*.

Warning:In the interest of of clarity, this book contains graphic descriptions and strong language.

Pat Califia's *The Sexpert* is everything you've ever wanted to know about gay sexuality—but never dared to ask.

034-2 $4.95

ORDERING IS EASY!

MC/VISA ORDERS CAN BE PLACED BY CALLING OUR TOLL-FREE NUMBER

1-800-458-9640

OR MAIL THE COUPON BELOW TO:
**MASQUERADE BOOKS
801 SECOND AVE.,
NEW YORK, N.Y. 10017**

SP 028-8

QTY	TITLE	NO.	PRICE
	SUBTOTAL		
	POSTAGE and HANDLING		
	TOTAL		

Add $1.00 Postage and Handling for first book and 50¢ for each additional book.
Outside the U.S. add $2.00 for first book, $1.00 for each additional book. New York
State residents add 8-¼% sales tax.

NAME _____

ADDRESS _____ **APT #**_____

CITY————— **STATE**————— **ZIP** ——————

TEL (   ) ————————————————————

PAYMENT: ☐CHECK   ☐MONEY ORDER   ☐VISA   ☐MC

CARD NO. _____ **EXP. DATE** _____

PLEASE ALLOW **4-6 WEEKS** DELIVERY. NO C.O.D. ORDERS. PLEASE MAKE ALL
CHECKS PAYABLE TO MASQUERADE BOOKS. PAYABLE IN U.S. CURRENCY ONLY.

THE GENERAL STRIKE
OF 1926

Other books in the Historical Perspective series

THE FENIANS IN ENGLAND 1865-1872: *A Sense of Insecurity*
   Patrick Quinlivan and Paul Rose

HISTORICAL PERSPECTIVES

THE
GENERAL STRIKE
OF 1926

*The Economic, Political
and Social Causes
of that Class War*

R.A. Florey

JOHN CALDER · LONDON
RIVERRUN PRESS · NEW YORK

First published in Great Britain 1980 by
John Calder (Publishers) Ltd.,
18, Brewer Street
London W1R 4AS

First published in the U.S.A. 1981 by
Riverrun Press Inc.,
175, Fifth Avenue
New York NY 10010

BRITISH LIBRARY CATALOGUING DATA
Florey, R A
  The General Strike of 1926. - (Historical
  perspectives; vol. 2).
  1. General Strike, Great Britain, 1926
  I. Title   II. Series
  331.89'25'0941   HD5365.A6   80-40574

  ISBN 0-7145-3698-9

Typeset in 10 on 12 point Janson by Alan Sutton Publishing Limited
Printed by Whitstable Litho Ltd., Whitstable, Kent
Bound by Redwood Burn, Esher

Contents

Chapter 7 119
The Class War Intensified; Battle; Betrayal;
Rout and Reprisal.

APPENDICES

List of Illustrations

Introduction

The use of the term 'Class War' to define the conflict between the working class on one side, and the middle and upper classes on the other, is as open to objection as any other generalization is. However if we see the past as it appears from the standpoint of that age,[1] we shall begin to see the truth of that term. A government faction in Baldwin's second cabinet, (November 1924 - June 1929) had long prepared for the particular battle which became known as 'The General Strike'. These men were determined at the outset to not only defeat the organized working class, but afterwards to attempt to utterly demoralize and humiliate them, so that it could never happen again.

The leaders of the General Council of the Trades Union Congress betrayed their own troops during the actual conflict by secret negotiations with the enemy, and afterwards moved over to join the ranks of their former foe. The leaders of the workers in the field of battle were totally unprepared for the slaughter and rout which followed. The use of military metaphors may seem unnecessary, but after reading contemporary newspapers, periodicals, pamphlets, books and letters, and listening to people who were actually involved, or merely looked on, one can get the feeling of a military operation — a military operation with a few people killed and many wounded. The antagonists in the war — a class war — were then more clearly defined.

What needs to be emphasized, and will be in this book is the fact that the working class of 1926 were a more homogeneous group. They had suffered together, and lived more intimately than they do now. The miner's cottage was as near to the pit head as possible; the rows of houses rented by the textile workers, were within walking distance of the mill, and so on. The workers were in fact segregated according to the particular industry of the areas where they worked. In the case of the several million other tradesmen or labourers, the homes of the workers were usually grouped together at the 'East End' or in some clearly defined part of the city or town. The coal-miners, who bore the brunt of the class war, lived for the most part in rows of mean little cottages clustered together in villages. Theirs was a close knit community life which made for a common bondage and comradeship, hard to be visualized by the middle-class, and difficult for them to understand in their narrow, insular, self-seeking existence.

During the General Strike the middle class was drawn together because of the recognized threat to the growing power they had wrested from the aristocracy since the Reform Act of 1832. They joined forces with the aristocracy in order to bring about the defeat of a common enemy — the organized working class. The election of a minority Labour Government in 1924 caused them great concern. To them Socialism and Bolshevism were synonomous, and had to be crushed and eradicated.

The Anti-Socialist Constitutionalist who in 1924 fought a Conservative candidate, was to lead the Conservative Party against the workers in 1926. He was to have as a collaborator, a man who had attempted inside that party, to set himself up as the 'most progressive social reformer.'[2] These two men were Winston Churchill and Neville Chamberlain. The former as Chancellor of the Exchequer in 1926, by a 'combination of deflation and free imports which he stubbornly maintained bore its immediate fruit in wage reductions, long-drawn industrial conflict and continuous heavy unemployment; its long-term results in the conviction of the working class that Socialism alone could provide a remedy for unemployment.'[3] The latter as Minister of Health, introducing his Board of Guardians (Default) Bill, proved himself to be not progressive but reactionary. The policy of both ensured a Labour victory in the elections of 1929, but because the socialists again required Liberal support, they were allowed to be a government provided they did not behave like socialists.

In the General Election of 1924 the Conservatives had an overall majority of more than 200 seats, won on Baldwin's plea for a 'sane, commonsense government', and the added motive of the Zinoviev letter. 'The fear of the socialist party was then very real, and the wilder speeches of their wilder men was taken as proof.'[4] In fact the Labour Party had even in 1924 lost sight of its original aims and objectives, and was being led by a man who three years after the General Strike became premier of a coalition government. The day after this was formed a Labour colleague remarked that he would now be finding himself popular in strange company. The former Labour leader, Ramsey Macdonald, replied 'gleefully rubbing his hands: "Yes, tomorrow every Duchess in London will be wanting to kiss me!" '[5]

One socialist writer in 1926 posed the question: 'Are we not indeed a middle-class party, with middle-class leaders, who can shake as good a leg in any drawing rooms of the great?'[6] Certainly J.H. Thomas the railwaymen's leader had then for years been moving in upper class circles and was described as 'probably one of the best waltzers in London' by a chatty little column in one of the Northcliffe papers. He lived on the Astor estate, and often shared Lord Derby's box on National Day.[7].

It is significant that the *Labour Magazine*, journal of the Trade Union Congress, in no way indicated that there was any preparation by that body to counteract the known, well prepared plans of the then Home Secretary to resist any strike action which was inevitable as a result of deliberate government action. *The Social Democrat* magazine recognized that the Home Secretary, Sir William Joynson Hicks, had welcomed help from the 'Fascisti',[8] and, 'spoke of Mussolini in a way that suggested that worse might be done than follow the example of the man who is head and front of the attempt to crush all freedom in Italy,[9] but it offered no advice to workers when they, like everyone else with some political insight, knew that a General Strike was inevitable.

Fascism in Italy was having its repercussions on the rest of the world. Many leading figures in this country recognized it as a means of combating socialism and were prepared to defend its evils. In 1925 Austin Chamberlain wrote of Mussolini: '. . . I believe him to be accused of crimes in which he had no share, and I suspect him to have connived unwillingly at other outrages which he would have prevented if he could.'[10] We shall see that Mussolini and his regime was frequently referred to and quoted as able to deal with industrial strife by the Government organ, *The British Gazette*, in some of its eight issues during the strike. Its editor was Winston Churchill, who proved eventually to be the nation's leader against fascism, although he was largely responsible for Britain lagging behind in the armament race of the 1930s.[11] Austin Chamberlain also realized in 1933 that German fascism was a force to be deplored,[12] but like most of the establishment he was years behind the organized working class in recognizing that fascism threatened everyone's freedom. This was because, as we shall see, the working class were the first to feel the organized brutality of the 'fascisti'.

Just as the middle and upper class saw Bolshevism and Socialism as synonymous, so the working class saw Capitalism and Fascism as two forces which at times were so similar that they were given the label 'reactionary'.

It was in the Duke of Northumberland's paper, *The Patriot* that six advertisements appeared in 1923, put there by Miss Rotha Linton-Orman, founder of the British Fascists. The advertisement asked for recruits for a British Fascisti to act as an organized force to combat the Red revolution.[13] That 'extreme right-wing conservative',[14] the Duke of Northumberland, wrote a letter to the *Morning Post* on the eve of the General Strike. It was headed, 'COAL WAR PLOT. Miners under the thumb of Moscow. The vanguard of Revolution.[15] The *Morning Post* became the *British Gazette*. The future leader of the British fascists, Oswald Moseley was elected as M.P. for Smethwick in 1926 having miners' support. He was then a Left Wing Labour M.P.

The leading left-wing miner was however a member of the Communist Party and the communist inspired Minority Movement. He was described by Beatrice Webb in her diaries as 'an inspired idiot, drunk with his own words, dominated by his own slogans. I doubt whether he even knows what he is going to say or what he has just said.'[16] Despite such scathing criticism, Arthur J. Cook 'confined his agitation to two points, the need for unity and the need to fight. He never wavered from the course he had set himself, which was to win justice for the miners by an uncompromising class war and a policy of direct industrial action.'[17] That he failed was not due to lack of support from the miners, which he represented, but to circumstances outside his control.

From what has been written so far the reader will have realized that the General Strike demands a great deal of research in order to arrive at the truth of what actually happened and why. Without some attempt to understand the people involved, the economic circumstances, the political background, and the social causes and effects of what was a class war, the General Strike of 1926 can never properly be understood.

Just as the middle-class gloated over their political victory in the Reform Bill of 1832, the same class proclaimed their trouncing of the workers in 1926. The working class reaction to the great betrayal of 1832, when their agitation for reform brought them nothing, was to turn to industrial action — a general strike. The Chartist leaders immediately grasped their opportunity. 'The trades of Great Britain,' they said, 'carried the Reform Bill. The trades of Great Britain shall carry the Charter.'[18] However they were not to repeat their success of using the workers as they had done in 1832. One reason being that at the height of the strike action the Chartist leaders did an about face, and condemned those who followed them.

The failure of a Labour minority government in 1924 caused the workers to turn from political to industrial action in 1926. The general strike of that year had no political movement to back it, but it too was betrayed.

When the General Strike of the 1980s begins, as seems possible, will the organized Trade Union Movement learn from history, or will it again trust in its leaders and let history repeat itself? This book attempts to clear the fog which has long surrounded the great General Strike of 1926, and should give a clearer view of the future for all those about to be involved in the struggles ahead.

Notes to Introduction

1. Collingwood, R.G.: *The Idea of History*. Oxford. 1946. p.60
2. Macleod, Iain: *Neville Chamberlain*. Muller. 1961. p.119
3. Amery, L.S.: *My Political Life*. Hutchinson. 1953. p.300.
4. Macleod, Iain: *Op. Cit.* p.99.
5. Mowat, Charles Loch: *Britain Between the Wars*. Methuen. 1964. p.396.
6. Article by S.B.M. Potter: *Socialist Review*. Dec. 1926.
7. Blaxland, Gregory: *A Life for Unity*. Muller. pp.161 and 152.
8. *The Social Democrat*. Nov. 1925.
9. *Ibid.*
10. Petrie, Sir Charles: The Life and Letters of the Right Hon. Sir Austin Chamberlain. Cassell. 1940. p.296.
11. 'Churchill the Outsider'. Review in *The Observer*, 4 Sept. 1966. p.16
12. *Hansard* 13 April 1933.
13. Cross, Colin: *The Fascists in Britain*. Barrie and Rockliffe. 1961. p.57.
14. *The Concise Dictionary of National Bibliography*. Part 2. 1964.
15. Martin, Kingsley: *The British Public and the General Strike*. Hogarth Press. 1927. p.28
16. Bullock, Allan: *The Life and Times of Ernest Bevin*. Vol. 1. Heineman. 1960. p.264.
17. Bullock, Allan: *Ibid.* p.264.
18. Cole, G.D.H, & Postgate, Raymond: *The Common People*. U.P. p.290.

Chapter 1

A Grand National Holiday

In the 'Poor Man's Guardian' of the 28 January 1832, William Benbow put forward what is believed to be the first idea of a General Strike in Great Britain since the beginning of the Industrial Revolution. The title he used was: 'Grand National Holiday and Congress of the Productive Classes.' Overproduction was then said to be the cause of the widespread poverty of the working classes. To this theory Benbow replied:

> Our Lords and Masters tell us we produce too much — very well then, we shall cease from producing for one month, and thus put into practice the theory of our Lords and Masters.

In the 'Introductory Address' he wrote:

> All men enjoy life, but do not enjoy it equally. The enjoyment of some is so very limited, that it does not deserve the name of enjoyment . . . The only class of person in society, as it is now constituted, who enjoy any considerable portion of ease, pleasure, and happiness, are those who do the least towards producing anything good or necessary for the community at large.

Benbow declared that these lucky and powerful members of society constituted scarcely one in five hundred of the population:

> The 499 who create the state, who are its instruments on all occasions, without whom it cannot go on for a single second, who dig deep, rise early, and watch late, by whose sweat and toil the whole face of nature is beautiful, rendered pleasant to the sight and useful to the existence; the 499 who do all this are reduced to less than nothing in the estimation of the *unit* who does no one thing, unless *consuming* may be called doing something . . . the 499 are *his* purveyors, they procure him everything; and, more to be pitied and worse treated than the jackal, they are not left even the offals.[1]

Benbow then turned to the 499, accused them of never fighting for
themselves, and asserted it was ignorance that permitted the
majority to toil incessantly for others. Moreover, the knowledge
that the 499 needed most was not book learning, but rather 'a
knowledge of ourselves: a knowledge of our own power, of our
immense might, and of the right we have to employ in action that
immense power.' The remedy he offered for this parlous condition
of the workers was 'unity of thought and action.' Hence, in his
introduction, Benbow already voiced the gist of the modern theory
of the general strike: that the many are subject to the few through
ignorance of their own power. Did they but know it, the state
could not 'go on for a single second' without them. All that was
required for remedy was united action — or, rather, 'cessation of
all action.'[2]

Benbow proposed that every care should be taken to organize the
workers for the proposed 'national holiday'. 'Committees of
management of the workers had to be appointed in every city,
town, village, and parish, to carry through the project as effectively
and quickly as possible. Frequent meetings were to be held to
instruct the people as to the necessity of a national holiday and the
need for extreme sobriety and economy.'[3]

Although Benbow's ideas spread throughout the Chartist movement from 1836 to 1842, when the general strike came widespread
organization amongst the workers was lacking. It was in July 1842
when the 'colliery owners of Staffordshire reduced wages from four
shillings to three shillings and sixpence, with but 48 hours' notice,
whereas two weeks' notice had hitherto been the custom. The
miners naturally resisted the wage reduction and appealed to the
magistrates.'[4] The owners proceeded to lock-out the miners, who
'marched to adjacent districts and forced other miners to join in
with them. The resultant failure of the coal supply threw the
employees of the pottery industry out of work.'[5] The strike spread
'to Cheshire, Lancashire, Warwickshire, Yorkshire, Scotland, and
Wales.'[6] At the same time as the miners' strike, the so called 'plug
plot' of August 1842, spread from Stalybridge and Ashton over the
Pennines into Yorkshire. This strike was started by Richard
Pilling, who declared at his trial 'that he earned sixteen shillings for
the first week he worked as a weaver, when he was but ten years of
age. Thirty years later, in 1840, working hard all the week, he
earned only six shillings and sixpence.'[7] In 1841 he found work in
Ashton, and in 1842 wages dropped again, which led Pilling to

propose the removal of the plugs from mill boilers as a protest.

The strikers' demands were purely economic at first, but later the Chartists' political demands were added. The authorities reacted with large displays of military force. 'There were, for example, over two thousand soldiers and six pieces of artillery in Manchester alone.'[8] Nevertheless the greater part of the delegates (to the Chartist Conference in August 1842), believed that the strikers should be encouraged to remain out till the Charter was law.[9] Feargus O'Conner, the Chartist leader, decided to leave the decision 'to the people' and departed to London, where he asserted that the strike was a crafty device of 'the mill owners and of the Anti-Corn-Law League to reduce wages and divert men's minds from the Charter!'[10]

Thus, basely deserted by the political leaders who had so long promulgated the notion of the 'sacred month' or the general strike, the workers slowly were driven back to work. The riots had commenced in July; before the end of August the disorders were virtually at an end. In the course of September the strike wore itself out, the workers going back with no assurance as to their wages. 'Persecuted by the authorities, who made wholesale arrests; oppressed by misery, which was rendered more acute by the strike, the workmen gradually returned to the factories, but even at the end of September the strike still possessed a partial character.'[11]

Just as in 1842, it was an unprepared working class in 1926 that supported a miners' strike against a reduction in wages. The miners of 1926 were locked out prior to their strike action as had their predecessors been in 1842. However, in 1926 there was no political organization prepared to use the general strike for political ends, although there was much said about the possibilities by left-wing agitators, and fear of a revolution by extreme right-wing Conservatives. Just as the Chartist leader deserted his followers in spite of an overwhelming response to the strike call, so did the leaders of the great strike of 1926.

There are other similarities in these two outstanding dates of working class history which shall be discussed in the following chapters.

Notes to Chapter 1

1. All references to Benbow are taken from Crook, W.H.: *The General Strike. A Study of Labor's Tragic Weapon in Theory and Practice*. The University of North Carolina Press. 1931. pp.5, 6 and 7.
2. Crook, W.H.: *Ibid*. pp.7, 8 and 9.
3. Crook, W.H.: *Ibid*. pp.7, 8 and 9.
4. Crook, W.H.: *Ibid*. p.20.
5. Crook, W.H. *Ibid*. p.20
6. Crook, W.H.: *Ibid*. p.20.
7. Crook, W.H.: *Ibid*. p.18.
8. Crook, W.H.: *Ibid*. p.25.
9. Crook, W.H.: *Ibid*. p.26.
10. Crook, W.H.: *Ibid*. p.26.
11. Crook, W.H.: *Ibid*. p.26 and 27.

Chapter 2

The Mines and Collieries Act, 1842.
Invalidated in Principle and made Inoperative

The reduction in wages by the Staffordshire colliery owners in July 1842, followed quickly on Lord Ashley's attempts to forbid the labour of women and girls underground, all boys under thirteen, and all parish apprentices. (7 June, 1842)[1]

The Marquis of Londonderry, owner of several mines, fought the Bill tooth and nail. 'The measure,' he said, 'might be regarded as the commencement of a series of grievances which would be got up for the purpose of working upon that hypocritical humanity which reigned so much.' This was too much for the Bishop of Gloucester who in the House of Lords, on 14 July 1842, asked Lord Londonderry to withdraw the words 'hypocritical humanity'. But the most noble Marquis, who had stated that 'some seams of coal required the employment of women, was not thus to be put down by his spiritual peer; he continued his opposition to the last, and the Bill was returned to the Commons so altered as to be, in the words of Lord Ashley, 'invalidated in principle and made inoperative.'[2]

The Bill, greatly altered by the coal owners, became law on 10' August 1842. It fixed the age limit of boys at 10; it allowed parish apprentices to be sent down the mines, but laid down that they could not be employed before ten; it forbade the employment of women and girls underground. In the Bill, as originally amended in the House of Commons, the Inspectors were to report on the state and condition of the mines, but Londonderry persuaded the House of Lords to strike out these words, and to allow the inspectors to report only on the state and condition of the persons working in the mine. Hours were unrestricted by the Bill.[3]

'None but the most glaring abuses which clearly require reform was suppressed,' wrote a mining engineer, 'but even this fragment of legislation met with the disapprobation of the colliery owners.' He added that, on the other hand, 'the measure was almost

received by indifference by the colliers . . . the measure in fact, did
not touch many of the grievances under which the colliery population had suffered for a long period.' In addition that year wages
were lowered and many were discharged.[4]

Drawing of a child opening a trap door for two child 'hurriers' (taken from
Commission of Inquiry into the Employment of Young Persons in Mines report of 1842)

It is often assumed and categorically stated that after 1842 child
labour stopped. An example is a B.B.C. caption of the above print:
*This child was called a 'trapper'. This terrible work for children was
stopped by Lord Ashley, afterwards Lord Shaftesbury, in a Bill passed by
Parliament* (taken from a B.B.C. Schools pamphlet, Summer Term
1961). This was not the case. 'By the terms of the Mines Regulation Act of 1842, the employment of boys underground was re-
stricted to those who had attained the age of ten years. This Act,
however, remained a dead letter for some years and children continued to work underground in the mines,'[5] in some cases 'being
concealed by the men during times of inspection.'[6] On page 520 of
the *First Report of the Commission of Inquiry into the Employment of
Young Persons in Mines* (1842), we are given a clue as to the reason
for this in the evidence of Witness 96. Thomas Slatheral of Dinas,
Rhonda, stated; 'My father took me down to claim his tram.' In
those days a man and a 'helper' could get more trams than a man
working alone, i.e. instead of getting two trams to load, the collier
would get three and this would increase his coal output for the
day.'[7]

The print on the previous page shows a 'door-boy' or 'trapper', whose job it was to check as far as possible the wastage of ventilation air through the underground doors. The door-boy's special duty was to open the door for anyone who wished to pass through — and then shut it again as quickly as possible. In most cases, the door-boys were in total darkness and quite alone. 'Were it not,' said the 1842 Report, 'for the passing and repassing of the coal carriages, this would amount to solitary confinement of the worst order.' Though not in itself difficult or arduous, their work was nevertheless of great importance; indeed the whole safety of the mines depended on these lads of six or seven years of age. Boys were sometimes put in charge of pumps and others worked as hauliers or actually filled the trams.[8]

But let the actual child witnesses of 1842 speak for themselves:

Evidence of Witness 103 at Dinas Colliery
William Isaac, Aged 11
(Air-door keeper)

Has to keep the air-doors in the coal mine, goes down the shaft at four to five in the morning and returns at five or six at night; works frequently at night; been four years below ground; was burned by fire damp 20 months since, and laid ill 18 months; only returned to the pit two months since; the accident took place from a collier incautiously entering an old working with his candle near the roof; several were burnt and the horse which brought up the train of carts was killed. (The commissioners wrote; 'This witness was neglected; the whole skin of his face was burned and he has a very disagreable appearance; the eyes are much inflamed.')[9]

Evidence of Witness 97 at Dinas Colliery
Philip Davies, Aged 10
(Haulier)

I have been driving horses below ground three years, and was 12 months before at a trap door; when at the traps used frequently to fall asleep; work 12 hours; would go to school if the work were not so long; cannot go now as I have to work on the night as well as the day shifts; the night work is done by group who work about (alternate weeks); never was at school. (The commissioners added; 'This witness cannot read, is much neglected and in appearance sickly'.)[10]

Drawing of children pushing and pulling coal cart in mine (taken from report of 1842)

Children were also employed to push and pull carriages filled with coal along the passages, and as the passages were often very low and narrow, it was necessary to use very small children for this purpose. 'In many mines which are at present worked,' reported the Commission, 'the main gates are only from 24 to 30 inches high, and in some parts of these mines the passages do not exceed 18 inches in height. In this case not only is the employment of very young children absolutely indispensable to the working of the mine, but even the youngest children must necessarily work in a bent position of the body.' As a rule the carriages were pushed along small iron railways, but sometimes they were drawn by children and women, 'harnessed like dogs in a go-cart,' and moving like dogs, on all fours.[11]

The employment of girls and women was confined to certain districts; Scotland, South Wales, the West Riding, Cheshire, and parts of Lancashire. In Scotland girls were set to work at an earlier age than boys. Women were employed, like the children, to push, or, to use the Yorkshire term, to 'hurry' the corves of coal.[12]

Drawing of girls carrying sacks of coal on their backs up steep ladders (taken from report of 1842)

In Scotland, women and children were also used to carry coal in baskets on their backs up steep ladders and along the passages from the workings to the pit bottom; in some cases girls of six were found carrying ½ cwt. of coal.[13]

Southwood Smith, a doctor and one of the commissioners responsible for the report on the mines, argued that Members of Parliament, who might have thought themselves too busy to read the text of the report, would at least turn over its pages to glance at the illustrations.[4] The illustrations in this text are copies of those same illustrations, drawn on the spot, of women and children at work.

Lord Londonderry, an employer of women and children in his mines considered that the commissioners' methods were 'underhand', and their 'disgusting pictorial illustrations' had given a false impression. 'Their instructions were to examine the children themselves, and the mode in which they had collected their evidence — communicating with artful boys and ignorant young girls, and putting questions in a manner which in many cases seemed to suggest the answer, was anything but a fair and impartial mode.'[15]

The following month, Londonderry made a passionate speech against education for the workers. 'Enthusiastic advocates for the education of the labouring classes [forgot] that our fields could not be ploughed, our mines wrought, nor our ships sailed by the use of the pen alone. The national community might be compared to a great machine or manufactory, all its wheels and parts must be duly proportioned to enable it to move smoothly, and the requisite proportion of education would always be supplied without making all this stir and effort about it. If it should preponderate, the equilibrium of society would be destroyed.'[16]

Drawing of girl pulling cart of coal underground with a chain around her waist and between her legs (taken from report of 1842)

Another coal owner, Lord Fitzwilliam of Yorkshire, assured the House of Lords that it was misleading to talk of women working in chains, since the chains were merely used to draw the carriages.[17]

Lord Londonderry, who had extensive mining interests in Northumberland and Durham, claimed that there were over ten million pounds invested in that area alone, and as for the masters of that industry, there was 'no set of men in the world who did more justice in every way to those who were employed by them.'[18] The 1842 Report however, makes the following general comment concerning the physical effects of children working down mines:

> That they aquire a prenatural development of the muscles, especially about the arms, shoulders, chest and back; that for some time they are capable of prodigious muscular exertion; that in a few years their strength diminishes and many lose their robust appearance; that they become pallid, stunted in growth, short of breath, sometimes thin and often burnt, crooked, crippled, and that, in addition, they are peculiarly subject to certain mortal diseases, the direct result of their employment and the state of the place in which they work.[19]

Drawing of woman winding two children to the pit head by windlass (taken from report of 1842)

One would have not been surprised if the following had been found in the 1842 Report;

The seams in this Somerset coalfield are thin, and the galleries are too narrow for ponies. No less than 1,500 boys and young men are employed as tuggers. Stark naked, on all fours, with a rope round their waist, and a chain between their legs hitched on to a waggon, they pull the coal through the workings. The rope rubs off the skin, until callosites are formed. The dirt gets in, and the septic wounds are the result. A doctor in the district has commented on the increase of septic sores owing to the poor nourishment of the boys. A woman in one cottage told me how she wept every time she had to wash her son's back, all bleeding and chaffed from the rope. The nation prosecutes if a pit pony is worked with bleeding sores and abraded skin.[20]

In fact the above was written by Helen Wilkinson M.P. after her tour of the mining areas of this country during the General Strike of 1926.

A retired miner wrote to this writer in 1967 and said that he was employed as a door-boy (trapper) at the age of 13 in 1906. He then worked 12 hours or 'often more' a day, receiving 1/8d per day for his 'solitary confinement'.[21]

Notes to Chapter 2

1. Hammond, J.L. and Barbara; *Lord Shaftesbury.*London, 1969. p.74.
2. Arnot, R. Page; *The Miners; Years of Struggle*, Vol. II. London. pp. 34 and 35.
3. Hammond, J.L. & B. *Op. Cit.* pp. 79 and 80.
4. Arnot, R. Page. *Op. Cit.* p.35.
5. Lewis, E.D.: *The Rhondda Valleys.* London, 1959. pp.153 and 154.
6. Lewis, E.D. *Ibid.* p.154.
7. Lewis, E.D. *Ibid.* p.154.
8. Lewis, E.D. *Ibid.* p.151 and 152.
9. Lewis, E.D. *Ibid.* p.152 and 153.
10. Lewis, E.D. *Ibid.* p.152 and 153.
11. Hammond, J.L. & B. *Op. Cit.* p.71.
12. Hammond, J.L. & B. *Ibid.* p.72.
13. Hammond, J.L. & B. *Ibid.* p.72.
14. Hammond, J.L. & B. *Ibid.* p.72.
15. Hammond, J.L. & B. *Ibid.* p.77.
16. Hammond, J.L. & B. *Ibid.* p.79.
17. Hammond, J.L. & B. *Ibid.* p.77.
18. Hammond, J.L. & B. *Ibid.* p.78.
19. Lewis, E.D. *Op. Cit.* p.153.
20. *Lansbury's Labour Weekly.* 5 June 1926. p.7.
21. Letter from Mr T. Croome, 25 Treharne Street, Pentre, Rhondda. 1967.

Chapter 3

Safety Last, Profits First. A Brief History of Coal Mining Progress from 1842 to 1911

In The Mines and Collieries Act of 1842, 'as originally amended in the House of Commons, the Inspectors were to report on the state and condition of the mines, but Londonderry persuaded the House of Lords to strike out these words, and to allow the inspectors to report only on the state and condition of the persons working in the mines. This alteration had important consequences. Hours were unrestricted by the Bill, although children's hours in the mines were longer than children's hours in the mills.'[1]

That same year the Miners' Association of Great Britain and Ireland was formed, headed by Martin Jude. They began by sending petitions to Parliament asking for the appointment of more inspectors, and pointing out the reasons why there were so many accidents. 'Many accidents occur in the mines from persons being entrusted with the care of engines who have served no regular apprenticeship.'[2] The petitioners also observed 'with much satisfaction the laws compelling the masters in factories to provide some amount of education for the children who work there, and your petitioners submit to your Honourable House that a similar plan would be of great use to the children of colliers. . . .'[3]

The first 'Inspector' appointed (they were called Commissioners under the Act), was Mr Seymour Tremenheere. Martin Jude had this to say about his methods of inspection: 'Tremenheere did not come to get a correct report, or at all events if he did, he had not gone the way to get one. Instead of taking evidence from all parties, he only went among the petty officials who had been raised up into situations, some of them from working men, and who were now cutting high capers over the poor miners; the commissioner was shown over the houses these little bodies were then living in, taken to the colliery office, and courteously escorted to the station by the officials; but the men were not in any single instance consulted. . . .'[4]

Tremenheere was not allowed of course, to inspect the conditions of the mines themselves, and pressure was kept up 'throughout the 'forties from the M.A.G.B. and reinforced by numerous petitions, by recommendations of men of science and by reports of departmental and parliamentary committees,'[5] to change the law so that this could be done. On 28 September, 1844, at the Haswell Colliery, 95 lives were lost after an explosion. This tragedy, together with the mounting pressure mentioned, forced the government to yield, and the principle of inspection of coal mines was conceded in the Act of 1850. Lord Londonderry and Lord Lonsdale opposed the Bill in the Lords, and in the Commons, Disraeli said that he had had communications from several coal-owners complaining that the interference with their property would be seriously injurious. He was answered by a coal-owner, who reminded him that 2,000 persons lost their lives every year, and declared that two-thirds of the coal-owners approved the Bill.[6]

The accidents however continued, and a Select Committee of the House of Commons was appointed in 1852 which recommended doubling the number of inspectors from six to twelve. This did not satisfy the workmen, who continued the agitation for more inspectors. Eventually after more accidents, and another select committee, the twelve inspectors were duly appointed in 1855.[7] Some understanding of the miners discontent can be appreciated when we read the first detailed list of rules sent to a Rhondda coal-owner by H.M. Inspector Herbert Mackworth in 1854. The owner was J.H. Insole of Cymmer. Mackworth advocated that a qualified engineer should be appointed at Cymmer; that the working places should be examined daily; that artificial means of ventilation should be employed to produce a regular and active current of air throughout the workings; that where fire-damp was perceptible, entrance to it should be barred; that the Davy safety lamp should be used instead of naked lights; that all safety lamps should be locked; that a list of printed rules for the colliery should be placed at the pithead. All these recommendations were completely ignored because of the indifference of the owner and manager and their objections to the cost involved in their operation. Consequently, on the 15 July 1856, 'the most lamentable and destructive explosion which had ever occurred in any country, either this or abroad' took place at the Cymmer Old Pit. Out of 156 men and boys who were underground at the time of the explosion, 114 were killed, and of the 42 who escaped, the majority were severely injured.

Mackworth could report with truth: 'I think the explosion arose from the persons in charge of the pit neglecting the commonest precautions for the safety of the men and the safe working of the colliery.'[8] The Davy safety lamp was invented in 1815, and improvements were expected as a result, but 'mines were driven deeper and operations were carried on with greater recklessness than before.'[9] A writer in 1929 commented: '. . . how far the labours of Davy . . . fell short of fulfilling the high expectations that were aroused in 1815 was amply demonstrated on almost every coalfield during the following century.'[10]

The courageous work of the H.M. Inspector Mackworth should be carefully noted by the reader. Despite his warnings, and the many others which followed, accidents through the neglect of the owners to carry out obvious precautions, increased. In 1862, through lack of an upcast shaft, 204 lives were lost at Hartley Colliery.[11] All inspectors were not like Mackworth, and the Miners' National Union demanded that 'inspectors should be drawn from the same class as the miners,' and that 'measures used at collieries should come under the Survey of the Inspector of Weights and Measures.'[12] The Coal Mines Regulation Act of 1872 called for the appointment of sub-inspectors, which enabled the mines to be more frequently inspected, and the principle was established that in future all coals (except those mixed with dirt and dross) were to be paid by weight, which went a great deal of the way to meeting union demands.[13] From 1879 to 1886 a Royal Commission inquired into accidents in mines. This Commission met after several hundred miners had lost their lives. During the course of the inquiry, there were the following principal disasters:

Disasters involving the loss of 100 or more lives

DATE	COLLIERY	KILLED
15 July, 1880	Risca, Monmouth	120
8 Sept., 1880	Seaham, Durham	164
10 Dec., 1880	Naval Steam Coal, Glamorgan	101
9 June, 1885	Clifton Hall, Trencherbone Seam, Lancaster	178

'The final report of the Commissioners contained a comprehensive statement of existing knowledge on the subject of mine gas, and on the subject of the dangerous properties of coal dust which by a series of elaborate experiments they proved could cause or propa-

gate explosions.'[14] Pit disasters however continued, and in 1906 the
Miners' Federation of Great Britain, (M.F.G.B. formed in 1889
replaced the M.A.G.B.I.) was invited to send three of their
Executive Committee to sit upon yet another Royal Commission,
which was to 'inquire into and report on certain questions relating
to the health and safety of miners . . .'[15] The outcome was the Coal
Mines Act of 1911. Two years later, 14 October 1913, no less than
439 lives were lost at the Senghenydd Pit, in Glamorgan. No
special precautions had been taken in this pit despite an explosion
in 1901, which caused considerable loss of life, and as late as 1910
there had been an outburst of gas which was not got under control
for four days. The 1911 Act had been blatantly ignored by the
owners, yet the local magistrates aquitted the company of all four
charges brought against them by the Divisional Mines Inspector for
Wales.[16] The Manager's fines were nominal. 'Miners' Lives at 1s
1¼d Each' was the heading in a local Labour paper at the time.
Children under 12 were involved in the accidents listed in the
previous table (see p.31), because it was not until the Coal Mines
Regulation Act of 1887, that children under 12 could not be
employed underground. At Senghenydd boys of 13 would be
involved, because the Mines (Prohibition of Child Labour Underground) Act of 1900, raised the age limit by one year. Lord
Shaftesbury (formerly Ashley) died five years previously, his
struggle to prevent boys under 13 working underground had taken
almost 60 years to win.

The 1911 Coal Mines Act 'marked a great step forward'[17] for the
miners. At the time 'it was the most advanced ameliorative mining
law in Europe or America.[18] Needless to say, as previously
explained, the mining companies were slow to carry out sections of
the Act. From 1911 to 1926 no Acts were passed which greatly
improved the safety or the working conditions of the miner. In
1908 the M.F.G.B., after a struggle which lasted some twenty
years, succeeded in winning an eight hour day for their members.
'The reduction in hours involved readjustments of wage rates and
piecework prices, and over these considerable friction arose, and
there were big strikes in Yorkshire, South Wales, and other areas.
At the same time, the Conciliation Boards in most of the coalfields
awarded substantial reductions in wages on account of the fall in
the price of coal, which, despite the abolition of the sliding scale
system, remained still the chief factor governing miners' wages.
1910 began with a further crop of mining strikes. In consequence

of the Eight Hours Act, the coal-owners in Northumberland and Durham introduced changes in the method of working, including in many collieries, a three shift system.'[19] Unofficial strikes resulted, and were defeated by the employers. At the Cambrian Combine, 'the most powerful colliery concern in South Wales, trouble arose over a new list of piece work prices. No agreement could be reached, and the men struck, alleging that the firm was trying indirectly to cut wages and was refusing to give proper regard to the vexed problem of the "abnormal place", i.e. to the working place in which, by reason of the special difficulty of coal getting, the hewer could not, at piece-work prices, earn a reasonable wage.'[20] The strike lasted nearly twelve months, and achieved little for the miners except near starvation, but the problem of the 'abnormal place' became a national issue and led eventually to a national miners' strike for a minimum wage in 1912. It was during this strike of 1910-11 against the powerful Cambrian Combine, that the then Home Secretary, Winston Churchill, sent in troops[21] to suppress the strikers. At Tonypandy it was alleged that rioters were disrupting law and order. In fact no more than 100 men were involved in damage to private houses, looting, and window smashing. Local opinion was quite sure that if the local police had been in the streets at the time of the incidents, instead of almost all at the colliery guarding the owners' property, there would have been no need for such a ridiculous show of force.[22] The main cause of the rioting was the importation of blackleg labour. Police and troops, (the latter, according to General Nevil Macready, used their bayonets against the strikers to provide, as he put it, 'gentle persuasion'), could not force the miners back to work, hunger and poverty did.

1911 then was a significant year as far as the General Strike of 1926 is concerned. The miners realized that they must act as a national movement if they were to succeed in their aims. The same man who tried military force at Tonypandy was to use it again against the nationally organized working class in 1926. Before we move on however, some attention should be given to the other workers in the great struggle that was yet to come.

Notes to Chapter 3

1. Hammond, J.L. and B: *Lord Shaftesbury*, London, 1969. pp. 79/80.
2. Arnot, R.Page: *The Miners; Years of Struggle*, Vol.II. London. p. 37.
3. Arnot, R.Page: *Ibid*. p. 36.
4. Arnot, R.Page: *Ibid*. p. 39.
5. Arnot, R.Page: *Ibid*. p. 38.
6. Hammond, J.L. and B: *Op. Cit*. p. 83.
7. Arnot, R.Page: *Op. Cit*. p. 40 and 41.
8. Lewis, E.D: *The Rhondda Valleys*. London 1959. p. 149.
9. Arnot, R.Page: *Op. Cit*. p. 33.
10. Ashton, T.S. and Sykes, Joseph: *The Coal Industry of the Eighteenth Century*, Manchester, 1929. p. 53.
11. Arnot, R.Page: *Op. Cit*. p. 42.
12. Arnot, R.Page: *Ibid*. p. 43.
13. Arnot, R.Page: *Ibid*. p. 43.
14. Arnot, R.Page: *Ibid*. p. 45.
15. Arnot, R.Page: *Ibid*. p. 47.
16. Arnot, R.Page: *Ibid*. pp. 51 and 52.
17. Arnot, R.Page: *Ibid*. p. 50.
18. Arnot, R.Page: *Ibid*. p. 50.
19. Cole, G.D.H: *A Short History of the British Working Class Movement, 1789-1947.*, London, 1960. p. 319.
20. Cole, G.D.H: *Ibid*. pp. 338 and 339.
21. Lewis, E.D. *Op. Cit*. p. 176. The Lancashire Fusiliers, 218th Hussars, the West Riding Regiment.
22. Lewis, E.D. *Ibid*. p. 176.

Chapter 4

Railwaymen and Dockers and their Struggle for Justice to 1911.

Between 1801 and 1845 there were more than 360 private Acts of Parliament authorizing the construction of railways passed into law. In the latter year the capital authorized for new railway undertakings reached nearly £60,000,000 in the one year, nearly treble the previous record of 1836. 'These sums far exceeded any which had previously been raised by way of public investment. That they could be raised, and in addition very large sums provided for industrial development in mining and manufactures, shows clearly how rapidly wealth was accumulating in the hands of the richer classes; for clearly the bulk of the new investments must have come out of the profits of industry and commerce.'[1]

Before 1870 strikes occurred during periods of retrenchment and drastic economies which followed the weeks of incautious expansion by the many railway companies. The companies then endeavoured to economize at the expense of the men's wages, hours and security of employment and provoked them into an organized, if rudimentary, resistance.[2] Discipline became stricter as the railways expanded. Towards the end of the period just mentioned the Taff Vale Railway warned its employees:

> . . . not an instance of intoxication, singing, whistling or levity will be overlooked, and besides being dismissed the offender will be liable for punishment.[3]

The editorial board of the *Lancet* in 1861 appointed a Commission 'to inquire into the influence of railway travelling on public health.'[4] The report of the Commission revealed, however, that its members had discovered that the most urgent need for reform was in the condition of employment of railway servants:

> Suppose that men wearied out by long journeys and exhausted by fatigue and want of sleep are ordered, on pain of dismissal, to undertake immediately fresh duties for which they are

rendered incapable by previous exhaustion of body and mind.
Would it not then appear little short of miraculous if some
accident did not result? The worn out engine driver nods, and
a hundred lives are in jeopardy; the signalman, dazed by want
of sleep, becomes confused, and in a moment the engines are
pounding up human beings between them. The acute faculties
of the guard are blunted by long unrest, the danger signal
passes unnoticed, the brake does not second the efforts of the
alarmed engine driver, and next morning there is recorded in
the paper another railway accident.[5]

In 1870, a Board of Trade Inspector, Captain Tyler, reported that
accidents 'had been 57% above, and the proportion of passengers
killed to the number of journeys made 200% above, the average of
the five preceding years.'[6] 'He found it "inexcusable" the regular or
periodic employment of signalmen for 18, 25 or even 37 hours at a
stretch.'[7]

On 19 December 1871, a feature writer of the *Daily Telegraph*,
James Greenwood, gave the following account of a guard at Leeds,
who after he had completed 18 hours work, was told to take a train
to London.

The tired and sleepy man went to the superintendent and
asked to be informed how many hours a day he was expected
to work.

'That's our business', was the official answer, 'you've got 24
hours in a day like every other man, and they are all ours if we
want you to work them . . .'.

When Greenwood questioned why the man did not complain
to the General Manager, the guard replied:

'That's been done, sir, and I'll tell you how it has worked. As
soon as the words are out of your mouth: "If you please I have
to complain," you are cut short with the question, "Have you
your clothes with you? . . ." That means your private clothes,
which a man would naturally require if he were called upon to
give up the company's livery on the spot. Well, what can a
poor man do with a hint like that flung at him? He's shut up,
sir, and only too glad to get out of the office with no more
damage than when he entered it.'[8]

A few weeks before Greenwood published his article, a meeting
took place in the People's Hall, Holbeck, Leeds. Delegates from all
grades serving the five railway companies linked to Leeds, met

there on the 26 November, to make the decision to form a railwaymen's union. On 8 December 1871, other railwaymen met at the Lambeth Baths, Westminster Road, London. There was to be great rivalry between the various groups that sprang up at that time, but eventually out of the above meetings the first great national union of railwaymen was formed, the Associated Society of Railway Servants.[9]

That conditions did not improve with the forming of a union, can be judged from the following comment of a North British Railway guard in 1888:

> How about food? There is no stopping for that. It's a case of go as you please. The tea is always hanging on the stove and properly inky it becomes. It would do the directors good to drink some out of a lid. And your education? We have to thank the school and mother wit for that. And the church? Trains don't stop there. . . .
> So the upshot seems to be this; for twenty four to thirty shillings a week you give yourself up body and soul to the public service and a good two-thirds of your life are spent in the guard-van? Yes, it is a common saying that in the winter months a guard never gets the chance of seeing his children. That is the other side of the four percent dividend.[10]

The following year something was to happen which stirred all trade unionists out of their apathy. 'An inconspicuous report tucked away at the foot of a column of *The Times*, 16 August 1889, told of 2,500 London dockers who had come out on strike the previous day for a minimum rate of pay of 6d an hour and the guarantee of four hours work per day. Before the successful conclusion of the dispute on September 15th, nearly 100,000 disgracefully 'paid, impoverished men had joined the original strikers.'[11] These 'despised undernourished mortals' also showed that they were capable of distributing 'with impeccable honesty' the sum of '£51,000 contributed by sympathizers, and of organizing the daily feeding of the 250,000 belonging to the families directly effected by the strike.'[12]

The railwaymen realized that if the dockers, who were even worse paid than the poorest of their members, could gain substantial improvements, why should not the porters, guards, signalmen and others enter the fight for more tolerable conditions of employment?[13] Railwaymen flocked to join the A.S.R.S. and

1890 was a year of seventeen railway strikes involving some 12,000 men.[14] On the North Eastern Railway, 'about 2,000 men handed in their notice' when the A.S.R.S. Northern District's wages and hours demands were not agreed to by the directors. A six day guaranteed week and a two shilling a week increase for platelayers resulted without a strike.

The A.S.R.S. had changed its character. In the first seventeen years of its existence it had been a trade union of a friendly society type.[15] Its General Secretary, E. Harford, in his report to the October 1890 A.G.M. said:

> We have now, while still adhering to our old principles, adopted methods which are associated with robust and even aggressive trade unionism. . . .[16]

The union continued its fight to improve safety on the railways, and in 1900 the Railway Employment (Prevention of Accidents) Act was passed. That its recommendations, too detailed to enter into here, were not carried out is seen by the fact that the Parliamentary Labour Party on 12 February 1914, moved an amendment to the King's Speech, calling attention to the high accident rate in mines and railways.[17] Also before 1914 only signalmen in busy boxes, shunters employed in busy yards and some locomotivemen employed on main line routes, worked less than sixty hours a week in a normal working week.[18] Just after the 1900 Act was passed (Prevention of Accidents), Richard Bell, General Secretary of the A.S.R.S. was in the House of Commons as the new member for Derby, and representative of the newly formed Labour Representation Committee. He was the first railwayman to enter the House; the only other L.R.C. candidate elected was a miner, Keir Hardie. Hardie had previously been Independent Labour Party member for West Ham (1892 together with John Burns for Battersea, and J. Havelock Wilson, the leader of the then militant Sailors' and Firemen's Union, for Middlesborough), but lost his seat in the 1895 election. Bell, Burns and Wilson all moved rapidly to the right, only Hardie remained in the Labour ranks.[19]

Despite Bell's defection from the Labour movement, his union played a greater part than any other trade union in the formation of the Labour Party. Two events in legal history, the Taff Vale and Osborne Judgements, not only served greatly to strengthen the foundations laid by the A.S.R.S., but after the General Strike of 1926 provided means of attacking the movement.[20] It was the

A.S.R.S. who sponsored a resolution at the Plymouth T.U.C. of 1899 which led to the setting up of the L.R.C.[21]

The men working for the Taff Vale Railway company in South Wales came out on strike on 19 August 1900 in favour of a two shillings a week rise for signalmen, and an half penny an hour increase for brakesmen, shunters and guards, besides the reinstatement of a signalman who had refused to be moved sixteen miles from his home. The General Manager inserted advertisements for men in a large number of newspapers. His main source of supply of non-union labour came from the company's two guinea a year membership subscription to William Collinsons' National Free Labour Association in London. Some of the blacklegs were roughly handled by the union pickets, but a much larger number were persuaded to return home by the offer of free meals, beer, and their return ticket paid by the A.S.R.S. The Society turned the tables on the strike-breakers by using management methods. The Taff Vale company, however, sent letters to all strikers who occupied company owned cottages ordering them to vacate their homes forthwith. The evictions were carried out. A settlement of the dispute of sorts was eventually reached by Mr Bell on 30 August, when the company agreed to take back all the strikers within one month, and the Board of Trade were to decide the signalman's fate. The Taff Vale General Manager, Mr Beasley, was granted an injunction against the union officials, (and the union), by Mr Justice Farrell. The outcome was that the Taff Vale Case cost the A.S.R.S. £42,000, and made the whole legal position of trade unions uncertain. Whilst striking was still legal, almost all forms of picketing, without which strikes are necessarily ineffectual, were not. Within a fortnight of the judgement, Ramsey MacDonald, secretary of the L.R.C., sent a circular to the trade unions in which he claimed: 'The recent decision. . . should convince the unions that a Labour Party in Parliament is an immediate necessity.' Trade unions quickly responded, and many affiliated. A notable exception was the M.F.G.B.[22]

The Taff Vale case had rallied trade unionists to the L.R.C. and in the General Election of 1906 the Labour Party, which is what the L.R.C. became, returned 29 successful candidates. Keir Hardie produced the Trades Disputes Bill that same year which to everyone's surprise gained support, not only from Liberals, but from many Conservatives. The new Bill fully legalized peaceful picketing and declared that inducing a breach of contract was not action-

able if done in pursuance of a trade dispute. The union's funds
were to be fully protected. The Taff Vale judgement had been
reversed.[23]

In 1902 the A.S.R.S. had agreed, by ballot, that each member
should pay a levy of one penny to support the L.R.C. candidates.
In 1905, because the legality of this had been questioned by a
branch secretary, Walter Victor Osborne, the Society decided to
seek legal advice. The advisors assured them that all was in order,
so a second ballot was taken later in the year to include in the
Society's rules provisions to raise a compulsory Parliamentary levy
of three pence per quarter for each member. 81% of the members
who took part in the ballot voted in favour of the compulsory levy.
Had not this money helped to bring about the remarkable success
at the polls in 1906, Osborne's complaints would perhaps have
never been heard of again. The right-wing press however, became
alarmed. The *Daily Mail* noted how:

> . . . these working men by the simple device of collecting one
> penny per month per man from their trade unions, had placed
> themselves on so firm a financial basis that they are able to
> meet the representatives of capital on even grounds at the
> polls. . . . Their present success will be found to prove the
> beginning of a movement that will require much watching by
> capitalists of all conditions.

The *Daily Express* conducted a sustained campaign to protect
'honest trade unionists' who were standing up to the 'pernicious
doctrines of socialists'. It warned its readers of the 'Fraud of
Socialism'.

Greatly encouraged by such support, Osborne took out a writ
against the Society to test the validity of the compulsory Parliamentary levy. Osborne's action failed and he had to pay costs (22
July 1908). Later that same summer the Miners' Federation decided
to affiliate to the Labour party, increasing its funds. This action
appears to have spurred Osborne on to appeal against the court's
previous decision. Judgement this time was given against the
Society, who immediately appealed to the House of Lords. It was
not until 21 December 1909, that the five law lords published their
verdict and unanimously dismissed the appeal made by the
A.S.R.S.

The Times could not conceal its delight, and commented that,
coming as it did on the eve of a General Election the decision

would be 'peculiarly inopportune' to those who would now have to look to voluntary subscriptions instead of 'forced exactions'.[24] *Punch* also joined the rest of the press in attempting to influence voters against the Socialists.

'Forced Fellowship' cartoon by Bernard Partridge

Suspicious-looking party: Any objection to my company, Guv'nor? I', agoin' your way — (*aside*) and further.

Despite the decision of the House of Lords, and the anti-socialist propaganda in the press, the Labour Party won 40 seats at the General Election of 1910. With funds rapidly shrinking, the new party had to face another election in December that year, and gained only two seats.

The Liberals, who now depended on Labour support to hold a majority in the House, were pressed to reverse the Osborne judgement. In 1906 they may have been scared of the new party, but by 1911 they thought they had taken its measure, and consequently did nothing to help their allies against the Conservatives. Ramsey Macdonald, now the leader of the Labour Party, knew that his party had no prospects of becoming a government, and decided that their easiest course was to keep the Liberals in power at any rate till Home Rule for Ireland had been achieved, and a new Trade Union Bill passed. To some these arguments seemed convincing, but to the new militant trade unionists and many of the rank and file party workers it appeared as if the Labour Party had merged with the Liberals, losing not only its independence but its principles. This was at least a powerful contributory cause of the shifting of working-class activity from politics to industrial action. We shall see that a similar situation occurred in 1926, and the men who laid the base of this new militancy were active in the General Strike of that year. Before we examine this new movement and the men involved, we must continue following the course of events after the second General Election of 1910.

The Cambrian Combine strike of the miners was discussed in the previous chapter. Whilst that strike was in progress the National Sailors' and Firemen's Union put forward a National Programme, demanding the formation of a National Conciliation Board, the granting of a national wage scale and a minimum wage, and a number of other concessions. Later that same year, Ben Tillett, secretary of the Docker's Union and his old colleague, Tom Mann, set to work to organize a National Transport Workers' Federation. This organization included all types of transport workers except railwaymen. The railwaymen, discontented with the working of the Conciliation Scheme of 1907 had reached breaking point in 1911. In June of that year Tom Mann's Transport Worker's Federation in conjunction with the seamen who came out on strike first, took all England by surprise with the solidarity of the men involved. 'The achievement of the underpaid dockers [who won substantial concessions] in defeating the powerful employers' federation and in refusing to be cowed by the dispatch by Mr Winston Churchill of two warships and 7,000 troops to the Merseyside was an "eye-opener" to the thousands of railwaymen employed in the area.'[25]

On 5 August goods porters employed by the Lancashire and Yorkshire Railway at Liverpool struck when their demands for a rise in wages and a reduction of hours were refused. Within three days 2,500 railwaymen were out in the city; 'the men marched from one station to another calling out groups of men as they proceeded.'[26] The strike then rapidly spread to London, Bristol, Sheffield, Birmingham, Cardiff and Glasgow — to mention only some of the places affected — and as yet there had been no union recognition of the strike. It was, in fact, 'a soldiers battle with 50,000 men, or about a quarter of those ultimately involved, prematurely engaging the enemy before the General Staff took over control.'[27]

On 15 August the Executive Committees of the A.S.R.S., A.S.L.E.F., the General Railway Workers Union and the Union of Pointsmen's and Signalmen's Society, met to consider what action should be taken. They reached the unanimous agreement to a resolution which gave the railway companies twenty-four hours in which to decide 'whether they were prepared immediately to meet the representatives of the unions to negotiate the basis of a settlement.'[28]

On the 16 August, the President of the Board of Trade met first the managers of the main line railway companies, and later that day the union representatives. After the meeting Sir Guy Granet, General Manager of the Midland Railway, revealed that:

> The Government at our conference today have undertaken to put at the service of the railway companies every available soldier in the country.
> In this dispute the Government and the railway companies are necessarily working together . . . we have got to stand firm, and if the men wish it, there will be a fight to the finish. The companies are prepared even in the event of a general strike to give an effective, if restricted, service.[29]

The workers were offered by the Prime Minister, Mr Asquith, a Royal Commission to look into their grievances. When the men's leaders indicated that they did not consider the proposal for a Royal Commission adequate the Prime Minister murmured 'Then your blood be on your own head' and the meeting broke up.[30]

After informing the Prime Minister formally of their decision to revert to their previous position, the following telegram was sent to nearly 2,000 centres: 'Your liberty is at stake. All railwaymen must strike at once. The loyalty of each means victory for all. (Signed) Williams, Fox, Lowth, Chorlton.' The fact that the telegram was signed by the general secretaries of all four unions must have raised the moral of the strikers.[31]

The magnificent response to the telegram is all the more remarkable in view of the many inducements offered to those who were prepared to stay at work. The Managing Director of the London Underground Electric Railway circularized officials, 'Please inform staff that men remaining loyal throughout will receive double pay.' Similar offers were made by the managements of the Central London and Taff Vale Railways, while on the Midland a bonus of 50% of wages was offered. Free beer was plentiful, for the 'right types' of railwaymen only.[32]

From 17 to 19 August large areas of the country were placed under martial law. 58,000 troops were mobilized for disposal in the areas affected by the strike. Despite strike committee manifestoes disclaiming any connection with rowdyism and violence, some occurred, which the unions were quick to point out as the work of 'rowdy youths to be found in any big city' and called upon 'all who wished well to the men to refrain from all violence themselves and to check it on the part of others.'[33] From the evidence Mr Bagwell has collected it appears as if in most cases the local police were able to control any disturbances. It was the arrival of troops with fixed bayonets which aroused the people's anger. When troops arrived in Llanelly the crowd threw stones at them. 'The soldiers, retaliating, killed two persons.'[34]

It is difficult to escape the conclusion that the ostentatious placing of sentries with fixed bayonets at the entrances to the main line termini and the flamboyant establishment of an army signalling station on the Golden Gallery of St. Paul's Cathedral was intended rather to impress the strikers with the odds against them and to cow them into surrender, than to protect those who wished to continue at work.[35]

'As against these blandishments all that the union leaders could offer was strike pay at the rate of ten shillings a week to members of the four unions participating, a gratuitous allowance of six shillings to non-union members who came out, and the distinct possibility — if previous experience was anything to go by — of failure to get reinstatement after it was all over. Nevertheless an estimated 200,000 came out on strike.'[36] Miners in Dowlais and Nottingham came out in support of the railwaymen, and many others were thrown out of work because there was no movement of coal. 'At this time motor vehicles could form no substitute for the railways since there were but 120,000 of all kinds in the country.'[37]

The strikers who had shown such solidarity against tremendous odds expected something as a result of their struggle against the employers, police and armed troops. Their leaders did, for the first time in history, participate in round table discussions with the spokesmen of the railway managers as a whole. They also obtained a promise that the strikers would be reinstated without suffering any penalties. As to wages and hours of work the union leaders accepted that the Conciliation Boards would consider the men's complaints, without delay. In addition a special Commission of Inquiry was to report its findings much quicker than was usually the case. The workers were told by their leaders that 'before many weeks were over railway workers would have won a charter long enjoyed by every other class of the community.'[38]

Such 'pie in the sky' did not fool thousands of the men who had risked their livelihood. At a meeting of 3,000 railwaymen in Manchester only six hands were raised in favour of acceptance. At Newcastle-upon-Tyne it was resolved that there should be no return to work until the men had gained an eight-hour day and an advance of two shillings a week.[39] In London however 20,000 railwaymen were influenced by the General Secretary of the A.S.R.S., Mr J.E. Williams, and his assistant secretary, J.H. Thomas. Mr Thomas was confident that the dispute would 'sweep out of existence all the petty tyranny'.[40] By Monday, 21 August practically everyone, except on the North Eastern, was almost back to normal.

On October 20 the Commission presented their report. J.H. Thomas found it 'bitterly disappointing', while C.T. Cramp declared that it was 'a bitter farce'. The union executives eventually decided to hold a ballot to decide whether they were prepared to accept the findings of the Commission, or whether they were prepared to strike in favour of recognition of the trade unions and a programme for all railwaymen to be agreed upon by the members of the union executives.

Whilst the ballot was in progress the railway directors prepared

to involve the country in another national railway strike. A
volunteer police force was organized, whose members were to be
available like light infantry to serve anywhere in the country.
Before the result of the ballot was due the representatives of the
companies and of the men met to discuss the findings and recommendations of the Royal Commission. This was only after much
pressure was brought to bear on the employers in the House of
Commons. The outcome was that the Central Conciliation Boards
were to be abolished, and the main work of conciliation was placed
in the hands of Sectional Boards, the final say in the event of disagreement being with the Chairman-Arbitrator, appointed by the
Board of Trade. This 'accentuated grade consciousness which was
inimical to the interests of railwaymen as a whole as it enabled the
companies to pick and choose and pit the members of one grade
against another. It tended to give a new lease of life to sectional
unionism. It was a tragedy that this happened in the very year of
the greatest triumph of united trade-union action by the
railwaymen.'[41]

The main outcome of the confrontation between the worker's
representatives and the employers was the fact that the latter had
accepted that the unions existed and had to be negotiated with. In
addition the railwaymen did obtain an average increase in wages
from 25s 9d (1910) to 27s 4½d (1912), and other minor concessions.
On the other hand most railwaymen continued under the burden
of the 60-hour week.[42] Four workers had lost their lives, and
hundreds had felt the blows of the policeman's truncheon and
rolled cape. The two deaths at Llanelly, were followed with the
killing of two men by soldiers of the 18th Hussars in Great Homer
Street, Liverpool. Sunday 13 August is known as Bloody Sunday
to this day by older workers who saw what happened outside the
St. Georges Hall at Liverpool in 1911. The persuasive tongue of
Tom Mann had managed to unite even Orangemen and Catholics
in support of the dockers, railwaymen and seamen then on strike.
Some 40,000 men, women and children were assembled at Lime
Street, when three youths were pushed from the window ledge of
an hotel by the police. Foot police then began indiscriminately to
attack the crowd with their truncheons. These were followed by
mounted police. The *Manchester Guardian* commented: 'It was a
display of violence that horrified those who saw it.' Bessie
Bradock M.P. was there on Bloody Sunday, and saw starving
women knocked about. She was only 12 years old at the time, but

nothing 'short of the end of the world' could erase such memories.[43] At Rotherhithe ten months later complaints were made against the police for the way they attacked innocent people during a second transport workers strike. In the Report of the inquiry which followed (see appendices) the reader will discover that in no incident where ample evidence was provided did any of the police admit to using unnecessary force.[44] An average increase in wages of 1s 7½d a week for railwaymen was no victory for the workers. Members of the Transport Workers' Federation won an extra two pence an hour to the sixpence conceded in the great dock strike of 1889 as a result of their strike in 1911. The 1912 strike, despite incidents like Rotherhithe, was a failure. When the London Dockers struck, the Federation called a national strike, but there was little response. Lord Davenport, chairman of the newly formed Port of London Authority, refused to attend a conference of the parties involved which was called by the Board of Trade.

The men of 1926 would have vivid memories of some of the times just outlined in this chapter, and unless we have some knowledge of what they lived through, we can not hope to understand the General Strike of 1926.

Notes to Chapter 4

1. Cole, G.D.H. and Postgate, R: *The Common People.* pp. 295 and 296.
2. Bagwell, Philip, S: *The Railwaymen*, London, 1963. p.29.
3. Bagwell, P.S. *Ibid.* p.26.
4. Bagwell, P.S. *Ibid.* p.36.
5. Bagwell, P.S. *Ibid.* pp. 36 and 37.
6. Bagwell, P.S. *Ibid.* p.48.
7. Bagwell, P.S. *Ibid.* p.48.
8. Bagwell, P.S. *Ibid.* p.50.
9. Bagwell, P.S. *Ibid.* p.52 to 54.
10. Bagwell, P.S. *Ibid.* p.128.
11. Bagwell, P.S. *Ibid.* pp.128 and 129.
12. Bagwell, P.S. *Ibid.* pp.128 and 129.
13. Bagwell, P.S. *Ibid.* pp.128 and 129.
14. Bagwell, P.S. *Ibid.* p.133.
15. Bagwell, P.S. *Ibid.* p.149.
16. Bagwell, P.S. *Ibid.* p.149.
17. Bagwell, P.S. *Ibid.* p.110.
18. Bagwell, P.S. *Ibid.* p.173.

19. Cole, G.D.H.: *A Short History of the British Working Class Movement, 1789-1947*, London, 1960. pp. 247 to 249
20. Cole, G.D.H.: *Ibid* pp. 305 and 423.
21. Bagwell, P.S.: *Op.Cit.* p.199
22. Bagwell, P.S.: *Ibid.* Chapter 8.
23. Bagwell, P.S.: *Ibid.* Chapter 9.
24. Bagwell, P.S.: *Ibid.* Chapter 9.
25. Bagwell, P.S.: *Ibid.* p.290
26. Bagwell, P.S.: *Ibid.* p.290.
27. Bagwell, P.S.: *Ibid.* p.291.
28. Bagwell, P.S.: *Ibid.* p.291.
29. Bagwell, P.S.: *Ibid.* p.292.
30. Bagwell, P.S.: *Ibid.* p.293.
31. Bagwell, P.S.: *Ibid.* pp.293 and 294.
32. Bagwell, P.S.: *Ibid.* pp.295.
33. Bagwell, P.S.: *Ibid.* pp.295 and 296.
34. Bagwell, P.S.: *Ibid.* pp.295 and 296.
35. Bagwell, P.S.: *Ibid.* pp.295 and 296.
36. Bagwell, P.S.: *Ibid.* p. 296.
37. Bagwell, P.S.: *Ibid.* p.298.
38. Bagwell, P.S.: *Ibid.* p.299.
39. Bagwell, P.S.: *Ibid.* p.299.
40. Bagwell, P.S.: *Ibid.* p.299.
41. Bagwell, P.S.: *Ibid.* p.303.
42. Bagwell, P.S.: *Ibid.* p.305.
43. Toole, Millie: *Bessie Bradock M.P.*, London, 1967.
44. *Report by Mr Chester Jones on Certain Disturbances at Rotherhithe on June 11th 1912, And Complaints Against the Conduct of the Police in Connection Therewith.* H.M.S.O. 1912. For full report see appendices.

Chapter 5

They did not Create the Unrest; They were Only Its would-be Interpreters and Leaders.

There is little doubt that the years 1906 to 1909 were rich in measures for social reform, and any good text book will supply a list of the Acts which the Liberal government with Labour support, pushed through Parliament. Yet there was more industrial unrest after these Acts became law than in all the previous 68 years since the Chartist Riots of 1842. It would take many volumes to detail all the reasons why this was so. Some reasons have already been presented on the previous pages, and more will be given here and in other chapters.

The social causes of the 1926 General Strike, the real fundamental causes, are dealt with in this chapter. The seeds of unrest were planted in the minds of the workers by the incapability of the capitalist system to recognize the producers of wealth as human beings. The growth of large-scale production, the formation of trusts and monopolies, the predominance assumed by banking and finance, the action and reaction of overseas investment, had all affected the British Empire and had begun to disturb the relations of the various classes and races within it. Faced by the growth of trusts and employers organizations, the trade unions were compelled to resort to ever wider mass formations and to defensive activities on a national scale — defensive because they were called forth in response to the attack made on the livelihood of the working class by the ever rising cost of living. The formation of the National Transport Workers Federation in 1910, was followed by the fusion of three railway unions in 1913 in order to make the National Union of Railwaymen. What followed then is best told in the words of Robert Smillie, the miners' President:

> One definite concrete result of the industrial unrest of recent years is the formation of the Triple Alliance proposed at a conference of the Miners' Federation of Great Britain, the

National Union of Railwaymen and the National Transport
Workers' Federation, held on 23 April 1914. The idea of such
a conference was first brought into prominence at the Miners'
Annual Conference in 1913, when a resolution was passed . . .
That the Executive Committee of the Miners' Federation be
requested to approach the Executive Committees of other big
Trade Unions with a view to co-operative action in support of
each other's demands. (9 October, 1913.)[1]

Trade union membership almost doubled between 1906 and the
outbreak of the first World War.[2] The Co-operative Movement also
made rapid, though less sensational advances. The idea of independent working class political action also captured the imaginations of many young men of those days. Some, notably the
followers of Marx, preached that capitalism was in the death throes
and only required a push to send it to its grave. The facts and
figures however show that 'the last years of the nineteenth century
and the first thirteen years of the twentieth, despite the continued
alteration of relatively good and bad times, were on the whole a
period of astonishingly rapid advance.'[3] To those who 'looked
below the surface the situation was not so reassuring as trade
statistics made it appear. The British producer was, indeed, competing successfully with his newer rival (i.e. Germany) and was to
some extent increasing his trade because of the growth of theirs.
But, because of competition, he was trading on a narrower margin,
and was less willing to incur higher wage costs which might
hamper him in his competition with the foreigner. In the period of
falling prices, the workers had done well as long as they could keep
money wages relatively stable;'[4] but in the period between 1906
and 1913 the workers needed wage advances to compensate them
for rising prices — and as we have seen in chapters 3 and 4,
advances were not easy to get.

Once the workers began to unite and act on a national scale, a
new factor was introduced. The State, under the 1911 Asquith
Liberal Government, participated directly in the railway strike.
The State claimed to be acting solely on behalf of the community,
but none the less the part it played in that strike was an effective
aid to the railway companies and a blow to the strikers. From this
time onwards it was clear that the sort of encounter that took place
was bound to be repeated on an ever increasing scale.

The war and its aftermath again brought about economic

changes which necessitated greater centralization in trade union affairs. Skilled engineers formed the Amalgamated Engineering Union, nearly all the societies of vehicle and waterside workers came together in the Transport and General Workers' Union, the old Gas Workers' Union became the National Union of General and Municipal Workers, embodying a large number of societies of less skilled and miscellaneous workers, and so on. After 1920 a period of severe depression set in, and just before the General Strike trade union membership fell from 8,300,000 to 5,250,000.

What caused the strikes of 1910 and the following years were really bread-and-butter reasons. 'The percentage of Trade Unionists out of work rose from under four per cent in 1906 and 1907 to nearly eight per cent in 1908 and 1909. Wage rates fell back by an average of two per cent, to a level barely higher than that of 1906, though in the meantime the cost of living had risen by a further six per cent.[5]

In the industrial areas of the North of England, South Wales, and Scotland, the workers lived in conditions which would not be tolerated today. Conditions in Bradford and Leeds then were typical of most industrial cities. Fred Jowett, who had been First Commissioner of Works in the 1924 Labour Government, later described them:

> The houses were built in long streets, intersected by passages, with privy middens for each block of houses in the backyards. All these houses were built back to back and therefore they had no through draught for ventilation. Only where an intersecting passage leading to a backyard enabled an extra bedroom to be built over the passage were there two bedroomed houses. Privymiddens, which in those days were the common form of sanitary provision for all sorts of refuse, including human excreta, are a forgotten monstrosity in our days. (1943) The best arranged of them served four households, two families living in houses fronting to the street, and two facing (in some cases actually adjoining) the privy middens in the backyard. All four families used the same ashpit, the large central part of the structure which had two privies at each end of it. In the front wall of the ashpit was a wooden door about two feet square, through which the accumulated refuse and excreta of four households were thrown into the yard when the middens were emptied. There were many larger privy middens serving eight households.

The contractor employed 'night soil men', as they were called,
who clambered through the ash pit doors, and pitched out the
refuse into the backyard, to be reshovelled into carts later.
As the carts rumbled into the yards and the reshovelling proceeded, the noise kept the occupants awake for hours, and the
stench increased the nuisance. Next day there was the swilling
to be done, often necessary after working hours: tired women
scrubbing their respective shares of the paved yard, with
water carried from the house taps in bucketfuls by husband or
grown up son or daughter, or by neighbours for each other.
These insanitary conditions and low wages made life difficult
for working class parents with young children. They looked
forward expectantly to their children reaching working age,
for the small weekly additions to the family income which
they would bring into the home. Working class families were
much larger than they are today, although more children died
in infancy and in their early years. Whilst children were under
working age, food and clothing was insufficient. Yet going to
work too early in life stunted growth, weakened constitutions
and therefore was a heavy price to pay for the few extra
shillings a week. . . . children grew up knock-kneed and bow-
legged in large numbers, probably due to untreated rickets in
childhood — a disease so common at one time in this country
that it was often referred to abroad as 'English disease'.[6]

Of course the above description was not of the worst housing
conditions, nor the very best. In 1924 Jowett visited Chester-Le-
Street, a mining area in Durham, and was particularly interested
because it was where a thousand of the six thousand war-time
structures were still occupied which he had insisted should be put
into healthy, habitable conditions when he was Minister of Works.
'They were one-storey wooden dwellings' he wrote, 'intersected by
unpaved streets, A real shanty town.'[7]

Until the first Town Planning Act of 1909, which gave the local
authority power to plan areas of unbuilt land, there was no official
control over the siting of houses. In Leeds for example, some
12,000 houses of the type described by Jowett in Bradford, were
built just prior to the Act. The photograph opposite shows a group
of late Victorian back-to-backs, built in a block of eight with yard
privies, later w.c.'s to conform with bye-laws. These houses,
unlike the ones Jowett described, have attics and cellars. It was

estimated in 1948 that Leeds still possessed 90,000 houses, out of a total of about 154,000, which were substandard and fit only for demolition: the 90,000 included 56,000 back-to-back houses of which about 16,000 were pre-1844.[8]

Group of eight late Victorian back-to-backs with yard privies in Leeds (taken from *Leeds and Its Regions*)

In Scotland conditions were much worse than in England. In evidence presented to the Sankey Commission of 1919 it was stated that amongst miners' houses in the Upper Ward of Lanarkshire, 665 shared common middens, 57 had private middens, 103 had pail closets, 265 had w.c.'s, and 75 were without any toilet facilities. In addition to this 809 of these houses were without sinks. Amongst a wealth of evidence of insanitary conditions for Scottish miners was also the following:

> Armadale (Linlithgow) — Population, 4627; overcrowded 77.5%, with 27.1% living in houses of one room. One-roomed house dimensions — 15 feet by 14 feet by 9 feet, from which must be deducted 12 feet by 4 feet by 9 feet for two recess

beds. It is in such houses that the coals are stored under the
bed. (Six people per room was the average in this area).[9]

Statistics however tend to lose sight of the human beings involved.
The following account of just one English family after the First
World war is typical of thousands:

> One family which I visited lived in an odd little house con-
> sisting of one bedroom, one ground floor room, and a base-
> ment kitchen opening into a high-walled yard, more like a tank
> than a yard, and from which almost all light was obscured by
> surrounding buildings which pressed right up against it. In
> these quarters lived a respectable hard-working man, a kind,
> good hard working mother and seven children. There had
> been nine, but the eldest boy had been killed in the war (Oh,
> he was a good lad to me, sighed the mother) and the eldest
> girl, aged seventeen, was out in service.
> In the bedroom the bugs were crawling on the walls and
> dropping on to the beds. 'We have tried everything' our
> hostess explained, 'but as fast as we get 'em down, they come
> in fresh from houses on either side.'
> Father, mother and two youngest children slept in this room.
> Three girls slept in the ground floor room and the two boys in
> the kitchen. The mother took in washing. It was a hot June
> day when we visited her, and the kitchen was an inferno of
> heat, and thick with steam. . . . The 'Sanitary Lady' told me
> that the children of this family were sickly, but admirably
> brought up, and that every week on her afternoon out the
> eldest girl came to lend a hand with the ironing and to bring a
> few sweets for the little ones.[10]

The above account refers to post-war conditions, they could have
been written about pre-war Britain of either the 1914 or the 1939
war.

It has already been mentioned that the period of the first 13
years of the 20th century was a period of astonishingly rapid
advance for the capitalist. Profits soared. The pace of accumulation
of capital out of profits became swift beyond all precedent. But for
the most part the new capital did not flow into British industry. It
was invested to an increasing extent abroad, in the British
Dominions or in foreign countries — where even higher profits
than at home could be secured by the opening up of new areas or
the exploitation of cheap labour. Great Britain was in fact fast

equipping less developed countries with instruments of production which would enable their cheaper labour to be used in competition with that of the British workers. This simultaneously put up the price of capital, i.e. the rate of interest, in Great Britain, and caused British exporters to cut their prices in order to compete with the products of the newer countries. But, when prices had to be cut in the face of rising interest rates, there was only one resource left. Wage costs had to come down.

This is the economic explanation of the curious phenomenon of falling real wages side by side with rapidly advancing trade and capitalist prosperity. The workmen, even with the aid of their Trade Unions, could not meet their employers on equal terms, because they were face to face with a capitalism that could invoke against them the unorganized labour and the unexploited resources of the less developed parts of the world.[11]

Industrial action between 1910 and 1913 did gain something for the workers. It restored real wages at least to where they were in 1906, though they were still well below the standards of 1900. Even then, in 1914 'when the poverty line for a man, his wife and three children was set at about 24s a week, nearly a quarter of all the male wage earners in the country were receiving less than 25s a week.'[12]

Before the 1914-1918 war, education for the working class was limited by the needs of industry, (education in organized schools that is). An act of 1880 required that no child between the ages of ten and thirteen should be employed without a certificate showing that he had passed through the minimum standards in school or put in a certain amount of attendance; but this only enforced a school leaving age of 10. Not until 1893 was the age raised to 11, and in 1899 to 12. In 1901 School Boards were permitted to raise the age of attendance from 13 to 14, but, by statute, some provision had to be made for either total or partial exemption below 14. With so many people living near or below the poverty line thousands of children were sent out to work part time, the worst industry being that of the cotton mills in Lancashire. Apart from textile workers the whole labour movement spoke out against a system that was cruel and unjust to the children and wasteful both morally and financially, and a standing blot upon our professed civilization. But the workers had to wait until 1920 before the school leaving age was raised to 14. The Federation of British Industries, with their powerful spokesmen in the House of

Commons were able to hold back the educational advance. This employer's organization issued a memorandum in 1918 which argued openly for a strictly stratified system of education, as well as for a restrictive educational policy. R.H. Tawney wrote in a contemporary article that it expressed the view that the aim of education 'is to reflect, to defend, and to perpetuate the division of mankind into masters and servants . . . . The Bourbons of industry who drafted it have learned nothing and forgotten nothing. Europe is in ruins; and out of the sea of blood and tears the Federation of British Industries emerges jaunty and unabashed, clamouring that whatever else is shaken, the vested interest of employers in the labour of children of fourteen must not be disturbed by so much as eight hours per week.'[13] This class structure of society was not to be disturbed by Education Acts which enforced secondary education later.[14] The schools were places where, in the main, children were indoctrinated to believe that the capitalist system and the British Empire must be protected at all costs. *The Times* 22 May 1926, reporting on the Empire Celebrations of the previous day, gave the following account of a typical 'indoctrination' in a London school:

> The Lord Mayor unfurled the Union Jack and the children saluted the flag and gave three cheers for the King. . . . The Lord Mayor reminded the children of the extent and influence of the British Empire, of which they were the future citizens and exhorted them to remain loyal and patriotic members of the Empire. It was a delight at any time, he said, to take part in a demonstration of that kind, but after the stirring and anxious days of the past fortnight, they were intensely proud of the patriotism and discipline and the regard for law and order exhibited throughout the country during that unfortunate period. He impressed on the children the value of education and urged them to make themselves fully aquainted with what the words 'British Empire' meant.

In view of the above example, which is representative of the period under discussion, it is not surprising that at the Labour Party conference of 1926 the Teachers Labour League should submit a resolution (which was passed unanimously), 'condemning the widespread reactionary and imperialist teaching in schools, particularly with regard to Empire Day celebrations and the use of history and other text-books with an anti-working class bias.'[15]

The Socialist Sunday Schools started in 1892, whose aim was to bring children to an understanding of the meaning of socialism, as well as of the structure and nature of the existing society. By 1910 about 100 schools were in existence attended by some 5,000 children — there are still a few left today — and many of these 5,000 probably attended classes organized by the W.E.A. and the N.C.L.C., in adult life.[16]

The Workers' Educational Association came into being in 1903, and saw education as a means of transforming the individual, but not society. Tawney who so attacked the F.B.I. in 1918, said in 1914 of those who attended W.E.A. classes:

> To these miners and weavers and engineers who pursue knowledge with the passion born of difficulties, knowledge can never be a means, but only an end; for what have they to gain from it save knowledge itself?[17]

The National Council of Labour Colleges came into being in 1920. The Plebs League out of which it sprang was formed in 1909, and published the *Plebs* magazine. The full details need not be entered into here, but by contrast with the W.E.A. the Plebs League and the N.C.L.C. were political organizations with a partisan rather than an impartial approach to education. At the formation of the first Labour College (Central Labour College) in 1909 the aims are clearly set out:

> The Labour College teaches the workmen to look for the causes of social evils and the problems arising therefrom in the material foundations of society; that these causes are in the last analysis economic; that their elimination involves in the first place economic changes of such a character as to lead to the eradication of capitalist economy.[18]

On the 22 November 1916, *The Times* carried an article characterizing South Wales as 'the industrial storm centre of Great Britain,' when the South Wales miners came out on strike that year.

'The causes of disaffection in South Wales,' wrote *The Times*, 'were two-fold.' In the first place 'seething discontent' was promoted by the mining industry itself which was no more than a 'de-humanized, commercial machine for the extraction of gold out of labour'. Second, to the 'fiery temperament' of the Celts, there was added 'a degree of education which would astonish some of their absentee employers. There are scores of men working in the Welsh pits who could pass an examination in Ibsen or Shaw or Swinburne, or could hold their own in an argument on economics or politics with the average member of Parliament.' These men owed their training 'not to the state or the municipalities' but to the educational facilities provided by the I.L.P., the Central Labour College and the Plebs League. 'For years past free evening classes in economics, industrial history, and similar subjects have been held in I.L.P. branch rooms in the various mining centres'; another educational movement, the Central Labour College, was centred in the Rhondda where ex-students took classes and were making special efforts to extend their work throughout the district, 'chiefly by lectures in the workmen's institutes and co-operative society rooms.' The Plebs league aimed to educate the workers by classes in sociology, industrial history and Marxist economics.'Not only do hundreds of miners absorb their teaching,' but others had gone to college and returned to preach what they had learned. Men so educated attended Lodge meetings so that decisions were taken by a handful of extremists; to a large extent the Miners Federation 'has been captured by men of advanced and even revolutionary views.'[19]

Arthur James Cook took three of the N.C.L. classes mentioned in the *Times* article of 1917. Cook was born in 1889 at Wookey in Somerset, and because his father was a soldier he was brought up by his grandparents who were Tory farmers at Cooksby. When Arthur was 12 his father wanted him to become a drummer in the army, but he ran away from home to find work with a farmer near Cheddar. He worked on the farm for three and a half years, during which time he learned much from his Radical employer who lent him books on the speeches of Cobden and Bright. Cook also became a Baptist local preacher, but proved to be too radical for the local squire and the parson, so he left the farm at 16 for South Wales. The coal mines were booming at that time and Arthur became a collier. One day he heard an I.L.P. speaker and was so impressed that he joined the movement. In 1906 he became chairman and secretary of his local union branch, and worked with Noah Ablett on a paper they produced called *The Rhondda Bomb*. The strike of 1910, as we have seen, was defeated but laid the foundations of the success of 1912. Before the strike of that year Cook won a scholarship at the Central Labour College (The M.F.G.B. and the N.U.R. were amongst the first unions to support the college). He left his wife and child in South Wales,

borrowing money to pay his fare to London. He took one useful
precaution. He was living in a company house so he let the rent fall
in arrears, because he calculated that the Colliery Company would
not refuse him work when he came back as they would want him
to be able to pay off his arrears in rent.[20]

About this time some members of the Plebs League, notably
Noah Ablett, published *The Miners' Next Step*. This pamphlet
caused a stir throughout the mines of Great Britain. Its five authors
advocated a minimum wage of eight shillings for a seven hour day,
but also aimed at getting into the hands of the workers the control
and ultimately the ownership of the mines.

Although this pamphlet could not have greatly influenced the
members of the Executive of the M.F.G.B. they did propose about
the time of its publication, a minimum wage of five shillings for
men and two shillings for boys, largely to offset the injustice of the
'abnormal place'. A ballot amongst union members gave a two
thirds majority for a national strike if the owners refused the
proposal. They refused, and the Asquith government immediately
intervened. Some owners accepted the miners' proposals, but those
of South Wales refused. The miner's leaders, after conversations
with the Prime Minister, were led to believe that the government
was going to push through parliament a Bill to enforce the coal-
owners to meet the miner's demands. When it was realized that Mr
Asquith's cabinet did not intend to include any figures in the Bill
the men knew they had been misled. It was one of many such
instances in years to come. On the very day of the first reading of
the Bill, the Attorney General ordered the arrest of Tom Mann, on
a charge under the Incitement to Mutiny Act of 1795. The
Government were aware of Mann's part in the 1911 Cambrian
Combine Strike, (Tonypandy), and when he began to issue 'Don't
Shoot' leaflets in this 1912 dispute they acted quickly.[21] Lord
Robert Cecil complained in the House of Lords that the miners'
strike was no ordinary strike, but 'part of a great conspiracy' and an
attempt to gain 'dictatorial powers over the industries of this
country by a small band of revolutionaries.' In proof of this he
cited the agitation begun eighteen months earlier by Tom Mann,
and the unexampled growth since then in the number and size of
strikes. He perhaps was not aware of the conditions under which
people had to live at that time, although perhaps he had seen
references to *The Miners' Next Step* in the *Morning Post*. If he had
read the full document he would have noticed that it attacked the

old leaders of the M.F.G.B. and urged a complete change. Yet it was these old leaders who had been forced into the position of calling a strike ballot because of the stubbornness of the employers, particularly in South Wales. Most of the coal owners in England had agreed to the miners' demands, so that the strike call was a united action in an attempt to win justice for all. Even the Prime Minister considered 'it is an unselfish demand on the part of the great bulk of the miners.'[22] On 29 March 1912 the National Minimum Wage Act became law. It did not meet the demands of the M.F.G.B. but gave powers to set up District Boards of the employers and the workmen in the districts. This was a 'victory' for the miners in the sense that unity of action had forced the government of the day to produce an Act setting out the basic idea of a minimum wage. Unfortunately the Act was full of loop-holes which the coal-owners were quick to find. A special conference of the M.F.G.B. expressed its strong disatisfaction with the working of the Act on 16 August 1912.[23] It should be pointed out that a ballot was taken by the miners before the strike took place, and before a return to work was called. The Trades Disputes Act, 1906 made it lawful, 'for one or more persons, acting on their own behalf or on behalf of a trade union or of an individual employer or firm in contemplation or furtherance of a trade dispute, to attend at or near a house or place where a person resides or works or carries on business or happens to be, if they so attend for the purpose of peacefully obtaining or communicating information, or of peacefully persuading any person to work or abstain from working.' Mr Winston Churchill, who had used the bayonet and the battleship to overawe the strikers of August 1911, was moved to the admiralty on the 23 October that same year. Tom Mann gave out thousands of 'Don't Shoot' leaflets to the troops whose appeals, especially after four workers had been shot, were justified. They read;

> Men! Comrades! Brothers! You are in the army. So are we. You, are in the army of Destruction. We, are in the Industrial Army of Construction.
> We work at the mine, mill, forge, factory, or dock, etc., producing and transporting all the goods, clothing stuffs, etc., which makes it possible for people to live.
> You are Workingmen's Sons.
> When we go on strike to better Our lot, which is the lot also of Your Fathers, Mothers, Brothers and Sisters, YOU are called

upon by your Officers to MURDER US. Don't do it.

No troops were to be used against the miners when they struck for a minimum wage in 1912, perhaps because Mr Churchill was no longer Home Secretary. Mr Asquith did however take the precaution of arresting Tom Mann on the same day that he introduced the first reading of the Minimum Wages Bill into the House of Commons (19 March 1912).[24]

Tom Mann, Noah Ablett, and Arthur Cook, to mention only three, were leaders of a new movement active before the first world war. They belonged to the Syndicalist movement, the prime mover of this influential organization being Tom Mann. The word 'Syndicalist' is merely a French word for trade unionism. Essentially the trade unions were urged to bring the downfall of capitalism without recourse to a political party. It also advocated the use of the General Strike as a means of overthrowing capitalism. The Anarchist Movement also pressed for a 'Social General Strike' at this time. A pamphlet, written by Arnold Roller and printed in 1912, propounded the theory that 'the General Strike idea puts an efficient and sure remedy in place of the craving for the "Mother of Freedom, Revolution"; in place of the fruitless Social Democratic declamations about evolution in distant futures in which no one dares to believe, which seems to us like veiled ideals, suspended far distant, and which, at one time or another, after a long wait, we are told, will come to us "over the mountains"; a remedy which will remove capitalism and bring freedom and welfare for all.'[25] Add to these ideas those of the Industrial Workers of the World brought to this country also by Mann, which advocated that 'all the toilers (should) come together on the political as well as on the industrial field, and take hold of that which they produce by their labour through an economic organization of the working class, without affiliation with any political party;'[26] and one can understand the growing concern in ruling circles. The concern was not only shown in Parliament. The Trade Union leaders saw these movements as a threat to their leadership and attacked Syndicalism, the Anarchists, and the I.W.W.. Ramsey MacDonald wrote a book against Syndicalism; Philip Snowden, in *The Living Wage*, set out to show the futility of the strike weapon as an instrument of social change.[27] Against such assaults however the *Daily Herald* emerged. First as a printer's strike sheet in 1911, then in 1912 as a daily paper, opening its columns to the revolutionary left. In May 1912 it said of strikes: 'We have considered the matter. We have considered every phase of it and we say: Prepare your organization and then strike. STRIKE AND STRIKE HARD.'[28] The Trades Union Congress then withdrew its support and sponsored a rival *The Daily Citizen*, but this died a natural death in 1914, whilst the *Daily Herald* (under the editorship of George Lansbury until 1926) continued freely to function until 1922, when it was taken over and muzzled by the Trades Union Congress.

It is not surprising then that all this agitation had some effect on people who were suffering from rising food prices, without being able to obtain higher wages. Especially when all around them they could see 'the rich getting the lion's share of the increasing wealth'[29] of the nation. Also as Mr Shackleton, the right honourable member for Clitheroe pointed out in the House of Commons 1906: 'No workman, or any person near the status of a workman, ever found a place on special juries; and whether the action of trade unions was for the purpose of peacefully persuading or communicating information, there was a disposition not in favour of workmen in any trade dispute.' With regard to peaceful picketing he went on to say that the issue was between 'workmen and employers, and the jury to try the question was composed entirely of employers.'[30]

We return for a moment to Arthur Cook, whom we left on a course at the National Labour College, just before the miners' strike of 1912. When this strike broke, Cook returned to Wales, and because he owed the colliery company arrears in rent, was able to get his job back when the strike was over. He immediately started seven classes in economics and industrial history, one of which had an average attendance of 500. As soon as he had paid off his rent the colliery company put him 'on the road.' He found work at other pits but because of his agitation became unemployed several times. When the first World War began in 1914 he, along with many other similar agitators, was accepted back into the pits because of the shortage of labour. Thousands of other miners had volunteered to go to the front. Empire Days and biased history books had played their part, and many young men volunteered for 'national service' leaving their bug infested slums for the rat infested trenches of France. A few, like Arthur Cook, resisted the recruiting campaign launched by the Government with Conservative and official Labour support. Even the *Daily Herald* offered no opposition at first. By the winter of 1914 however the *Daily*

Herald became anti-war, as did the *Labour Leader* (I.L.P.) and the Glasgow *Forward*. It should be pointed out that miners were exempted from conscription when it came in 1916, yet 40% of the

A.J. Cook addressing a crowd at Trafalgar Square in 1926
(Photograph by courtesy of the T.U.C. Library)

miners of military age were absorbed into military service, and by far the greater number left the mines in the early weeks of the war in the Autumn of 1914.

When the Lloyd George Government came into power late in 1916, it proceeded to take over all the remaining vital industries and by 1918 state control of industry had become an almost all-embracing system. The railways and some shipping had been put under state control in 1914, the munitions factories in 1915 and the South Wales coal fields in 1916. Rationing and price fixing followed, which naturally resulted in the rising amount and intensity of organization amongst the employing class. The Federation of British Industries previously mentioned, was founded during the war.[31]

Food naturally became scarce as the war progressed, and prices soared. Throughout the war the unions had to do battle with the employers and the government in order to keep pace with the rising cost of living. Wages did rise, but usually because of the 'War Bonus' which helped to avoid industrial unrest, but could be easily removed when the war finished.[32] Food rationing did not come until 1918.

When the men returned from the war they expected things would be changed; whereas those who had fought on the industrial front were equally determined and continued their fight. The struggle lasted until 1926 when the workers were forced into the General Strike. By that time Arthur Cook was the secretary of the Miners' Federation of Great Britain.

Notes to Chapter 5

1. Arnot, R. Page: *The Miners*, Allen Unwin, 1953. p.174.
2. Cole, G.D.H.: *A Short History of the British Working Class Movement*, Allen & Unwin, 1960. p.484.
3. Cole, G.D.H.: *Ibid*. p.281.
4. Cole, G.D.H.: *Ibid*. p.283.
5. Cole, G.D.H. and Postgate, R.: *The Common People* p.498.
6. Brockway, Fenner: *Socialism over 60 years. The Life of Jowett of Bradford*. London, 1946. pp. 15 and 16.
7. Brockway, Fenner: *Ibid*. p.246.
8. Beresford, M.W. and Jones, G.R.J.: *Leeds and Its Regions*. Leeds, 1967. p.177. Photograph from p.180 (facing).

9. Robertson, John: Chairman of the S.M.W.U. *Scotland's Shame. How the Miners Live and Work.* Glasgow, 1919, (Published on evidence presented to the Sankey Commission in pamphlet form).
10. Laver, James: *Between the Wars.* London, 1961. pp. 18 and 19.
11. Cole, G.D.H. and Postgate, R: *Op. Cit.* pp. 497 to 502
12. Briggs, Asa: *Social Thought and Social Action.* London, 1961. p.51.
13. Simon, Brian: *Education and the Labour Movement*, London, 1965. p.355.
14. Simon, Brian: *Ibid.* pp.362 to 364.
15. *Bradford Pioneer.* Organ of the I.L.P. 27 May 1927. From a report of a speech by H. Stanley Redgrove, B.S.C., A.I.C. p.6.
16. Simon, Brian; *Op. Cit.* pp. 49 and 50.
17. Simon, Brian: *Ibid.* pp.304 and 329.
18. Simon, Brian: *Ibid.* p.330.
19. Simon, Brian: *Ibid.* pp. 334 and 335. (From *Plebs*, Vol. viii, No. 11, December 1916, quoting *The Times*, 22 November 1916).
20. *Socialist Review*, September 1926. Article, 'Who A.J. Cook Is' by John Strachey.
21. Arnot, R. Page: *Op. Cit.* pp. 114 and 115.
22. Arnot, R. Page: *Ibid.* p.98.
23. Arnot, R. Page: *Ibid.* p.121.
24. Arnot, R.Page: *Ibid.* p.115.
25. *The Social Strike.* Arnold Roller. London 1912. (Pamphlet) p.30.
26. Arnot, R. Page: *Op. Cit.* p.113.
27. Cole, G.D.H.: *Op. Cit.* p.326.
28. Cole, G.D.H. and Postgate, R: *Op. Cit.* p.486.
29. Cole, G.D.H. and Postgate, R: *Ibid.* p.497.
30. *Hansard*, 9 November 1906.
31. Cole, G.D.H.: *Op. Cit.* pp.363 to 371.
32. Cole, G.D.H.: *Ibid.* p.354.

Chapter 6

The Great War Ends But The Class War Really Begins

In the previous chapters some attempt has been made to show the conditions under which the working class lived and worked; how they organized together and fought to change these conditions; how also the idea of a general strike was advocated during the times of the Chartists, and revived again just before the first World War. We shall now follow some of the events which forced even moderate trade union leaders into reluctantly calling on the Triple Alliance, forcing the Government to change its mind about reducing railwaymen's wages. Then having proved its possible power as a weapon, we shall see how the Triple Alliance was merely a 'paper alliance'.

In the first months of the war, several mining districts were working short time and unemployment was prevalent. Several coalowners were threatening reductions in wages. In the West Yorkshire coal-field a dispute over the refusal of certain mine-owners to carryout an award under the Minimum Wages Act dragged on for six months. Taken in relation to recruitment from other industries the number of men who joined the forces in 1914 was in itself a terrible commentary on wages and conditions in the mining industry. A quarter of a million had enlisted by August 1915. This outflow of men naturally curtailed coal production, and proposals were put for lowering the age limit for boys,† and the employment of women at the surface. These proposals were resisted by the M.F.G.B. and there is no record of boys below 14 being sent underground, though women were employed on the surface.[1]

The problem of labour shortage became acute in other industries too, and the employers were insisting that Trade Union rules must be abrogated in order to give them full freedom to reorganize the

†Coal Mines Act of 1911 had established the minimum age at 14 years.

workshops in view of war needs, and to employ unskilled workers
in jobs ordinarily reserved for skilled men.

The Committee on Production (set up earlier), in March 1915,
proposed that the Trade Unions should accept both compulsory
arbitration and the abrogation of Trade Union restrictions, on
condition that the Government should pledge itself to the restoration of the status quo at the end of the war. Most of the unions
accepted these terms, but the Miner's Federation refused to be
bound by them. In July, Lloyd George, at the head of the newly-
established Ministry of Munitions, secured the passage of the
Munitions of War Act, 1915, which made compulsory arbitration,
as well as suspension of Trade Union customs, legally binding.[2]

Such actions, and many others, caused the Triple Alliance to
meet in April 1916 and demand from the Government: full restoration of trade union rules and regulations, demobilization by
industry and not by military unit; full maintenance for discharged
members of the armed forces and munition workers. The Prime
Minister gave his pledge that there would be a full restoration of
trade union rules and regulations.[3]

The pledge was imperfectly carried out by the Government. Far
from intervening to obtain the actual restoration of rules, the
Government, after much delay, passed the Restoration of Pre-War
Practices Act which enabled a worker to proceed in the law courts
against any employer who failed to restore the old conditions. Such
a restoration in any case was made obligatory only for one year.[4]

It should also be noted that a Coal Controller heading a new
department of the Board of Trade, controlled the whole distribution and output of coal from the end of February 1917. This
control was to some extent rendered futile through the fact that the
first charge on the industry was the profits of the coal owners.
There was a complex financial arrangement by which the coal
owners were to be guaranteed their profits from a profits pool to
which the Government would contribute three quarters of the
excess profits tax proceeds.[5]

The miners of course were not the only dissatisfied workers,
many other groups were driven to take strike action between 1914
and 1918. The men and women out on the several war fronts
anticipated that the end of the war would bring a happy and far
better society at home. They were, along with those who had
remained at the factory, office, mill and mine, to be very disappointed.

The first shock came with the 'coupon election' instigated by Lloyd George. Only one man in four in the forces cast his vote.[6] As a consequence 338 Conservatives were elected on the 'coupon', and 48 not on it, making a total of 386. 136 Liberals under Lloyd George, and 10 Labour and other supporters made up the 1918 coalition Government. In opposition were 59 Labour members, and 26 Asquith Liberals, besides 16 others. It was a decisive victory for 'the hard faced men who looked as if they had done well out of the war.'[7] The Representation of the Peoples Act of 1918 gave all men over 21 the vote, and with certain property qualifications, women over 30. Before and during the election the press came heavily down on the side of the 'hard faced men'. The Russian Revolution of 1917 had shaken the capitalist world and the most absurd statements were made about the attitude of Labour candidates. Lloyd George declared: 'The Labour Party is being run by the extreme pacifist, Bolshevist group' and attacked it as a class party, a bad thing — 'Look at what has happened in Russia.'[8] People kept looking at 'what happened in Russia' and the hysteria grew until by 1926 it had reached such a fever pitch that even Lloyd George was calling it 'dishonest slosh'.[9]

The Labour Party had polled 22% of the votes cast, but received only about 10% of the members elected. Organized labour, not unnaturally, felt that it had been let down, and again turned to industrial action. Before it did so however, the Government took steps to prepare for a class war.

At the begining of January 1919 there were demonstrations by soldiers against the slowness of demobilization. At Kempton Park the soldiers formed a 'soldiers council' and declared their intention to fraternize with the workmen of the neighbourhood. On 6 and 7 January there were three separate demonstrations near Whitehall and soldiers in lorries carried signs such as: 'We won the war. Give us our tickets'; 'We want civvy suits'; 'Promises are not pie crusts'.[10] It was obvious that the returning workers were not going to stand for any nonsense. Before January was out the Secretary of War, Winston Churchill, acted. A circular was sent in secret by the War Office to the commanding officers of troops stationed in Great Britain. These officers were to send weekly reports, for the information of the Secretary of State, so that the Army Council 'could keep its fingers on the pulse of the troops.' The questions asked leave no doubts about the strike breaking intentions of the author of the circular:

> Will troops in the various areas respond to orders for
> assistance to reserve the public peace?
> Will they assist in strike breaking?

The various station commanders were also requested to provide
information on the following points, in regard to the troops under
their command:

> Whether there is any growth of trade unionism among them.
> The effect outside trade unions have upon them.
> Whether any agitation from internal or external sources is
> affecting them.
> Whether any soldiers' 'Councils' have been formed.
> Whether any demobilization troubles are occurring. . . .

One other question is of especial interest when one considers
Churchill's intervention in Russia later:

> Will they parade for draft overseas, especially to Russia?

Churchill's secret army circular was sent out at the beginning of
January. By the end of that month the call had gone out for a
general strike, initiated by the Clyde Worker's Committee, and
later joined by local trade union leaders. The strike leaders wanted
a 40 hour week because they anticipated widespread unemployment as a result of demobilization. When the strike began
Churchill concentrated troops, with machine guns and tanks, to
surround the city. The class war involving the use of troops against
the civilian working population was to become a common feature of
the next seven years. It is true, as we have seen, that such military
action was not uncommon. From now on however, white collar
workers, the middle class and even the aristocracy were to join the
state military machine against the working class.

The *Daily Herald* somehow obtained a copy of the Churchill
circular and published it in full on 13 May 1919. This caused
questions to be asked in the Commons. Mr Churchill defined what
action was necessary in other than 'ordinary disputes':

> The expression strike breaking, for instance, was bound to
> give offence, and moreover it was not what the military
> authorities meant. Strike breaking means using soldiers or
> sailors to take the place of workmen who are carrying on an
> industrial dispute with their employers, in order to improve
> their wages or conditions of their trade. No one ever thought

of doing that. It would be entirely contrary to the law of the land, and the whole custom and practice of the country. . . . To use soldiers or sailors, kept up at the expense of the tax-payer, to take sides with the employer, in an ordinary trade dispute, to employ them as what are called blacklegs, would be a monstrous invasion of the liberty of the subject. . . . But the case is different where vital services effecting the health, life and safety of large cities or great concentrations of people are concerned. . . . Light, water, electric power, transport, the distribution of food, all these are indispensable to the existence of these mighty cities which cover our land. If any of these commodities or facilities are suddenly cut off, the State must intervene and come to the rescue of the population whose lives are in danger, by every means in its power, including the use of military and naval forces, so as to avoid a general catastrophe.[12]

Tanks stand by in the Glasgow Cattle Market during the 1919 strike (Photograph courtesy of George Outram & Co. Ltd.)

We shall see that 'the liberty of the subject' as defined by Mr Churchill, would be violated on his orders.

The mineworkers too were concerned about the plight of ex-soldiers and on 14 January 1919 put in a claim for 'full maintenance at trade union rates of wages for mineworkers unemployed through demobilization.'[13] At the same time the M.F.G.B. claimed an increase in wages, and a reduction of working hours. The Government offered a shilling per day with the promise of a committee of inquiry. True to their democratic tradition, the union executive held a ballot, urging their members to vote in favour of a stoppage to obtain their demands. The Government, at the expense of the taxpayer, inserted advertisements in most of the newspapers urging the miners to vote against executive decisions. In the event over 500,000 miners out of over 700,000 voted to strike on 15 March. The Prime Minister offered a Royal Commission, which would issue its first report by 20 March. It took all the persuasive powers of Secretary Frank Hodges and President Robert Smillie at the Miners' Federation to postpone the strike for three weeks. The Sankey Commission, (see previous mention in chapter 5) was made into a 'grand jury' by the miners. The gross inefficiency of 'private enterprise' was exposed, as well as its inhuman cruelty. Many houses being, the Commission reported, 'a reproach to our civilisation [for which] no judicial language is sufficiently strong or sufficiently severe to apply to their condemnation.'[14] The miners were offered an increase of two shillings per day for adults, and a 7 hour day. Recommendation IX stated:

> Even on the evidence already given, the present system of ownership and working in the coal industry stands condemned, and some other system must be substituted for it, either nationalization or a method of unification by national purchase and/or joint control.[15]

Bonar Law, on the day the Sankey Commission gave this first report, declared unequivocally on behalf of the Government that: 'The Government is prepared to adopt the report in the spirit as well as in the letter, and to take all the necessary steps to carry out its recommendations without delay.' A similar letter was sent to the Miners' Federation. They held a national ballot and also accepted the Commission's report.

No sooner had the Sankey Commission issued its fourth and final report than the Yorkshire mine-owners caused a dispute by changing the piece rates in consequence to the reduction of the working day. Troops were hurried to the coalfields and naval ratings manned the mine pumps in direct contradiction of the principle expressed in Churchill's speech quoted earlier. This strike lasted four weeks before it was settled.

On 30 August 1918, the National Union of Police and Prison Officers had called a strike to protest at the delay in raising the wages of the force. Six thousand of the Metropolitan Police and almost all of the City of London force came out on strike. Lloyd George acted quickly, granted swift redress of the grievances over wages and hurriedly installed a new commissioner — none other than the man who commanded the troops at Tonypandy in 1911. On 1 August 1919, the police were out again because the new commissioner, Sir Nevil Macready, had forbidden policemen to belong to a union. 1,083 men in London, out of some 19,000, were sacked when they came out on strike. 932 men out of a force of 2,100 came out at Liverpool, and these too were sacked.[16] The 2,000 raw recruits who replaced the sacked men had no sympathy with trade unions or trade unionists in the battles yet to come.

Once the police threat to strike had been removed, Lloyd George announced in the House of Commons on 18 August 1919 that Mr Sankey's recommendation of State ownership could not be accepted by the Government! This refusal to fulfil a solemn pledge convinced the miners that the ruling class could not be trusted, and anyone who has followed this book carefully, would wonder how the miners' leaders could be so naive when they and their fathers before them had been so often deceived. It was however nothing to the deception that was to come.

It was next the turn of the railwaymen to be misled by the 'Welsh wizard', ably supported by the 179 company directors then in the House of Commons.[17]

Both the N.U.R. and the A.S.L.E.F. had claims for wage increases and had been negotiating with Sir Auckland Geddes since February. The footplatemen were to be treated generously, but the porters, guards and ticket collectors, all members of the N.U.R., were to have their wages reduced. For example a porter was to have his wages reduced from 51s to 40s, and a passenger guard was to lose between 4s and 7s a week. It soon became clear that here was a policy of 'divide and rule'. The footplatemen of the A.S.L.E.F. were to be placated, and the N.U.R. members scorned — or was it 'provoked'? Certainly Beatrice Webb thought so as she wrote in her diary that the strike had been '. . . desired, if not engineered, by the Geddes brothers, and subconsciously desired by the Prime Minister. The Geddes brothers represent the universal determination of the capitalists to reduce wages to pre-war level, a possible pre-war money level but in any case a pre-war

commodity value level.' Sir Eric Geddes took over the new
Ministry of Transport in September 1919, exchanging places with
his brother who had controlled the railways from the Board of
Trade.[18] That the railwaymen's reductions was to be a 'try on' for a
reduction of other workers' wages was made clear by Lloyd George
when he said to J.H. Thomas, Secretary of the N.U.R. during the
negotiations:

> Whatever we lay down with regard to railwaymen, you may
> depend upon it, it is going to be claimed throughout the
> country; and therefore we have to consider not merely your
> case but the cases of all the other trades in the Kingdom.

Thomas answered, 'We feel equally well that we are doing
something for the rest of the workers.'[19]
On 26 September the rail strike began, and the A.S.L.E.F.
unselfishly joined in with the N.U.R. The attempt to split the
workers had failed.[20]
Again Churchill went into action, sending troops in all directions, hopefully anticipating the outbreak of a revolution. Not only
was the Minister of War ready, but the whole cabinet was prepared
for the strike. Lloyd George wrote in 1926 that:

> Even before the end of the war, preparations were being made
> by my cabinet to meet any industrial crisis which would
> involve interference with transport and food supplies of the
> country.
> After the Armistice a very complete organization was created
> by the Ministry of Food, at my desire, for that purpose.
> At that time the vast machinery of food control was still in
> existence, and, utilising in part the existing machinery,
> arrangements were made to divide the country into sixteen
> divisional areas, each with its own commissioner and staff,
> ready to act at a moments notice, in the event of a transport,
> or general strike.
> The 'Powers of the Food Controller Road Transport
> (Requisition) Order of 1919' gave the food controller for the
> time being, on a state of emergency being declared, ample
> powers of requisitioning motor and other vehicles, and a
> complete system of road transport was organized.
> Retailers throughout the country were encouraged to hold
> reserve stocks of food, and in addition depots of emergency
> stocks were created and placed under the control of the district

commissioners. Full and detailed particulars of the transport and drivers whose services would be available were registered by the Ministry of Food, and if a general strike came, the sending of a one word code telegram to sixteen district commissioners was all that was necessary to set the whole machinery in motion. On 26 September 1919, these preparations were tested by the railway strike, which commenced on that date and lasted until 6 October.[21]

On 6 October the railwaymen found that their wages had been stabilized at the level then existing, until 30 September 1920. No adult railwayman was to receive less than 51s a week so long as the cost of living stood at not less than 110% above the pre-war level; the arrears of wages which had been withheld were to be paid; the unions agreed that their members should 'work harmoniously with the railway servants who have remained at or returned to work.' The Government and the unions agreed that no man should be prejudiced in any way as a result of the strike.[22] In 1919 this agreement was kept because it was not one sided. In 1926 the Government assured railwaymen that it was not their business 'to triumph over those who had failed in a mistaken attempt.'[23] We shall see that there was a ruthless victimization of strikers.

Churchill used troops to put down a revolution that was merely in the minds of extremists in the Government and amongst the barons of the press. What little possibility of revolution there was, arose from the provocative attitude of the Government, and the bias shown by the press, which freely repeated the myth about 'anarchist conspiracy'. In spite of press exaggeration there was practically no disorder and no attempt to injure property. The Government was allowed, without any obstruction, to bring into force its elaborate plan as outlined by Lloyd George.[24] The press published full-page advertisements of the Government case,[25] and because 'compositors and printers' assistants . . . threatened to strike and stop the newspapers completely,'[26] the railwaymen were allowed to advertise their case. The silent cinema screen was also used as a vehicle of propaganda by both sides.[27] So effective was the N.U.R. case, (put by the Labour Research Department), that even the press began to change its attitude. The *Daily Express* 'which on 29 September claimed that this "was a strike against the whole nation" organized by "a little band of conspirators who forced their duped followers" was carrying a headline on 3 October: "The railwaymen have a case".'[28] On Tuesday 30

September, J.H. Thomas of the N.U.R. declared that he would no longer hold out against allowing other unions to strike in sympathy.[29] This threat of a call on the rest of the Triple Alliance may have influenced the *Express* and the Government. Certainly the Government called out its 'Citizen Guard', but on the Sunday the strike was called off. The Government had 'surrendered'.

The Citizen Guard proved to be men of the aristocracy. Lord Cholmondeley became a volunteer porter at Paddington where he might have also met the Earl of Portarlington, who engaged in moving churns of milk or milking goats stranded for want of a train. The Duke of Manchester, the Earl of Lathom, Lord Herbert Vane Tempest and Lord Drogheda were also there to lend a hand with the movement of goods or the collection of tickets. It was reported that Lord Grimthorpe was 'doing the work of two ordinary men in the provinder department' at King's Cross where Admiral Sir Drury Wake and Sir Frederick Banbury also found employment. Lady Meux, wife of an Admiral of the Fleet, served as a ticket collector on the Great Eastern. On 3 October a band of volunteers from the Carlton Club went to Liverpool Street Station, offering 'to go out with the vans, and take whatever measures were necessary in case the drivers were attacked.' According to the *Morning Post* report they were 'mainly young majors and captains' who looked 'fighting fit'.[30]

Similar enthusiastic volunteers were to turn up in 1926; but in the meantime the Government felt that its strike breaking machinery had some loopholes that needed stopping before they could tackle the next strike involving transport. The Emergency Powers Act (27 October 1920) set into motion a 'police state' with arrest and imprisonment on a large scale made easy. Several reasons for the introduction of this harsh legislation can be postulated: the rapid rise in Trade Union membership (1919-1920) from 6 to 8 million; the success of the 1919 rail strike in terms of counter-government publicity and prevention of wage reductions; the March, 1920 general strike in Germany; the Bolshevik victories over Wrangel, Kolchak, Yudenich, and Denikin, and the armies of intervention in 1919; Trade Union and Labour opposition to the war against the Soviet Government being waged by the Poles under Pilsudski with French support in 1920, and finally a real fear of the Triple Alliance after it appeared to be strengthened by the setting up of a General Council of the T.U.C. Perhaps in addition to these factors one could add the formation of a Communist Party in 1920, but this small faction of the Labour movement had little influence at this time. Certainly it was a time of genuine fear on the part of the ruling class, and the capitalist system which they could see was being questioned and attacked, had to be defended.

The M.F.G.B. had obtained the support of other unions to put pressure on the Government to carry out their promises of implementing the findings of the Sankey Commission. The sudden rail strike prevented any united action to this end, so the miners decided to press for wage increases instead. The price of export coal and industrial coal for home consumption had risen rapidly and consequently profits soared. The Government offered a 20% increase which the miners accepted after the usual ballot. Within two weeks of signing the agreement the price of coal was again raised by the Government. The Government was preparing the way to hand back control of the pits to the owners. Practically all prices were increasing at this time, (29 April 1920), but it was the end of a period of insatiable greed, a wild capitalist boom where millions had been made out of the devastated areas in need of reconstruction; a gullible public was persuaded to buy shares in new companies floated to take over existing concerns which could not possibly pay the buyers. It was at the end a period where capitalist profits rose to quite extraordinary heights.[31] The miners were demanding their share.

The negotiations dragged on from April to October, the Government and coal-owners refusing to give way. On 16 October 1920 the miners struck work, and five days went by without any change in the situation. On 21 October the N.U.R. decided to support the miners' claim, and C.T. Cramp sent a letter to the Miners' Federation Executive to this effect, which was received on the 23 October. On that same day Lloyd George wrote to the executive suggesting that they should meet together 'to arrive at a basis of settlement,' having introduced into the House of Commons the repressive measures already quoted the day before. Lloyd George then offered the miners a two shillings per week increase, with additional increases dependent on output. The M.F.G.B. had to put this to the membership so that a vote could be taken. In the meantime on 27 October, the Royal Assent was given to the Emergency Powers Act. On 3 November the returned ballot papers showed that a small majority of 8,459 were against accepting the government's terms. The Federation executive decided that this was insufficient, according to the rules, for the strike to be resumed, so the members were instructed to return to work.[32] That same month retail food prices had reached their peak. Wages did not keep pace and the miners' struggle had been cancelled out.[33]

The middle class suffered the worst financially, especially if they had indulged in the share market. The press campaign against the miners while they were out on strike built up resentment in the middle classes who saw the miners as the cause of their own misery. Consequently the white collar workers became willing recruits of strike breaking orgnizations later on.

Unemployment by December had passed the half million mark; within 6 months more than two million were out of work. When these men, most of whom had been promised 'homes fit for heroes', began to demonstrate against the Government and its failure to cope with the economic crisis, they were trampled down by mounted police, or brutally battered into submission. At Liverpool where the memories of 'Bloody Sunday' had not faded, the police trapped demonstrators inside the Walker Art Gallery. 'Cries for mercy could be heard outside, men ran round the gallery panic-striken and dropped from open windows like bundles of old clothes into the side street. . . . An eye witness said, "The tessellated pavement of the vestibule streamed with blood and there were smears of it upon the walls." '[34]

It was during this period of mass unemployment (1920-21) that the Communist Party, through its organization of the unemployed, gained wide support. Many members of the Plebs League were to join the Communist Party, but like many others of the left in the 1920's they were to find that the rigid ideas and the 'infallibility' of the Communist leaders was not their idea of socialism. Marxism continued to be the dominant theme of *Plebs* and the National Council of Labour Colleges which came into being in 1921; but the rigid 'party liners' moved out, especially after Stalin's take over in the Soviet Union in 1924.

The Coal Mines Act of 1920 laid down that the State control should cease on 31 August 1921. After the end of the 1920 miners' strike, negotiations began with the Government and the coal-owners to draw up a new wages settlement on 31 March, in preparation for the conclusion of the agreement which was negotiated as part of the strike settlement. The miners' wanted a national settlement under a National Wages Board, drawing upon a 'national pool' of revenues from coal-mining; coupled with this was the desire for a new system of calculating wages, which would replace the existing confusion. When the Miners' Federation met the Government on January 13, 1921, the President of the Board of Trade told them that 'in the temporary agreement (due to expire on 31 March), the Government took the big risk of guaranteeing prices, and they had been hopelessly wrong in their conclusions. As a result of the big decrease in export prices, the industry was now losing money rapidly, and their anticipations were that the surplus pool of profits already accumulated, would, as a result of wage advances awarded, be exhausted in 10 weeks . . . . The Government therefore proposed to decontrol prices and distribution entirely on 1 March, but to keep on with the pooling of profits for some time longer, say, to take a date at random, until the 30 June, 1921. By that time it was hoped the two parties in the industry would have come to their conclusions on the point.'³⁵

On 23 February however, Sir Robert Horne, on behalf of the Board of Trade and the Government, told the Federation that; 'the Government has decided . . . to decontrol the coal trade absolutely as at the 31 March.'³⁶

The recovery of the French and Belgian mines, German reparations reaching France, and United States coal flooding the European market, had all brought about the fall in British exports. The Government was to shift the losses to the coal-owners, they in their turn were to take the loss out of the miners' wages. Notices were posted at the collieries showing the new wages the owners were prepared to pay. The Government compensated the owners by paying the full standard profit up to the end of 1920 and nine-tenths of that up to the end of the first quarter of 1921. There was to be no compensation for the miners.³⁷ The pit-head notices told miners in South Wales that there would be reductions of between 40% and 49% per shift, whilst in South Yorkshire the lower-paid men would actually receive small increases. In South Wales a labourer's wage was to be reduced from £3-13-9d to £1-18-9d.³⁸ The men refused these terms, and decided that all notices 'should be allowed to expire regardless of occupation.'³⁹ The coal-owners' had given notice of the new terms to all the miners, enginemen, pumpmen and all concerned with keeping the pit in working order. They were surprised when every man accepted this universal lock-out. The coal strike began on 1 April 1921.

In September of the previous year when the miners had called on the rest of the Triple Alliance for support in their October strike of that year, Ernest Bevin of the Transport Workers

passionately complained about the organization of the Alliance. He
said, 'When the test comes, if you do not make it a real organization it will be found to be a paper alliance.'[40] His prediction
proved to be correct. It was Friday 8 April before the Executive
Councils of the N.U.R. and Transport Workers' Federation
threatened to use their power to add weight to the miners' demand
for a National Wages Board and a National Pool; and this action
was not to be set in motion until midnight on the following
Tuesday. Then there was a further postponment until 15 April.
The miners could not be supported until they agreed to man the
pumps. One Colonel C. Lowther had pleaded that it was 'a terrible
thing that at this moment there may be ponies in the mines, and I
believe they are none too rare, either drowning bit by bit or
gradually starving to death.' In the same speech he drew a picture
of the miner 'told by Bolshevik agitators paid by German gold' that
the mine owners desired only 'to ruin him, to profiteer and to get
everything possible out of him.' The press worked on the 'poor
ponies', and the Government used the issue to delay the Triple
Alliance. (Needless to say, not one pony was in danger!) On the
evening of Thursday, 14 April, a group of coalition M.P.s invited
Frank Hodges, the miners' secretary, to discuss the miners' case
with him and some other M.P.s. No reporters were present, and
no one took notes, so it is impossible to say what exactly was said.
The press reported that Hodges had indicated that he would be
prepared to consider a return to district agreements, which was
what the owners wanted. J.H. Thomas claimed that someone
asked if the Triple Alliance would support a temporary return to
district agreements and he immediately told the gathering, 'Yes, I
am quite sure the Triple Alliance will support Mr Hodges action.'
Mr Thomas had dinner with Mr Hodges that very evening. It was
the same Mr Thomas who called out the railwaymen so suddenly
in 1919, and thereby prevented the Triple Alliance functioning
when the miners wanted to force the Government to honour their
promises to uphold the decisions of the Sankey Commission. It was
rather an odd coincidence; especially if we take into consideration
his future actions. Neither Mr Hodges nor Mr Thomas spoke with
the authority of those they represented. 'Black Friday and the split
in the Triple Alliance arose from the fact that whereas Mr
Hodges's statement was repudiated by the Executive of the Miners'
Federation on the following morning, Friday, 15 April 1921, Mr
Thomas was able to gain the support of the Executive Committees

of the N.U.R. and the Transport workers' for his actions.' It was Mr Thomas who ran down the steps of Unity House to tell the waiting reporters that the Triple Alliance strike was cancelled, the miners were on their own.[41] (Hodges later became a director of several companies; colliery, iron and steel, chemicals, finance, etc.)[42] The whole working class unity had been destroyed at one blow. A year later a three month strike of engineers was defeated; a two month strike in the shipyards ended in wage reductions; and during the year workers at the docks, in the building and printing trades, on the railways, and in the cotton industry accepted reductions.[43]

The miners, after 'Black Friday', stayed out until 1 July. They returned to work utterly defeated. The Government had moved troops into the coal areas at the commencement of the strike; the War Office cancelled all leave and on 8 April Army and Navy Reservists were called up; officers and men were re-enrolled in the Air Force; a new volunteer 'Defence Force' was asked for, and 75,000 came forward in the first 10 days.

One of Sir Philip Gibbs' novels of this period, *The Middle Road*, pictures a defence corps formed of ex-officers by the Government to defend 'us' against a revolution fomented by 'Bolshies' and agents paid with foreign gold — the chronic bugbears of those anxious years.

> (Us) . . . meaning the Decent Crowd, anybody with a stake in the country, including the unfortunate Middle Classes. All of us. Well, we accept the challenge. We're ready to knock hell out of them . . . . This clash has got to come. We must get the whole working classes back to their kennels. Back to cheap labour. Back to discipline. Otherwise we're done.[44]

If we turn back a page of this book we shall see that Colonel Lowther spoke of the miners as if they had been influenced 'by Bolshevik agitators paid by German gold' (See p.80). Another M.P., Mr Tom Johnston, writing about the unemployed demonstrations, was perhaps nearer the truth:

> Some of the hunger marches in London presented a pitiable and heart rending spectacle. Emaciated, starved, ragged, beaten, hopeless, not from these will come a social revolution. The press placards were yelling 'Moscow' and 'Communist Plot' but God knows the poor victims in that procession were concerned for a square meal — and for a Soviet, not at all.[45]

A trade unionist was able to claim unemployment benefit from his union. By the end of 1921, after the lock-out of the miners, £7,000,000 had been paid out and in many cases union funds were nearly exhausted.[46] The Government introduced the Unemployment Insurance Act of 1920, but its provisions were never fully enforced; instead, the Government, by a series of Acts in 1921 and 1922 (consolidated in the Unemployment Insurance Act of 1922), extended the period during which benefits could be drawn (originally only 15 weeks in a year) they also altered the rates of benefit, and increased the contributions. The most important of these Acts was that of March 1921, which, among other things, provided for two periods of extended benefit of 16 weeks each, separated by gaps when no benefits could be drawn as opposed to the original 15 weeks per annum. This was 'uncovenanted' benefit, beyond what the working man was entitled to from his contributions and in theory an advance against future contributions. Thus was born, if not named, the 'dole', hated by those it was meant to save from complete starvation and bitterly condemned by the comfortable classes who saw in it only the symbol of national demoralization.[47] *The Morning Post* on the 20 October 1922, for example, told its readers: 'The dole system cannot be abolished at once, but it may be reformed so that it shall no longer be said that it is less profitable to work than to do nothing.' Viscount Lymington opposed Unemployment Insurance as being bad for the independent spirit of the British people:

> But evil is not only done by adding £12,250,000 to the state commitments of this country. That is the least of it. The worst is the attack on the independence and the moral fibre of the people of this country. This is eating into the stubborn independence of our English character.[48]

This was after nine years of Unemployment Insurance. In a year when milk and potatoes were deliberately destroyed the *Glasgow Evening News* reported:

> The sudden death of a fourteen months old child in the Northern District of Glasgow provides a poignant example of the dire straights to which unemployment has reduced many working class families in the city . . . a distressing state of affairs was found in the house . . . there was no food . . . and without exaggeration it may be said that the entire family was starving. The total income was 15s per week.[49]

With the introduction of the dole, the unemployment insurance scheme 'became a form of inquisition. For to limit the numbers to whom aid was extended, it was laid down that payments were to be made only to those "genuinely seeking" work; and the Employment Exchanges and in time a vast machinery of committees and officials were called upon to make sure that only those thus qualified were granted the aid provided by the law.' Men in work paid for the support of those out of work; it was discovered in 1926 that 48% of insured workers had drawn no benefits at all in five years, though employees' contributions provided for about one-third of the expenditure of the fund. Families not covered by the unemployment insurance scheme or insufficiently aided by it, or stranded during the 'gaps' between periods of unemployment benefit (often about a month) all resorted to the Guardians, and sometimes received outdoor relief. 'Sometimes' because it was not uncommon for Boards of Guardians to refuse outdoor relief altogether.[50] (One correspondent informed this writer that he had been unemployed for five years after the ,1926 strike).[51] Relief varied from 15s a week for man and wife and 5s for each child to Poplar's more generous rate of 33s, plus 10s for rent. The dole was much less than the lowest Poor Law scales. The unemployed worker, 'genuinely seeking work' was paid 15s. Not until November, 1921, when the Unemployed Worker's Dependants (Temporary Provisions) Act came into force did his wife and dependent children get anything. The scales then received by the worker who was unable to find work because of the gross inefficiency and inability to cope with the capitalist system then prevailing was:

> Man 15s
> Wife 5s
> Child 1s

A man, wife and four children could then receive the magnificent sum of 24s per week. In the late 1930's the B.B.C. ran a series of talks called 'Time to Spare'. Several unemployed men and their wives told of their suffering on the 'dole'. Just prior to the 1950 General Election the Co-operative Party published a booklet called *So I'll Remember* with some quotations from that series. A number of quotations from the booklet are included in the appendices because, although biased in favour of the Labour Party, they do give some idea of working class conditions in the 1920s and 1930s.

Whilst the unemployed were struggling to make ends meet the coalition Government found itself under attack for spending too much. Lord Rothmere (the then owner of *The Times* and other newspapers) launched an Anti-Waste Party which won three seats in by elections. Sir Auckland Geddes, the Minister of Transport, was called upon to wield what became known as 'the Geddes axe'. Army, Navy and Air Force estimates were cut; education was cut by £6½ million; war pensions by £3½ million. Lloyd George's over generous 'sale of honours' brought down the wrath of men who indulged in this political corruption with equal fervour, given the opportunity. Three baronies in the Birthday Honours of June 1922 finally provoked an explosion in the House of Lords, the House of Commons, and the press. They were for Sir William Vesty, the millionaire meat packer of Union Cold Storage, who had transferred his business to Buenos Aires during the war to avoid English taxation; Sir James Waring of the furniture firm of Waring and Gillow, who had closed down one company in 1910 with considerable loss to the shareholders, and then formed another which made large profits on war contracts; and Sir Joseph Robinson, a South African financier, who thought he had been promised a title by Lord Birkenhead, but whose record did not bear examination. It seemed to *The Times* that Lloyd George would have to give way or resign, but Sir Joseph Robinson's dignified refusal of the honour helped to extricate the Government from the worst of its predicaments, and the crisis then was averted in a flurry of prevarications and downright lies.[52] Another press baron, Lord Beaverbrook, had abandoned the coalition and was urging Bonar Law, a Conservative, to return as a duty to public life. At the Carlton Club on 19 October, it was decided by leading Tories, who wanted a break from the coalition, that Bonar Law should become Prime Minister. The General Election which followed in November returned 347 Conservatives, 142 Labour members, 60 Asquith Liberals, and 57 Lloyd George Liberals. The 'rule of the pygmies, of the "second class brains" began, to continue until 1940.'[53]

That same year of 1922 a new President was elected to the Miners' Federation. Herbert Smith, born in the workhouse at Kippax in 1862 and soon an orphan, had entered the pits at 10 and was a member of the local school board at 30. In his youth he had been a fighter at public houses. Short of speech, brave, tough, kindly, he had been president of the Yorkshire miners since 1905, and in Barnsley where he spent most of his time, miners could do no wrong in his eyes.

Smith was to be president of the M.F.G.B. for seven years, but Bonar Law resigned after being Prime Minister for only seven months. In those seven months French and Belgian troops occupied the Ruhr, bringing to a halt most of Germany's coal production and thereby giving a boost to the British pits. However, this revival of the coal trade was not felt until later in 1923.

The Chancellor of the Exchequer in the Bonar Law administration was Stanley Baldwin. Because the American ambassador in London had encouraged the Government to believe that generous terms could be obtained from the United States for the funding of the British War Debt, then amounting to £978,000,000; Baldwin and Montagu Norman, the governor of the Bank of England, went to New York.[54] From New York they journeyed to Washington to negotiate with Andrew Mellon, Secretary to the U.S. Treasury. It turned out to be one of the costliest journeys in British history. Lloyd George subsequently wrote about the two leading negotiators:

> Mr Mellon was keen, experienced, hard, ruthless; Mr Baldwin casual, soft, easy-going, and at that time quite raw. Mr Baldwin admits that since then he has learnt a great deal. At that time he merited his constant boast that he was only a 'simple countryman'. A business transaction at that date between Mr Mellon and Mr Baldwin was in the nature of a negotiation between a weasel and its quarry. The result was a bargain which has brought international debt collection into disrepute.[55]

Mr Baldwin committed the Government to an annual payment of £33 million from 1923 to 1932, and £38 million thereafter until 1984. The high British rate may have been imposed because of the predictions that a Labour administration was soon to take office.[56] The rate of interest was twice as high as that later negotiated with France and eight times the rate negotiated with the Italian Government.[57] The Italian government was by then, a Fascist dictatorship. The low rate of interest was probably given in order to help promote Fascism. Certainly Mussolini's handling of trade unions and the working class in general, won high praise from established right-wing governments. Mussolini's bombardment and occupation of the island of Corfu on the 31 August 1923, was allowed to pass with little international protest, thus undermining the League of Nations, and encouraging future Fascist dictators to believe that might was right.

Mr Baldwin, 'the simple countryman' became Prime Minister in May 1923. He was soon to tell the country that, 'this unemployment problem is the most crucial problem . . . I can fight it. I am willing to fight it. I cannot fight without weapons . . . I have come to the conclusion myself that the only way of fighting this subject is by protecting the home market. I am not a clever man. I know nothing of political tactics . . . .'[58]

Despite his public statements, Baldwin's clever tactical manoeuvre of making protection a burning issue helped to unite the Conservative party. This intention was admitted by Baldwin later, and he found that the image of a simple not very clever politician continued to hide his true intentions.

Whatever his motives were, the outcome was an eventual Labour victory. In the election of December 1923 the Conservatives were still the largest party in the Commons, with 258 members compared with 346 before the dissolution, the Liberals elected 158 members, and Labour 191. Baldwin decided not to resign, but to face Parliament when it met on 8 January 1924. In the King's speech on 15 January, Baldwin was generous with promises his Government ran little risk of being able to honour: increased public works to relieve unemployment, increased old-age pensions, more housing. On the 17 January 1924 Labour moved an amendment that His Majesty's present advisers had 'not the confidence' of the House, which the Liberals supported. When the vote was taken on 21 January, the Government was defeated by 328 votes to 256. Baldwin resigned next day, and the King called MacDonald to form a government. The first Labour cabinet in British history was 'a cabinet of moderates, more representative of the upper and middle classes and of new recruits to the party than of the trade-union side and the old timers and left wingers; only five of the twenty members of the cabinet were trade unionists . . . Snobs were relieved by the presence of men such as Haldane and Chelmsford . . . *The Economist's* prediction of two years before, that the country would be "astonished at the bourgeois character of a Labour administration", was borne out.'[59]

Whilst in office MacDonald, in February 1924, announced Britain's recognition of the Soviet government, and by August had made arrangements to recommend to Parliament the guaranteeing of a loan to that Government. It was immediately attacked by both Conservatives and Liberals in the House. The Liberals went so far as to accuse the Government of adopting a definitely socialist course.

Just prior to MacDonald's decision to offer the U.S.S.R. a loan, in July a question was put down in parliament concerning seditious articles in the Communist Worker's Weekly. As a result the paper's office was raided on 5 August and the acting editor, J.R. Campbell was arrested and charged under the Incitement to Mutiny Act of 1797. He was author of an article on 25 July which urged soldiers not to fire on their fellow workers, whether in industrial disputes or in war. Several Labour M.P.s objected to the action taken by the Attorney General, Sir Patrick Hastings and at the end of September charges against Campbell were dropped.[60] The Labour Attorney General explained that as acting editor Campbell was not a responsible person, adding that he was also a crippled and decorated ex-serviceman.[61]

The Conservatives moved a motion of censure, which MacDonald insisted on making a matter of confidence, with the result that on 8 October the Government was defeated by 364 votes to 198.

The third general election in three years was held on 29 October 1924, but before it took place certain important events should be noted. Firstly, perhaps as a result of the Campbell case, at the annual Labour Party conference on 7 October, it was decided to reject the affiliation of Communists. It was also resolved that they were not eligible for endorsement as Labour party candidates nor even for membership in the party.[62]

That same month, on 21 October, the *Manchester Evening News* reported: 'There is a report to which much credence is attached that, before next polling day comes, a bombshell will burst and it will be connected with Zinoviev.' Then it came, just at the right psychological moment, in the newspapers of Saturday, 25 October, just four days before polling *The Daily Mail* announced in its then vitriolic language:

MOSCOW ORDERS TO OUR REDS
GREAT PLOT DISCLOSED YESTERDAY.
'PARALYSE THE ARMY AND NAVY.'
AND MR. MACDONALD WOULD LEND RUSSIA OUR MONEY!

**Document issued by Foreign Office
after 'Daily Mail' had spread the news.**

A 'very secret' letter of instruction from Moscow, which we publish below, discloses a great Bolshevik plot to paralyse the British Army and Navy and to plunge the country into civil war. The letter is addressed by the Bolsheviks of Moscow to the Soviet Government's servants in Great Britain, the Communist Party, who in turn are the masters of Mr. Ramsey MacDonald's Government, which has signed a treaty with Moscow whereby the Soviet is to be guaranteed a 'loan' of millions of British money.
The letter is signed by Zinoviev, the Dictator of Petrograd, President of the Third (Moscow) International, and is addressed to A. McManus, the British representative on the executive of this International, who returned from Moscow to London on October 18 to take part in the general election campaign.

This report then went on to link support of the Russian treaty with plans for the class war in Britain, and would have perhaps have had little effect if it had not been accompanied in the press by a letter from the Foreign Office signed by J.D. Gregory, head of its Russian section, to Rakovsky, Russian Charge d'Affaires in London, which protested against the letter as propaganda representing a direct interference in British domestic affairs from outside.[63]
The 'very secret' letter, which has never been authenticated, had the desired effect. Wavering Liberals were driven 'in shoals to vote for the Party that could best be trusted to oppose the Socialist menace', wrote Leopold Amery, soon to become colonial secretary in a victorious Conservative Government.[64]
While the Labour Government was in office, the miners, no less than the rest of the working class, had expected great improvements, especially in their conditions of work. The Miners' Federation wasted no time in giving notice that they wished to

terminate the 1921 wages agreement. In accordance with the Industrial Courts Act of 1919, the Government appointed a Court of Inquiry under the chairmanship of a Liberal, Lord Buckmaster. This led to a new agreement being signed providing for a substantially higher minimum wage. 'There can be little doubt that the principal reason for the coal-owners' acceptance of this was the fact that the Labour Government was in power, and, if they had not given way, would have probably framed a new Miners' Minimum Wage Act, raising the wages by law. The owners, therefore, signed; but the operation of the new agreement was limited to a single year.' Just before the election which was brought about by the 'Red scare' the Labour Party printed a document called 'The Mines for the Nation', (a copy of which is in the appendices). When the result of the election was made known, the Conservatives had obtained a large majority, 415 seats as compared with 152 won by Labour and 42 by the Liberals. Nationalization of the mines, was now out of the question.

The advantages gained from the Buckmaster inquiry were soon to be cancelled out by MacDonald's intervention in the French occupation of the Ruhr. A committee of experts — headed by the American, General Charles G. Dawes — had recommended that the German currency be stabilized on a gold basis and that Germany should pay an annual sum for reparations by raising the money from taxation, from bonds issued against the German railways, and from certain German industrial debentures. In addition, an international loan to Germany of £40 million was recommended. At a London conference attended by the newly elected French premier Edouard Herriot along with German delegates who included Chancellor Gustav Stresemann and British delegates led by MacDonald, all agreed that the French occupation of the Ruhr should end in 1924. Before the last French and Belgian troops had withdrawn, the Conservatives were in office under Stanley Baldwin. The minor boom in the coal trade now collapsed and the British coal-owners made their usual demands to cut wages in order to offset their losses. Baldwin's second cabinet included Austen Chamberlain as Foreign Secretary, Neville Chamberlain as Minister of Health, Lord Birkenhead as Secretary of State for India, Joynson-Hicks as Home Secretary, and Winston Churchill, who had just joined the Conservative Party after 20 years as a Liberal, as Chancellor of the Exchequer. Baldwin had succeeded in uniting the Tories. The trade union movement had watched political power taken from a Labour Government in which they were allowed to play little part.

On 30 June 1925, now confident with such a large Conservative majority to give them backing, the coal-owners served notice on the Miners' Federation to end the 1924 agreement in one month. They demanded a return to the wage conditions of 1921-24, and a repeal of the Seven Hours Act of 1919, and the resumption of the eight hours shift.[65] This meant not only a reduction in wages, but that the guarantee of a minimum wage would disappear. The owners were to retain their standard profit regardless of how low wages might fall. Led now by A.J. Cook (General Secretary), and Herbert Smith, (President), the miners were prepared to put up a fight, despite the odds being heavily against them. A quarter of all miners were unemployed and union funds were at their lowest ebb. Thousands were depending on unemployment insurance or poor relief for their daily existence. In May Cook had reported the grave condition of the British industry and, together with the rest of the Executive, had strongly dissuaded delegates from putting forward a claim for an increase in wages. It was also reported in *The Times*, 22 May 1925, that Cook had reminded the delegates of the experience in 1921 which had proved that with all the courage in the world the miners could not afford to take the offensive again alone.[66] Cook knew that a reorganization of the industry was necessary.[67] In the House of Commons on the 8 July, Vernon Hartshorn put the miner's case:

> Mr Harshorn opened the main debate with a speech of great sensibility and poise. He pointed out, in an absolutely non party way, the mass of human misery, hopelessness and humiliation implied by the figure of 301,000 unemployed miners — a figure which he thought might quite possibly be doubled if nothing were done . . . . The year 1924 showed a total profit of £14,250,000; yet of 254,000,000 tons mined, 84,000,000 were produced at a loss, even in such a good year. Again, every single district last month worked at a loss, yet in every one, the best mines showed a profit, and there were mines even now which could undersell the French.
>
> Quite obviously, he urged, some unification was necessary, and equally, certainly, recovery did not merely depend on reducing prices by a few shilllings a ton — or at least the reduction could come from neither profits nor wages. We

M.G.B. Delegation in 1926 with Herbert Smith on left with cloth cap and A.J. Cook on right with spectacles (Photograph by courtesy of the T.U.C. Library)

should try giving long credit terms like the Germans, or the development of low temperature carbonization at high speed. But in truth private enterprise had collapsed and the existence of 3,000 separate undertakings was at once the explanation of variable efficiency and the cause of the disaster.[68]

It should be emphasized that in the middle of May 1925 the Belgian Federation of Collieries estimated that two million tons of coal were on hand at the pit heads in Belgium: 'owing to the price of Belgian coal being higher than the foreign product.' Ten million tons of coal were lying at the Ruhr pitheads in July, quite 'unmarketable, owing to excessive world production and high German

prices.' Clearly greater output was not the essential in a world
already gravely overstocked with surplus coal, quite apart from the
inevitable increase of unemployment among miners that such a step
would have entailed.

Miners working on their knees at the coal-face in 1925 (Photograph by courtesy of
the T.U.C. Library)

The owners however, claimed that the coal industry could not
pay the existing wage rates with transport charges at their high
level in order to compete successfully with coal produced more
cheaply in foreign lands where labour conditions were more lenient
and currency depreciated. Yet as has been shown the 'foreign
lands' were complaining about their own coal being higher in price
than other foreign producers.[69]

The Court of Inquiry set up by the Government under the
Industrial Courts Act of 1919, was presided over by Mr H.P.
Macmillan. The Miners' Federation refused to be represented, they
had had enough of inquiries. Herbert Smith and Thomas Richards
(Vice-President), spent most of their time with the Minister of
Mines in order to back up the strong protest against the sealing

down of the Mortaque pit at Newcastle-upon-Tyne, before all the bodies had been got out and the causes had been thoroughly investigated in the pit explosion there.[70]

The Macmillan Report was issued on the 28 July 1925. *The Times* editorial on the following day found that 'in view of the findings of the Court, it will be impossible for the mineowners to maintain the ground upon which they have hitherto taken their stand. They will have no alternative but to suspend the notices and to withdraw their present proposals; and if they are wise they will do so with goodwill.' Even the *Spectator* declared that the Government must put the Macmillan Report into effect, that there could be no lockout, and that if the owners still refused to withdraw their notices the Government must take control of the coal industry as in war time.[71]

The same morning Mr Baldwin told the miners that the Government could grant no subsidy to the coal industry and that it would have to stand on its own economic foundations. The Macmillan Report had recommended that there should be a minimum wage provided, and that there was 'considerable room for improving the efficiency of the industry'. On the 30 July — or so the *Daily Herald* reported next day — the Prime Minister had urged the miners to make a contribution towards meeting 'the difficult situation with which the industry is confronted.' He told them that he had secured from the mine-owners a concession on Districts, followed reluctantly by the concession of a minimum wage. 'What have you to give?' he asked the miners. 'Nowt,' was the sturdy reply of the unyielding Herbert Smith, 'we have nowt to give.'[72] Then, according to the *Daily Herald*, the Prime Minister said, 'All the workers in this country have got to face a reduction of wages.' Miners:— 'What do you mean?' Prime Minister:— 'I mean all the workers of this country have got to take reductions in wages to help put industry on its feet.' That same evening a conference of one thousand trade union delegates at the Central Hall, Westminster, gave unanimous approval to the General Council's decision to put an embargo on the movement of coal, (which was decided upon on the 25 July 1925). At this meeting, held at the Caxton Hall on Saturday 25 July, at 10.30 a.m. the Unions were asked as a minimum requirement to refuse to handle coal, the movement of which was considered detrimental to the interests of the miners. The very cordial support and the united desire to assist was manifested by the Unions, and a sub-committee was set up to

work out the details of the practical application of the decisions.
The Sub-Committee on Wednesday morning, 29 July 1925, had
arrived at a concerted policy. The Unions met the following day,
Thursday, and having heard the miner's report of what the Prime
Minister had said, the decision taken by the sub-committee was
ratified. Notices were sent out by the General Council, counter-
signed by the appropriate trade union officials, ordering that the
stoppage of the movement of coal should operate from 11.59 p.m.
on Friday, 31 July. At 6.30 p.m. on that Friday the Cabinet met,
and later saw the miners' representatives. They agreed to
co-operate in an inquiry into means for improving the productive
efficiency of the industry provided wages and hours remained
unchanged during the inquiry: for that period, expected to be
about nine months, the Government promised the industry a
subsidy, estimated to be not less than £10 millions (in the event it
was over £23 millions). Under the terms of the subsidy announced
later, the owners were permitted a profit of 13% of proceeds
(including the subsidy), provided that when profits exceeded 1s.3d.
per ton the surplus would be used to reduce the subsidy.[73]

Many miners did not consider this a victory, although the *Daily
Herald* dubbed it as such, naming it 'Red Friday'. Certainly the
miners had suffered no reductions in wages, nor had they to suffer
from further strike action, but the owners had been assured of
profits higher than they had been used to, and these were to remain
constant for the next nine months despite a world surplus of coal.

The *Daily Mail* true to its character, charged the Premier with
changing his mind on the grant of a subsidy, under the threats of a
band of conspirators who had planned to blockade the nation. Mr
Lloyd George declared that 'the Government was taken by
surprise. No plan, no proposals, no suggestions. Even the strike
emergency organization was not ready.[74] On 3 August *The Times*
reported a speech made in Northampton by the Home Secretary,
Sir William Joynson-Hicks:

> He said to them, coming straight from the Cabinet Councils,
> the thing was not finished. The danger was not over. Sooner
> or later this question had got to be fought out by the people of
> the land. Was England to be governed by Parliament and by
> the Cabinet or by a handful of trade union leaders? If a Soviet
> were established here . . . a grave position would arise. On the
> other hand, if people were prepared to support the Govern-

ment . . . then he said quite frankly, quite seriously, there would be for a time grave trouble in the land, but if the heart of the people were sound, they could stand it.[75]

On the 6 August, after the Home Secretary had outlined his position, the Prime Minister then indicated his:

But peace was a matter of will, and those whose deliberate policy was war should reflect on the sad climax they would bring to the evolution of popular government. They would also learn that the community, when compelled to fight would develop forces which would astonish the crimes of anarchy. This warning was uttered in the spirit of one who knew that the greatest danger was the delay of reform, but who also knew that it was an expression of the instinct and belief of a free people.[76]

It appeared as if the Government was preparing for a battle — a class war. Any doubts about this were dispelled by the Chancellor of the Exchequer on the 10 December 1925:

The Government thought, moreover, at that juncture, the end of July, that they saw possibilities of actual trade revival. We did not feel justified in predicting it, but we believed from the evidence submitted to us from many quarters that there were good probabilities of an improvement, of a diminuation of unemployment, of an improvement in world prices in relation to our own, and, in consequence, an appreciable bridging of the gap between the ascertained wage and the minimum wage. We were also impressed with the fact that the country as a whole was not sufficiently informed about the character and immense consequences of such a struggle as that with which it was confronted.

It is quite clear that a conflict of this kind, launched in this way, might easily cease to be a mere ordinary industrial dispute about wages and conditions and might assume a character altogether different from such industrial disputes. If that were to ensue, then it is quite clear that such a conflict between the community on the one hand, with the Government at its head, and many of the great trade unions on the other, could only end one way, namely, by the community, at whatever cost, emerging victorious over an organized section of its citizens, however valuable, important, and even numerous that section was.

We consider therefore, that should such a struggle be found to be inevitable at the very last moment, it was of supreme importance that it should only be undertaken under conditions which would not expose the nation needlessly or wantonly to perils, the gravity of which cannot be over-estimated. We, therefore, decided to postpone the crisis in the hope of averting it, or, if not of averting it, of coping effectually with it when the time came.[77]

From the above speech, made by Winston Churchill, it is clearly admitted that 'Red Friday' was merely a deliberate decision by the Government in order to give themselves time to prepare for a victory over the working class. If the reader still has doubts about such deliberate preparations the following factual statement will perhaps provide additional proof:

The plan (of action) was outlined in a circular sent out in advance to Town Councils, Metropolitan Borough Councils . . . throughout the country. The circular was dated 20 November 1925, which date suggests two historical footnotes: (1) that in August 1925, when the so called general strike was first threatened, and averted by the Government's offer of a subsidy, the Government's machinery for dealing with the strike was not as complete as it might have been — hence no doubt the subsidy; and (2) that the organization which proved so effective in May 1926, was perfected as long ago as November, 1925 — five months in advance.[78]

If we return to Mr Churchill's speech of 10 December 1925 quoted earlier, we shall see that the Chancellor of the Exchequer then said that at the end of July, the Government saw the possibility 'of actual trade revival'. Perhaps Mr Churchill had high hopes of this happening when he announced in his budget speech on 28 April 1925, that he was to return to the Gold standard at the prewar parity. Sir Josiah Stamp and Sir Alfred Mond certainly did not agree with him if he did. They both had letters published in *The Times* of 8 August 1925. Sir Alfred wrote:

I pointed out in the debate on the Budget, when I got little support, the dangers involved in the premature return to the gold standard, or more correctly to the gold exchange forced upon the country by Mr Winston Churchill. The recent coal crisis was brought about by the unprofitable character of the export trade due to the resumption of the gold exchange. The damaging effect which has resulted in making the competitive price of English export coal higher by 1s to 1s.9d. per ton, and thus still further widening the gap between our prices and those of continental nations, has been specially emphasized by Sir Josiah Stamp in his report on the Coal Inquiry, by Mr Lee, the secretary of the Coal-Owners' Association and by Mr J.M. Keynes in Chapter 4 of his pamphlet, 'The Economic Consequences of Churchill'.

The financial policy of the Government having logically led to the depression of the coal industry, an increase of unemployment followed, and the consequent demand for a reduction of existing money wages to a new real wage standard, which is estimated should be 10% lower. The return to the gold standard has produced exactly the crisis which must inevitably result from such a policy.

The Mining Association of Great Britain also had a letter published in the same paper on the same day. Was this a coincidence or was it a deliberate pre-meditated attempt to influence the public? The letter leaves no doubt on this score, and this letter has a strange similarity to the report of the Joynson-Hicks speech at Northampton earlier in the month:

Mr Baldwin has secured the support of the House of Commons for his policy of Danegeld; Parliament is up; the public can continue its holiday. In due course a Royal Commission will be set up to 'inquire into the industry' but, as the P.M. himself admitted, no industry has been so frequently inquired into or so continuously interfered with by successive Governments. No inquiry, whether it is of a judicial character, or whether it is allowed to degenerate into a Socialist circus like the Sankey commission, or is contemptuously boycotted by the miners like the court presided over by Mr Macmillan, can put into the industry money which is not there, compel our foreign customers to buy coal they can obtain more cheaply elsewhere or enable the industry to pay wages out of losses. The Mining Association warns the public that the crisis will occur in exactly the same form next May unless the situation is resolutely faced in the interim. The Mining Association knows, if the public does not, that those who control the Miners' Federation never had any intention of

arriving at a settlement of the recent dispute, and they do not
want peace in industry, but the overthrow of private enterprise and the existing structure of society. . . . Are we to be
governed by Parliament or by a Soviet acting in the name of
the Labour movement. It will be the endeavour of the Mining
Association during the respite purchased by Mr Baldwin, to
expose the ramifications and activities of our English Reds, the
methods by which they control the Miners' Federation and
other unions, and their policy towards industry and the State.

The former Labour Prime Minister added his comments to the
issue and warned of revolutionaries, making his speech not in
England but New York!

Had the lock-out taken place the industries of our country
would have been paralyzed within a week. The railways
would have been involved from the first hour; other sections of
the transport trades would have followed quickly; gas and
electrical works were included in the trade union scheme of
united action. . . . The prospect was undoubtedly appalling,
and the sections which believe that governments yield only to
force, and that direct action against society offers great
prospects for improvement in working class conditions
naturally feel that they have scored a fine triumph. They are
now able to say that a threat of direct action wrung
£10,000,000 from the taxpayers . . . the mishandling by the
Government . . . handed over the honors of war to those who
may be inclined to toy with revolution.[79]

It should be stressed that gas and electrical works were *not* included
in the 'trade union scheme', nor did any trade unionist claim to have
'wrung' the subsidy out of 'the taxpayers'.

Arthur Cook, the secretary of the Miners' Federation and
enthusiastic supporter of the Communist dominated Minority
Movement, certainly confirmed some of the fears of MacDonald
the mine-owners, and the Government. At the end of August,
1925, he stated:

Next May we shall be faced with the greatest crisis and the
greatest struggle we have ever known, and we are preparing
for it. We shall prepare a Commissariat department. I am
going to get a fund, if I can, that will buy grub so that when

the struggle comes we shall have that grub distributed in the homes of our people.
I don't care a hang for any government, or army or navy. They can come along with their bayonets. Bayonets don't cut coal. We have already beaten, not only the employers, but the strongest Government in modern times.[80]

Like similar emotional outbursts made later, (although there are indications that Cook had anticipated getting the support of which he boasted), the miners' secretary was so deeply involved with the men he led, that he considered all other workers had the same fighting spirit. The mining industry and the men who worked in it were unique. The mines could not be worked by the importation of blackleg labour in the same way that for instance ships, trains, gas works, or electricity works could. In addition the areas where the mines were situated made for greater solidarity because they were usually the dominant industry, besides being concentrated. The miners too had every reason to back Cook and Smith in their slogan which they formulated at this time: 'Not a penny off the pay, not a minute on the day.' Their whole history left them no alternative. All their years of struggle would have been in vain. Robert Smillie, the old miner, when speaking in support of a Minimum Wages Bill the Labour Party had tried unsuccessfully to introduce in May 1925, summed up the miners' attitude to the coal-owners:

> Mr. Smillie ridiculed the idea that the passage of the Bill would kill the mining industry, for he remembered during his 40 years experience that the industry had been ruined eight times already; and the same tale was told 80 years ago, when it was proposed that women and children should be excluded from underground work.[81]

Cook was also unique in being a working miner whilst on the executive of his union. He knew from first hand physical contact, not academic theory, the extremely hazardous, arduous, and inhuman task the miner had to face in his daily work. He spent his week-ends at the pit-head talking to the miners, preaching socialism or rousing them to act against some injustice or other. Before and throughout the General Strike, and for several years afterwards, he gave himself to the miners' cause. Despite his obvious danger to the established society, which he constantly suggested should be overthrown, he was never arrested. This in itself suggests that he was respected as a leader who was being followed. The ruling class prefered to let him abuse them, because he would have become a dangerous martyr if put in jail. The Communist leaders on the other hand were never accepted by the majority of the miners (or the working class as a whole); they said similar things to Cook but they lacked his obvious sincerity, and what is more important, their motives were questioned whereas Cook's were not. They could be safely put out of the way without any fear of repercussions. Consequently on the 14 October, the police raided the Communist headquarters, seized a quantity of documents, arrested 12 of the leading members, and charged them with breaches of the Incitement to Mutiny Act of 1797.[82] Many other communists were arrested during the General Strike, but the leaders were put out of the way 'for the duration'.

Mussolini's success in Italy in 1922 led to the formation of Fascist organizations throughout the rest of Europe. The British movement was formed in 1923 by the grand-daughter of Field Marshal Sir Lintorn Simmons, Miss R. Lintorn-Orman. In its manifesto published in November 1925, it described itself as: 'A body of patriotic citizens who will place their resources at the disposal of a constitutional Government in the maintenance of law and order, and will be capable of resisting, by force if absolutely necessary, any attempt at a revolution which aims at the forcible overthrow of the British constitution and Empire.' It declared its intention to enforce 'severe measures against disloyalty', to suppress the Communist Sunday schools, to abolish the dole and to 'uphold the fundamental principles of free speech provided it be not seditious.'[83] About the same time this headline appeared:-

MUSSOLINI GAGS ITALY
NEWSPAPERS AND PARTIES TO BE SUPPRESSED
FASCIST "PURGE"
THE DEATH PENALTY EXTENDED
"Daily Express"
Correspondent.
ROME, Friday, Nov. 5.

The Morning Post, on the 13 October 1925, published a letter from Lord Ernest Hamilton. It read; 'Parliamentary candidates should realize what help the British Fascists' organization may be able to afford them where it is established and working and where the maintenance of thought and action of the votes is threatened by terrorist societies.'

In October 1924, the more militant fascists left the parent body to form the National Fascisti. 'They were a tougher, far more arrogant group from the middle and upper classes.'[84] They kidnapped Harry Pollitt, a prominent member of the Minority Movement, and prevented him attending a meeting. His assailants were arrested but aquitted. In October 1925 they also stole a *Daily Herald* van. On 16 November, George Lansbury asked the Prime Minister 'whether he was aware that widespread disatisfaction existed among the public at the action taken by the Director of Public Prosecutions in connection with the case of the four National Fascisti who admitted taking possession by force of a *Daily Herald* motor van and further damaging the van.' He also asked the Home Secretary if he 'was aware of the existence of certain Fascist and other organizations and societies organized like armed forces — drilling — in uniform.'[85] The British Fascists expressed their displeasure of the organization to which they had given birth:

> Any wilful provocative action by British Fascists, would do untold harm to the cause at this juncture; therefore it is more than ever the duty of patriots to eschew anything of the sort. This does not imply that, as common-sense citizens, we should shut our eyes to the fact that our foes aim at civil war, or that we should not make every possible preparation to resist such attempts if and when tried: but it certainly does produce such wanton and mischievous exploits as have recently been performed by the National Fascisti. We regard conduct of this sort as a direct encouragement to class hatred and condemn it without reservation.[86]

The Chief Constable of Liverpool was not worried about the wanton and mischievous exploits of the British Fascisti, according to *The Times* report of 5 October 1925:

> Liverpool will be the starting point of a new move on the part of the Fascisti. Arrangements have been made for members in the Liverpool area to become special constables and to drill at the hall of the City Police. Captain W.J. Lewis, Commander

of the Fascisti in the Lancashire and Wirral area stated that
officers of the organization were to take the oath at police
headquarters today, and the swearing in of other members
would follow in due course. It was expected that between
2,000 and 3,000 would thus be enrolled. 'We are asking all our
people', added Captain Lewis 'to do this, because as a
Constitutional movement, we ought to be in the Special Constabulary. If we should be called out we should act as special
constables under the command of the Chief Constable of
Liverpool. We are trying to show the way to the whole
country, but so far Liverpool is the only place where arrangements have been made with the police.'

From inquiries it is understood that the arrangements con-
templated will permit the Fascist special constables being
under their own officers. An official of the Liverpool Police
said on Saturday if members of the Fascisti offered themselves
as special constables there was no reason why they should not
be enrolled, provided they were suitable and met the requirements laid down. If they joined they would be drilled in
precisely the same way as the constabulary was drilled now.

The reader will not be surprised to learn that Mr Lansbury's
questions about the Fascist attack on the *Daily Herald* van met with
the answer that the Director of Public Prosecutions had dropped
the charges. The reason given was because the evidence was insufficient to support the charges.[87]

The Economic League also joined in the attack on 'preparations'
by the workers for a general strike. This was in spite of substantial
preparations being made for such an event by right wing organizations and the Government, but the organized workers and the
Labour movement in general made such half-hearted attempts to
resist these pressures, that when the struggle finally came, a defeat
seemed inevitable. Before an examination of Government preparations — preparations which should stir the conscience of anyone
who considers that we enjoy a democratic society — we will
examine the preparations of those who were well aware that a
general strike was inevitable.

Immediately after 'Red Friday' there was a feeling of victory
amongst a large number of trade unionists. At the Conference of
the Trades Union Congress held at Scarborough from the 7-12
September, the President, Mr A.B. Swales delivered an address of

which the keynote was high-pitched and confident. The Congress in a resolution on Trade Union aims, unequivocally declared that the 'Trade Union Movement must organize to prepare the Trade Unions in conjunction with the Party and the Workers to struggle for the overthrow of capitalism.'[88] Similar resolutions of a left-wing nature indicated that the workers were in a militant mood. However, when it came to the election of new officers, right-wing candidates gained office, thereby changing the whole mood of the congress with J.H. Thomas and A. Pugh being two examples. The resolution which revealed the weakness of the Trade Union Congress included the following:

> . . . in reference to the duties of the General Council (these should) be referred to the General Council with instructions to examine the problem in all its bearings, with power to consult the executive of the affiliated unions, and to report to a Special Conference of the executives concerned their considered recommendations on the subject.[89]

A slow, cumbersome machinery was set up against all the forces of reaction. We shall follow its progress.

Two weeks after the Scarborough Congress the Labour Party Conference was held at Liverpool. There every left-wing resolution was rejected, every Communist expelled, all talk of sympathetic strikes in support of other unions condemned.[90] There seems little doubt that the actions taken and the opinions expressed at this conference of Labour, presented the Conservative Government with a clear mandate to arrest the Communist leaders without any fear of opposition. Certainly they wasted no time in raiding the Communist Headquarters and taking documents which were to prove invaluable to them during the course of the General Strike, and of course putting out of the way the leaders mentioned previously. Ernest Bevin, who attacked the leadership of MacDonald, spoke for the majority of ordinary workers when he spoke to the resolution put by the Labour Party Executive which called for expulsion of the Communists. He said:

> If I thought for one moment that this resolution was put down by the Executive Committee merely because the Communists take an advanced line, I would be against the Executive. But having had the experience of the agitation carried on within my own Union, I feel that the Communists cannot con-

scientiously reconcile the Communist basis with the basis of evolutionary democracy that the Labour Party represents. I am tired of tactics. Working class men in this country want people to be straight with them.[91]

To say that he spoke for the majority of ordinary workers is born out by their actions during the strike to follow. It should also be emphasized that the left-wing of the Labour movement were well aware of the coming struggle. In January 1926 the *Workers' Weekly*, organ of the Communist Party, carried the headlines:

Vast Struggle Begins, Whole Class must Unite,
A common minimum wanted for All Workers.

That the trade unions, and particularly the General Council of the T.U.C. ignored such pleas is best illustrated by Bevin when he addressed the Conference of Executives in January 1927. Bevin, himself a member of the General Council, reported:

With regard to the preparations for the strike, there were no preparations until 27 April (1926), and I do not want anyone to go away from this conference under the impression that the General Council had any particular plan to run this move-ment. In fact the General Council did not sit down to draft plans until they were called together on 27 April, and it is better for everybody to know the task was thrown upon us from 27 April to 1 May and when that task is understood you will be able to appreciate, not the little difficulties, but the wonderful response and organization we had.[92]

To really appreciate the character and mood of men on the General Council we would have to examine each individual and attempt to discern their individual motives for the actions they did, or did not take. Some indications can be gained by quoting what they said in private and in public, but we never *really* know them. Some attempt however, has to be made, and by being selective one is open to the accusation of bias. Two events in the life of J.H. Thomas reveal the character of that 'leader' of the General Strike, biased or not. The first took place in 1924 when Thomas was a member of the Labour Government. 'Members of the N.U.R., under pressure from their National Secretary, Thomas, accepted wage reductions which the companies claimed under the sliding scale agreement.' The A.S.L.E.F. would not accept the verdict of the Central Wages Board. At a Privy Council meeting the King asked Thomas for his opinion of Bromley, leader of the A.S.L.E.F.

> 'Speaking to you as subject to your Majesty, sir, or as man to man?' he enquired.
> 'As man to man, please, Mr Thomas.'
> 'Then you can take it from me, your Majesty, he's a bloody 'ound.'

A strike followed this discussion, lasting for ten days, and ended in defeat.[93]

The second incident took place in 1926, but it is so closely related to one in 1918 that one is compelled to draw attention to them both.

In 1918 the railwaymen of South Wales had joined the miners there in a strike. General Smuts was sent to 'touch the patriotism' of the miners, and Thomas to appeal to the railwaymen. His speech was full of the politician's 'emotion':

> . . . over and above there was the thought of the great society that I love and that you love, the society that has done so much . . .
> It is unpleasant and it cuts to my soul to speak like this *to the people who have made me*, the people I worked with, but it is only duty that compels me to make you face the cold hard facts of the situation.

Early in 1926 (fully justifying the rallying call of the *Worker's Weekly*) the National Wages Board again threatened to reduce wages which the men resisted, in defiance of Thomas. But by force of personality as much as argument, Thomas persuaded the delegates to change their minds three days before a strike was due to begin.[94] The *Daily Herald* reported how it was done. Note italicized words in the following quote:

'J.H.T.' ON AWARD VOTE

27 JAN 1926

'No Section as Important as Whole Community'

Speaking at a dinner of the Empire Press Union, after the decision of delegates to accept the wages award, Mr. J.H. Thomas (who did not appear in evening dress) proposed the

J.H. Thomas M.P. with walking stick (Photograph by courtesy of the
T.U.C. Library)

health of the chairman. 'I don't apologise for not being in
evening dress,' he said, 'for after all dress does not count for
everything.'

'I had a choice between meeting 80 delegates who had determined on a strike, or of being here earlier. I knew that my

final speech would be at about 6.45, and I said to my wife, Aggie, what God's chance is there of carrying this resolution if I appear in evening dress?' (Laughter). I won. (Cheers). But what would have happened if I had appeared respectable? (Laughter).

'In connection with this dispute *I felt I had no right to throw overboard the people who have made me.* I acted as I did, not with the feeling of throwing them overboard, but with a true recognition that no section of the community, however important, is as important as the community as a whole, and for that reason my effort was directed as I hope it will always be directed, towards the channel of peace.'

The Miners' Federation was unprepared and although regularly Cook, Smith and the Minority Movement issued statements calling for preparations to be made, no preparations were ever made.

It will be remembered that the letter from the Mining Association (employers) referred to a Royal Commission being set up after 'Red Friday'. In the Sankey Commission, the Buckmaster Inquiry, and the Macmillan Inquiry, the workers were represented; but after 'Red Friday' the new Commission contained only members alien to the working class. The Chairman was Sir Herbert Samuel, who until recently had been High Commissioner in Palestine; the other members were: General Sir Herbert Lawrence, member of the banking firm of Glyn, Mills; Sir William Beveridge, director of the London School of Economics; and Kenneth Lee, chairman of the Tootal Broadhurst Lee Company, a large Manchester cotton firm. Its first public hearing was on 15 October 1925. Its report was completed on 6 March 1926. Its recommendations were: (1) the nationalization of the coal royalties — simply a repetition of the unanimous recommendation of the Sankey Commission, which had been ignored ever since; (2) the reorganization of the industry under private ownership (the Sankey Commission recommended nationalization); (3) improved arrangements for research and distribution with aid from the Government; (4) better relations between employers and labour through joint pit committees, pit head baths (promised 1911), etc. It suggested however that immediate consideration should be given to the lowering of wages.[95]

On the 11 March 1926, the day after the Samuel Report was made public, the miners not only accepted the proposal of the

Prime Minister, that the parties in the Coal Industry should make no pronouncement until after full examination of the report, but also requested the Industrial Committee of the T.U.C. to take a similar line. Included in a letter sent to the secretaries of all organizations affiliated to the Trade Unions Congress by this Industrial Committee, was the following:

> The Industrial Committee has been in regular consultation with the Miners' Federation, and while it would be premature at the present stage to attempt to formulate any detailed policy which may have to be pursued, the committee has already re-affirmed the attitude of the trade union movement as expressed in July last — namely, that it would stand firmly and unitedly against any attempt to degrade further the standard of life in the coalfields. There was to be no reduction in wages, no increase in working hours, and no interference with the principle of national agreements.
>
> The committee is not unmindful of the preparations which the Government and the mineowners are making, and is giving this matter due consideration. It is important, therefore, that the Labour movement should guard against any precipitate action. At the same time, the members of affiliated unions are specially asked to disregard the unauthorized and unofficial suggestions which are being made in many quarters regarding the mining problem.[96]

The letter was signed by Mr. A. Pugh (chairman) and Mr. W.M. Citrine (acting secretary).

Cook spoke for the miners in a speech at the end of March which summed up their attitude to the Samuel Commission. 'We are going to be slaves no longer and our men will starve before they accept any reductions in wages.'[97] This was in strict contrast to the guarded statement of the Industrial Committee.

The coal-owners would only talk of lowering wages and a return to district agreements. The Government, although taking part in the joint meetings, did nothing. It gave grudging acceptance to the proposals of the Report and promised the necessary legislation provided both sides agreed to it. It thus invited them to disagree, in effect giving a veto to the miners over reductions of wages and to the owners over reorganization.[98] Deadlock came at a meeting on

13 April which shall be returned to in the next chapter. We must now turn to examine the Government preparations for defeating the strike, a strike it had clearly provoked. Mr Churchill's speech of December 1925, and the circular sent out to all local authorities in November 1925, have already been mentioned. The first intimated the postponing of the strike (hence the subsidy), and then coping with it when the time came; the second dealt with the perfecting of an organization to deal with the anticipated strike of May 1926, (when the time would come).

The November Circular was numbered 636, and it was one of several of a similar kind issued since 1919. The first document was designed to combat the 1919 rail strike by the organized distribution of food and other essentials, under the control of the Ministry of Health. Essentially the same organization was in readiness for the threatened Triple Alliance Strike of 1921, which did not materialize. When the Lloyd George Government fell in 1922, the Bonar Law Government took over the existing organization, merely substituting its own Civil Commissioners. When the MacDonald Ministry assumed office in January 1924, they too changed the Commissioners, but the old strike breaking organization was maintained.

In 1919 the Government was able to use army trucks and R.A.S.C. drivers, but by 1926 the Baldwin Government had to rely almost wholly upon voluntary haulage, and voluntary business men's committees. The haulage contractors were organized into 150 committees, with the result that the total expense to the Government for carrying on emergency road transport during the nine days of the General Strike was only £20,000.[99] The consumers and not the Government paid the price of the emergency transport — milk, for example, rose by two pence a quart.[100] Circular 636 laid emphasis on the responsibilities of all local authorities for keeping essential services going in their own areas, and stated that the Government's organization was intended merely to supplement and assist such local efforts. These preparations were fully supported by another organization, details of which were revealed to the public on 25 September 1925. It was called the 'Organization for the Maintenance of Supplies', but became known better by the initials O.M.S.

The announcement ran as follows:

> For many months past it has been evident that a movement is
> being organized to take advantage of a trade dispute, excep-
> tionally difficult to solve, in order to promote a general strike,
> and by suspending supplies and arresting power, transport,
> and sanitary services to paralyse the national life. Such a
> danger was imminent on 6 August last, and it would have
> found the large majority of the people, who have neither
> sympathy with the movement, nor direct interest in the issue,
> wholly unprepared. Numerous suggestions have since been
> made from various quarters for organizing those citizens who
> would be prepared to volunteer to maintain supplies and vital
> services in the event of a general strike.
> It seems, therefore, that the moment has come to announce
> publicly that such an organization has already been constituted
> and is at work in many metropolitan boroughs, while steps are
> being taken to create corresponding organizations in all the
> principal centres of the Kingdom.[101]

At the head of this peculiar organization was Lord Hardinge of
Penhurst and on its Council were Admiral of the Fleet Lord Jellico,
General Sir Francis Lloyd, and several others of a similar class.

The *Manchester Guardian* wrote an editorial which deplored the
new step, and only the *Daily Mail* appeared to be enthusiastic.[102]
The Home Secretary, for reasons only he could give, found it
necessary to reply to an anonymous correspondent on the 1
October 1925:

> Thank you for your letter . . . I will be perfectly frank with
> you. I have known of the inauguration of this body (O.M.S.)
> for many weeks past; in fact, the promoters consulted me as to
> their desire to form some such organization. I told them quite
> frankly that it was the duty of the Government to preserve
> order and to maintain the necessary supplies for keeping the
> life of the country going in an emergency. This duty the
> Government is prepared to carry out. My plans have been
> long since made, and have been approved by the Government
> as a whole.
> On the other hand, we have not thought it necessary or
> desirable to make a public parade of our willingness and
> ability to do that which is our duty, nor have we desired to

assume that what might be considered a provocative attitude by enrolling several hundred thousand men who would be willing to assist in maintaining the services vital to the country's life. This being so, I told the promoters of the O.M.S. that there was no objection on the part of the Government to their desire to inaugurate the body to which you refer; that, if and when an emergency arose, the Government would discharge the responsibility which is theirs and theirs alone, but that it would be of every assistance to us to receive from the O.M.S., *or from any other body of well-disposed citizens* [author's italics], classified lists of men in different parts of the country who would be willing to place their services at the disposal of the Government.

From this statement you will see that not only is there no reason why you should object to the O.M.S. but that you . . . would be performing a patriotic act by allying yourself with this *or any other similar body* . . . [author's italics].

There *is no suggestion of Fascism about the movement* . . . [author's italics]. [103]

This last comment should be taken in the light of the parts of the Home Secretary's statement emphasized in italics, and a statement made by Lord Hardinge in *The Times* of 28 April 1926.

It is desirable that the position of the O.M.S. in regard to the British Fascists should be clearly defined. Our organization has announced that we welcome the cooperation of other *patriotic societies* [author's italics] in promoting the particular aims of O.M.S. We were however, unable to entertain any proposals for cooperation with the British Fascists so long as they adhered to their existing constitution. Only if they abandoned their quasi-military formation and made it clear that they would act under authority as citizens, and only then on requisition by a Constitutional Government, were we prepared to cooperate.

This statement led to the resignation of a number of men from the British Fascists, who then took the name of Loyalists. [104] Just because this was published in *The Times* does not mean that Fascists were unwelcome in the O.M.S. Proof of this came from the Secretary of the O.M.S. in a letter he sent to *The Social Democrat*. That journal, in its November issue (1925), criticized the Home Secretary for welcoming anything 'that may be offered voluntarily

— O.M.S., Fascisti, or what not — that he may have something
ready for emergencies without troubling the Home Office with
more than mere police work.' Its December issue published the
following, above the signature of C. Wykeham-Fiennes, General
Secretary, O.M.S.

> Sir William Joynson-Hicks has been roundly abused for
> announcing his willingness to accept aid of this kind. But
> why? Why should not the Government accept the services of
> men who are voluntarily banded together for — so they
> believe — the defence of their vital interests?
> The danger of a general strike may be remote; but it is not a
> figment of the brain of a few busybodies with 'cold feet'. It
> was definitely threatened last July, and it is well understood
> that this threat *was only postponed until the coal commission had
> finished its work.* There is plenty of evidence that the machinery
> for bringing such a strike into operation is being perfected.
> Who shall blame those who will suffer from the calamity if
> they take timely measures to avert its most immediate and
> direful consequences?

One can only wonder where this gentleman found his evidence that
'machinery' for bringing a general strike about was 'being
perfected' in December 1925, nearly three months before the
Samuel Commission published its findings.

Sir William Joynson Hicks, who above spoke of the
Government's 'duty to preserve order', was an ardent supporter of
the Ulster fire eaters under Sir Edward Carson, whose
gun-running exploits and open military training of the 'Ulster
Volunteers' were imperial scandals during the last years of the pre-
war Asquith Government. Sir William, speaking at Warrington on
6 December 1913, defied the Asquith Cabinet:

> The people of Ulster have behind them the Unionist Party;
> behind them the Lord God of Battles. In his name and your
> name I say to the Prime Minister — 'Let your armies and
> batteries fire. Fire if you dare; fire and be damned.'[105]

To Joynson-Hicks must be added Winston Churchill, the man who
sent out the questionaire to find out how many soldiers were
willing to act to suppress those comrades they had fought alongside
in the worst war in history; a man who had many times ordered
out military units against the working class. Add to those two the

Earl of Birkenhead. After the General Strike he was addressing a disorderly crowd in London. Voices from the front shouted, 'Wait till we put up the barricades!' In a second he strode to the front of the platform and shouted: 'Barricades! You dare to talk to me about barricades! — we've beaten you with brains, and if it comes to fighting two can play at that game! Put up your barricades, and we'll slit every one of your soft white throats!' Then followed long drawn yells of anger. 'Howl on you wolves of Moscow!' said Frederick Edwin, Earl of Birkenhead encouragingly.[106] A fourth member of this group was Mr Neville Chamberlain, the Minister of Health. With over 1½ million unemployed to deal with, this man was determined to keep a tight check on Boards of Guardians in case they *really* relieved poverty. On 11 August, *The Times* gave a clear indication of the policy of his Ministry: 'Extravagant Poor Relief', ran the headline. 'The Ministry have refused to sanction a further *loan* of £300,000 to West Ham Board of Guardians unless they reduced their scale of relief, which is held to be extravagent 'and make a closer scrutiny of the recipients. . . . The weekly scale upon which the relief is paid is as follows: 9s. 6d. per head for man and wife; 5s. for each child; rent up to 15s., coal in winter months, up to 2s. 3d. and the maximum allowed is £3.' On 17 August, the same paper carried another headline: 'Mother and Children Drowned'. It told of a mother who took her six children to the river Mersey and walked into the river with them — two managed to free themselves. 'Mrs Vaugham, who was about 35 years of age, was arrested (for theft) on the previous day . . . Mr Vaugham is a railway worker, and his wife had been worried about the health of one of her children, and the fact that she tried to borrow half a crown from a neighbour suggests that there was also financial stress.'

The four members of the Cabinet mentioned earlier provided the hard core of Conservative resistance to the working class, and they organized and prepared for a general strike by the workers, so that they could smash the working class resistance to wage cuts. A police state had been set up to this end. The O.M.S. was to provide willing volunteer strike breakers. Local Authorities had been given their orders to provide emergency transport arrangements, and make the public pay for it. British Fascists, National Fascisti, besides The Middle Class Union, the Citizens' Union, the Economic League, the Women's Guild of Empire, the Mineowners' Association, and many other reactionary organizations rallied to

Cartoon from *Punch* 19 May 1926 (By courtesy of *Punch*)

Man of the World (helping himself to private car in West End): Don't put yerself aht, Guv'nor — Anywhere in the Mile End Road'll do me — 'op in. Lizzie!

the strike breaking call. The middle classes and their allies, the aristocracy and leaders of big business, were fully prepared for fighting the class war. Their enemies, the working class, were totally unprepared, their leaders anxious only to negotiate terms less severe than those the ruling class were trying to impose. We shall follow the 'war' and the 'peace terms', in the final chapter.

Note.
The Times, 10 April 1926, carried a report of an attempted assassination of Mussolini by Miss Violet Gibson. Lady Chamberlain (wife of the Foreign Secretary) sent a telegram of sympathy to Mussolini. King George also sent a telegram: it read; 'Please express to the Prime Minister my horror at the dastardly attempt made on his life. I rejoice to hear that the wound has not proved serious and deeply regret that the assailant is a British subject. I hope the recovery will be rapid.'

Notes to Chapter 6

1. Arnot, R. Page: *The Miners*, Allen & Unwin, 1953, pp.159 and 161.
2. Cole, G.D.H. *A Short History of the British Working Class Movement*, Allen & Unwin, 1960, p.354.
3. Arnot, R. Page: *Op.Cit.* pp.179 and 180.
4. Crook, W.H.: *The General Strike. A Study of Labor's Tragic Weapon in Theory and Practice*, The University of North Carolina Press, pp.236 and 237.
5. Arnot, R. Page: *Op.Cit.* 170.
6. Mowat, Charles Loch: *Britain Between the Wars, 1914-18*, London, 1955. p.6.
7. Mowat, Charles Loch: *Ibid.* p.7.
8. Mowat, Charles Loch: *Ibid.* p.5.
9. Crook, W.H.: *Op.Cit.* p.380.
10. Mowat, Charles Loch: *Op.Cit.* p.22.
11. Crook, W.H. *Op.Cit.* pp.241 and 242.
12. *The Times*, 30 May 1919.
13. Arnot, R. Page: *Op.Cit.* p.184.
14. Mowat, Charles Loch: *Op.Cit.* p.33.
15. Mowat, Charles Loch: *Ibid.* p.33.
16. Mowat, Charles Loch: *Ibid.* pp.38 and 39.
17. Bagwell, P.S: *The Railwaymen*, London, 1963. p.375.
18. Bagwell, P.S: *Ibid.* pp.383 to 386.
19. Blaxland, Gregory; *J.H. Thomas: A Life for Unity*. London, 1964. p.128.
20. Blaxland, Gregory: *Ibid.* pp.130 and 131.
21. Glasgow, George: *General Strikes and Road Transport*. London. 1926.
22. Bagwell, P.S: *Op.Cit.* p.398.
23. Bagwell, P.S: *Ibid.* p.484.
24. Crook, W.H.: *Op.Cit.* p.254.
25. Bagwell, P.S: *Op.Cit.* p.394.
26. Crook, W.H.: *Op.Cit.* p.261.
27. Bagwell, P.S: *Op.Cit.* p.394.
28. Bagwell, P.S.: *Ibid.* p.395.
29. Crook, W.H.: *Op.Cit.* p.256.
30. Bagwell, P.S: *Op.Cit.* p.388.
31. Cole, G.D.H. and Postgate, R: *The Common People*. p.555.
32. Arnot, R.Page: *Op.Cit.* pp.270 to 278.
33. Mowat, Charles Loch: *Op.Cit.* p.27. (With the index number of retail food prices at 100 in July 1914, a peak was reached in November 1920 of 291). Mowat also claimed that the slump hit the middle class more than the working class. (See also p.27).
34. Toole, M: *Bessie Bradock M.P.*, London, 1967. p.68.
35. Arnot, R.Page: *Op.Cit.* pp.290 and 291.
36. Arnot, R.Page: *Ibid.* p.291.
37. Arnot, R.Page: *Ibid.* p.294.
38. Mowat, Charles Loch, *Op.Cit.* p.121.
39. Arnot, R.Page: *Op.Cit.* p.299.
40. Arnot, R.Page: *Ibid.* p.262.
41. Bagwell, P.S: *Op.Cit.* p.462.
42. Arnot, R.Page: *Op.Cit.* p.523.
43. Mowat, Charles Loch: *Op.Cit.* p.124.

44. Mowat, Charles Loch: *Ibid*. pp.121 and 122.
45. *Forward*, 2 December 1922.
46. Cole, G.D.H. *Op.Cit*. p.402.
47. Mowat, Charles Loch: *Op.Cit*. pp.127 and 128.
48. *Hansard*. 21 November 1929.
49. *Glasgow Evening News*, 24 November 1921.
50. Mowat, Charles Loch: *Op.Cit*. pp.128 and 129.
51. Mr. Owen Philips, 38 Gaynor Place, Yuyshir, Rhondda. 31 August 1976.
52. Bennett, Richard: *A Picture of the Twenties*. London, 1961. pp.58 and 59.
53. Mowat, Charles Loch: *Op.Cit*. pp.142 to 145.
54. Mowat, Charles Loch: *Ibid*. p.161.
55. Arnot, R. Page: *Op Cit*. p. 341.
56. *The Economist*, 21 October 1922.
57. Bennett, Richard: *Op.Cit*. p.71.
58. Mowat, Charles Loch: *Op.Cit*. p.166.
59. Mowat, Charles Loch: *Ibid*. pp.170 to 173.
60. Mowat, Charles Loch: *Ibid*. pp.184 to 186.
61. Bennett, Richard: *Op.Cit*. p.113.
62. Mowat, Charles Loch: *Op.Cit*. pp.185-186
63. Mowat, Charles Loch: *Ibid*. p.189.
64. Amery, S: *Op.Cit*. p.296.
65. Cole, G.D.H: *Ibid*. pp.415 and 416.
66. Crook, W.H.: *Op.Cit*. p.286.
67. Crook, W.H.: *Ibid*. p.287.
68. *The Times*, 9 July 1925.
69. Crook, W.H.: *Op.Cit*. pp.287 and 288.
70. *The Times*, 17 July 1925.
71. Crook, W.H.: *Op.Cit*. pp.291.
72. Arnot, R.Page: *Op.Cit*. pp.371 to 380.
73. Mowat, Charles Loch: *Op.Cit*. p.293.
74. *The Daily Mail*, 2 August 1925.
75. *The Times*, 3 August 1925.
76. *The Times*, 7 August 1925.
77. Arnot, R.Page: *The General Strike, Its Origin and History*. London, 1926. pp.58 and 59. Report of Mr Winston Churchill's speech on 10 December 1925, speaking on the Coal Mining Industry Convention.
78. Glasgow, George: *Op.Cit*. p.101.
79. Crook, W.H.: Op.Cit. pp.294 and 295 quoting from 'The Nation' (N.Y.) 26 August 1925.
80. Crook, W.H.: *Ibid*. p.295.
81. *The Labour Magazine*, (Journal of the T.U.C.), May, 1925.
82. Bennett, Richard: *Op.Cit*. p.131.
83. Mullally, Frederick: *Fascism Inside England*. London, 1946. p.19.
84. Mullally, Frederick: *Ibid*. p.21.
85. *The Times*. 17 November 1925.
86. *The Fascist Bulletin*. 21 November 1925.
87. *The Labour Magazine*. December 1925.
88. Arnot, R.Page: *The General Strike*. *Op.Cit*. p.63.
89. Arnot, R.Page: *Ibid*. p.70.
90. Arnot, R.Page: *The Miners*. *Op.Cit*. pp.395/6 and Bullock, Alan: *The Life and Times of Ernest Bevin*, Vol.I, Heinemann, 1960. p.285.

91. Bullock, Alan: *Ibid.* p.285.
92. Crook, W.H.: *Op.Cit.* pp.311 and 312.
93. Blaxland Gregory: *Op.Cit.* p.168.
94. Blaxland, Gregory: *Ibid.* pp.114 to 115 and p.184.
95. Arnot, R.Page: *The Miners. Op.Cit.* pp.402/405. also: *The Coal Crisis: Facts from the Samuel Commission*, 1925-26. London, 1926, and Mowat, Charles Loch: *Op.Cit.* pp.297 and 298.
96. *The New Dawn.* 13 March 1926. p.18.
97. Mowat, Charles Loch: *Op.Cit.* p.299.
98. Mowat, Charles Loch: *Ibid.* p.298 and 299.
99. Glasgow, George: *Op.Cit.* p.24.
100. Glasgow, George: *Ibid.* p.30.
101. Arnot, R.Page: *The General Strike,* p.49.
102. Arnot, R.Page: *Ibid.* p.54.
103. *The Times,* 1 October 1925.
104. Crook, W.H.: *Op.Cit.* p.301.
105. Crook, W.H.: *Ibid.* p.302.
106. Birkenhead, The Earl of: *Frederick Edwin, Earl of Birkenhead.* London, 1933. p.265.

Chapter 7

The Class War Intensified : Battle, Betrayal, Rout and Reprisal.

Only great boldness in the revolutionary struggle can strike the weapons from the hands of reaction, shorten the period of civil war, and diminish the number of its victims. He who is not prepared to go so far should not take up arms at all; he who will not take up arms should not think of serious resistance at all. The only thing that would remain would be to educate the workers in the spirit of complete submission, which would be a work of supererogation, as it is already being performed by the official schools, the governing party, the priests of the church, and . . . the Socialist preachers of the impropriety of force.

Leon Trotsky[1]

On the 13 April 1926, the Miners' Executive and the Central Committee of the Mining Association openly declared the deadlock, which had been apparent as soon as the Samuel Commission released its findings. The owners announced their intentions to proceed at once in the various districts to invite the miners' representatives to meet them for the purpose of considering the amounts of the minimum percentages or basis rates and of subsistence wages. On the following day a report of the meeting was put before the Special Industrial Committee of the General Council. A resolution protesting at the 'abandoning of national negotiations' and confirming that the Committee would 'render the miners the fullest support in resisting the degradation of their standard of life' was carried. The resolution made it clear that the committee's main aim was to obtain 'an equitable settlement of the case with regard to wages, hours, and national agreements.'[2]

This resolution was sent to the Prime Minister who then invited the Miner's Executive to meet him on the 15 April 1926. The result of this meeting was an understanding that Mr Baldwin would endeavour to bring the mineowners to agree to resume negotiations on a national basis.[3] Whilst these talks were proceeding, the owners posted notices terminating the current agreement on 30 April, but did not state the terms on which the men would be re-employed.[4]

On the 19 April, Mr J.H. Thomas expressed the view of the right-wing of the Trade Union movement, and Mr A.J. Cook that of the left. Mr Thomas, according to *The Times*, said:

> To talk at this stage as if in a few days all the workers of the country were to be called out was not only letting loose passions that might be difficult to control, but it was not rendering the best service either to the miners or anyone else . . . instead of organizing, mobilizing, and encouraging the feeling that war was inevitable, *let them concentrate on finding a solution honourable and satisfactory to all sides.* [author's italics]

Armoured cars and troops stand guard outside the Bank of England during the 1926 General Strike (Photograph by courtesy of the T.U.C. Library)

The Miners' Secretary, Arthur Cook had just returned from a meeting of the International Miners' Federation in Brussels, where he was assured of support in defence of the miner's standard of living, and if necessary, a sympathetic international mining strike, and was perhaps over enthusiastic. The International Transport Workers' Federation had also pledged their support, (when the strike came, some workers in Antwerp and Brussels 'acted even before instructions had reached them').[5] Cook declared that there would be no help for the miners from the British Government, who would certainly back the owners. The coming struggle must involve not merely the miners but the whole of the working classes:

> They had got the whole trade union movement in the country pledged to defend the miners' hours, wages and national agreements. Abroad they had made arrangements that no coal should come into this country. The Government and the owners knew they had got the organization that could fight and win. My last word to the Government is 'Count the cost. The cost of a strike of the miners would mean the end of capitalism.'
> Let me warn the Government that there is a new mentality in the police, the Army, the Navy, and the Air Force. Ninety-seven per cent of the recruits for the past two years have come from the working classes, and thousands of them miners, who will not shoot against their kith and kin, when the order comes, and we shall not be afraid to advise them. This is a war to the death, and it is your death they are after.[6]

Cartoon from the *St Pancras Bulletin* No 4 second edition 6 May 1926
(By courtesy of the Labour Research Department)

On the 20 April 1926, the Mining Association announced:

> There is not the slightest foundation for the rumours that the

coal owners have decided, or are prepared, to agree to the principle of a national minimum wage.[7]

Two days later the Miners' Executive met the owners' representatives, to consider the latter's draft agreement. No progress was made because the owners insisted on the settlement of wages by district negotiations. Mr Evan Williams admitted that many of the district wage offers that would shortly be made were undoubtedly low, but that if the workers would agree to longer hours, 'all of the districts would be in a position to offer wages of which no reasonable complaint could be made.'[8]

On the 23 April, under pressure from the Industrial Committee the previous evening, Mr Baldwin met both the miners and the mineowners. The owners drew up a series of wage offers based on an eight hour day.[8] These proposals were posted at the pit-heads. *The British Worker* of 5 May published a table showing a comparison of wages paid prior to the proposed lock-out, and wages to be expected in the future (see table following). In Northumberland the rates were found to be the same as those in force in July 1914 despite the rise in the cost of living.

Several meetings then took place between the Prime Minister, the owners' and the Miners' negotiating committees, and the Industrial Committee, before the lock-out notices were to take effect on 30 April 1926. The causes of breakdown were still the same; the owners thought only of longer hours and a reduction of wages; Baldwin made no proposals, and in particular none about reorganization which, for the miners, was the fundamental question. When one is aware of the fact that Mr Baldwin's right hand man, Joynson-Hicks, had spelt out Government policy in a speech on 1 August 1925, the Prime Minister's refusal to act is not surprising. 'Jix' as the Home Secretary was better known said: 'We have got to find a remedy (for the industrial depression), and, if need be, however disagreeable it may be, I am going to say straight out what the Prime Minister is alleged to have said in conference yesterday — namely, it may be that, in order to compete with the world, the conditions of labour, hours, and wages will have to be altered in this country.'[9]

With Joynson-Hicks' statement in mind, the Government's impartiality in the mining dispute was questionable. Furthermore with all the preparations outlined in the previous chapter for a conflict with the working class as a whole, it becomes more obvious that the Government was on the side of the owners. If any doubts

Comparative Table of Wages Offer from *The British Worker*

OWNERS' DRASTIC PROPOSALS

The Miners' Federation prepared a table showing a comparison of wages payable to certain representative classes of day-wage workers before the lock-out and the wages that would be paid under the terms of the owners' demands posted at the pit-heads.

The following figures were taken from the statement. Similar reductions were demanded in other districts.

On the basis of a 5½ day week the reductions range from 3s. 9d. to 17s. 2d. a week.

	Present wages s. d.		Owners' terms s. d.		Reduction per day. s. d.
Scotland					
Coal hewers	9 4	...	7 6	...	1 10
Labourers	6 8¼	...	6 0	...	8¼
Northumberland—					
Hewers	10 4	...	7 7	...	2 9
Labourers	7 7½	...	4 9	...	3 1½
Durham—					
Hewers	9 8	...	6 10	...	2 10
Labourers	7 6½	...	4 11¾	...	2 6¾
South Wales and Monmouthshire—					
Hewers	9 9¼	...	7 2½	...	2 6¾
Labourers (day)	8 0¾	...	*6 8	...	*1 4¾
South Yorks					
Hewers	10 7½	...	9 6¾	...	1 0¾
Labourers	8 8½	...	7 6½	...	1 2
Lancashire					
Hewers	9 6½	...	8 1½	...	1 5
Labourers	8 8½	...	6 2	...	2 5½
North Wales					
Hewers	9 4½	...	7 8	...	1 8½
Labourers	6 5	...	5 0	...	1 5
Derbyshire					
Hewers	11 8¾	...	10 6¾	...	1 2
Labourers (surface)	8 8½	...	7 6½	...	1 2
Notts—					
Hewers	12 1¼	...	10 10½	...	1 2¾
Labourers (surface)	8 5½	...	7 3¾	...	1 1¾

*If married. For single men the rate would be 5s. 9d. a day, a reduction of 2s. 3¾d. a day.

remain two events eradicate them. *The Sunday Times* of 25 April, provided space for Sir Robert Horne (Chancellor of the Exchequer during 1921-22), to attack the Samuel Commission Report. The report was emphatically hostile to longer working hours in the mines. Sir Robert however, demanded a return to the eight-hour day in order to reduce coal costs to a point where effective competition could be secured in the world markets. He belittled the fear that no markets could be found for the extra tonnage. On the following day, while Baldwin was talking to the Industrial Committee, a document was issued by the Central Office of the Conservative and Unionist party. It read as follows:

> You will no doubt be fully occupied with the Budget debate. Perhaps you will kindly pass on the enclosed to your labour correspondent. The Government are particularly anxious to draw the attention of the public to the serious economic position of the coal industry as disclosed in the statistical table given in the House of Commons last week, showing the percentage of coal which is raised at a loss. Reference may also usefully be made to the question of hours, upon which it is desirable to concentrate attention rather than upon the reduction of wages.[10]

Mr Baldwin denied any responsibility for the document.

On Thursday, 29 April the executive committees of 141 trade unions, numbering 828 in all, met in the Memorial Hall, Farringdon Street, London. Ramsey MacDonald and Arthur Henderson were there on the platform with the General Council. This Special Conference of Executive Committees did not disperse until Saturday, 1 May 1926. On the Thursday the Conference heard a full report from the chairman, Mr Arthur Pugh. A resolution was then moved by J.H. Thomas, and seconded by Mr Ernest Bevin, which 'endorsed the efforts of the General Council to secure an honourable settlement of the differences in the coal-mining industry.' The resolution went on to declare 'its readiness for the negotiations to continue providing that the impending lockout of the mineworkers is not enforced.' Bevin also made it clear that negotiations were to continue:

> You are moving to an extraordinary position. In 24 hours from now you may have to cease being separate Unions for this purpose. For this purpose you will become one union with no

autonomy. The miners will have to throw their lot and cause into the cause of the general movement, and the general movement will have to take the responsibility of seeing it through. But at the moment we feel that to begin wielding any sort of threat in connection with the negotiations, in the stage they are now in, would be to place a weapon in the hands of our opponents.[11]

W.J. Brown of the Civil Service Clerical Association broke through the woolly statements, when he spoke to the resolution:

> We are asked to adjourn today on the night before what may be the last day of negotiations, without any conclusive demonstration of where the movement stands on this particular issue. . . . The justification of the General Council is that they do not want, at this stae (the last moment), to use the big stick upon public opinion and upon those who are opposed to us. I want to ask them whether they have considered the effect which the absence of a definite lead this afternoon is likely to have upon our own people — a factor which is at least as important as its effect on the other side. If we are to go into this business; if it is in the mind of the General Council that the whole movement (i.e. Parliamentary Labour Party included) should back up the miners if peace cannot be got, then, in my opinion the time has come to say it.[12]

Mr Thomas replied to the above comments in the following words:

> Do not let there be any sneers at the Parliamentary Party, because that is the position. The other point is that this resolution means exactly what is said. It means that we must continue our efforts to get an honourable peace and report the situation to you tomorrow. No, this is not the time for bluff or a big stick. This is the time to face a serious issue in a serious way and do the right thing at the right time.[13]

One could hardly accuse the General Council of inciting the workers to start a revolution.

On Friday the 30 April the Conference met again at 11 a.m. and waited until 11.25 p.m. when Mr Pugh returned to report on the negotiations that had been continuing between the Industrial Committee (now called the Negotiating Committee), the Prime Minister, Lord Birkenhead, and Sir Austen Chamberlain. He told the delegates, who had passed the time smoking, talking or singing, that 'no definite proposals had been received either from the Government or from the employers upon which negotiations could be conducted.' Negotiations therefore continued until 1.30 a.m. on Saturday, 1 May. A letter dated 30 April, was sent to Herbert Smith by Baldwin, which Pugh had read out at about 11.30 p.m. (Friday). This letter told the miners that the coal-owners had at last made an offer. The Prime Minister's letter set out the offer thus: 'A uniform national minimum of 20% over 1914 standard on a uniform eight-hour basis, with corresponding hours for surface men.' Smith's reply interpreted these figures as follows: 'The proposals, stated briefly, provide for a reversion to the minimum percentage of 1921, i.e., 20% on 1914 standard wages, which means a uniform reduction of 13⅓% of the standard wages of the miners, and, further, is conditional upon the extension of the working day for over three years, such an adjustment to be reviewed after December, 1929.' (Baldwin offered to set up yet another Commission not later than 31 December 1929.) Smith pressed for the re-organization of the mines, and said:

It is only necessary to say that the present hours
(a)   Are long enough to supply all the coal for which a market can be found;
(b)   Are as long as men should be expected to pursue such a dangerous and arduous calling; and
(c)   That to extend hours in present circumstances is simply to swell the ranks of the unemployed;
(d)   That to increase hours is to invite similar measures on the part of our foreign competitors;
(e)   That such a proposal is contrary to the findings of the Royal Commission.

When the Industrial Committee returned at 1.30 a.m. Saturday, the miners had indicated that they were 'prepared to examine the Report from page one to the last page, and to stand by the result of the inquiry.' The Government were told, in other words, that the miners would consider wage reductions once the Samuel scheme for re-organization 'had been initiated by the Government'. The word 'initiated' was taken exception to, and Baldwin said bluntly, 'Will you accept the Report, Mr. Smith?' Herbert Smith, equally blunt, replied: 'When we see what the re-organization is going to be, all provided in the Report, we shall be prepared then to discuss the whole thing. If the policy of re-organization is worked out properly, we are bound to enter into a discussion but I am not prepared to accept a reduction in wages in advance. I want to tell you I want to see the horse I am going to mount.[14]

J.H. Thomas reporting on these negotiations of Friday and the early hours of Saturday, seemed bent on showing himself as a fighter for the working class. It should be remembered that he was then an M.P., and railwaymen's leader, and had been a Cabinet Minister in a Labour Government. He told the delegates at the Special Conference of Executive Committees (which began on 29 April 1926), about Baldwin's request to Smith, and then asked his audience: 'Is there any man worthy of the name of a leader or a negotiator who would so betray his trust, to ruin his case in advance by saying to the people "Yes, come and negotiate with me, and in advance I promise you I will accept a reduction?" They (the Miners) had asked the Government,' Mr. Thomas continued, 'merely for free negotiations in an atmosphere not hampered by the lock-out notices, which were at that moment already taking effect. When the Prime Minister in return asked for an assurance that if the notices were suspended a genuine attempt would be made to get an agreement, Again the Miners Federation met that magnificently, *and at our request — and we put to them specifically the paragraph of the Royal Commission dealing with interference with the minimum* — the Miners' Federation through their president, said, "Yes, we will agree to discuss it from end to end and consider anything, even if it involves reduction in wages, but we refuse, to say in advance that we are going to accept a reduction." . . .' Thomas went on: 'My friends, when the verbatim reports are written, I suppose my usual critics will say that Thomas was almost grovelling, and it is true. In all my long experience — and I have conducted many negotiations — I say to you, and all my colleagues will bear testimony to it, I never begged and pleaded like I begged and pleaded all day today, and I pleaded not alone because I believed in the case of the miners, but because in my bones I believed that my duty to the country involved it. . . . But we failed. The Cabinet was summoned — such additional members as had not previously been in the negotiations, a number of whom had heard nothing of what had taken place, were called in to give their final decision, and their final decision was a refusal to accede to your request. Please observe, not to effect a settlement, but a refusal to accede to your request for a suspension of the notices so that negotiations could continue.'[15] Thomas then produced the Conservative document sent out to the press, mentioned on page 124, and another document which read:

O.M.S. The Government has proclaimed a state of emergency. All loyal citizens who are able and willing to undertake any public service should register at once at the local office of the O.M.S.

'This was shown to the Prime Minister, who said that permission for its publication had been refused.' Thomas then asked the delegates: 'Where is it leading to? Whilst we have been striving for peace, whilst we have laid all our cards on the table and played cricket, what can be said of that kind of thing and what it means?'[16]

This pretence at being shocked at Government action could have only been made to blind the other trade unionists to Thomas's real intentions. He had already admitted that he had tried to push the miners into accepting a reduction in wages, and it should be remembered that the document sent out to the press was already four days old! Thomas knew full well of the Government preparations and of the O.M.S. As a former Privy Councillor he must have known about all the emergency regulations, and the Emergency Powers Act of 1920. Whilst he was 'grovelling' on Friday afternoon the King was meeting the Privy Council at Buckingham Palace, where a proclamation declaring a state of emergency was drawn up and signed.* On 8 July 1926, after Thomas had betrayed the General Strike, he declared that the Government 'would have been unworthy of office and unfit for their job if . . . they had not prepared for a struggle.'[17]

The Morning Post on Saturday morning had on its placards and banner headlines, 'ZINOVIEFF WINS', yet even then the General Strike had *not* been called. It is true that on the 28 April 1926 a small committee 'to consider ways and means of co-ordinating action in the event of a strike taking place' was hurriedly appointed. Of its six members, Bevin was the most active, and Purcell the chairman. Its report was put before the General Council on the same day, but its plans were kept in reserve.[18] The Executives of the various unions did not receive a copy of the document until the early hours of Saturday, 1 May 1926. They were asked to reassemble at 12.30 a.m. that day and

*This can be seen in *The Sunday Times* 2 May 1926 (See Appendix V).

state whether they supported the policy of the General Council. 3,653,527 voted for acceptance, and only 49,911 against. Bevin told the delegates:

> I desire to point out that, with a view to doing nothing at all which would aggravate the position, these proposals were not ready to hand to the General Secretaries, or rather the documents in the form in which you received it, until after we had received in our room the news that the Emergency Powers Act had been signed, and after the O.M.S. had already placed upon the printing press their preparatory literature . . . We look upon your 'yes' as meaning that you have placed your all upon the alter for this great movement, and, having placed it there, even if every penny goes, if every asset goes, history will ultimately write up that it was a magnificent generation that was prepared to do it rather than see the miners driven down like slaves.

Cartoon from *St Pancras Bulletin* No 9 of 10 May 1926 (By courtesy of the Labour Research Department.

It was made clear, and stated that 'in the event of . . . trade union agreements being placed in jeopardy, it be definitely agreed that there will be no general resumption of work until those agreements are fully recognized.' MacDonald made the closing speech of the conference, concluding with: 'On Monday we will raise a debate in the House of Commons, but I hope, I still hope, I believe, I must believe, that something will happen before then which will enable us to go about our work cheerily and heartily and hopefully during the next week. If not, we are there in the battle with you, taking our share uncomplainingly until the end has come and until right and justice have been done.' The Red Flag closed the three day meeting, and the General strike had been declared.[19] From midnight on Monday, 3 May 1926, trains, buses, trams, and other forms of transport would cease.

Before the actual strike began, May Day was celebrated by the working class. Huge demonstrations took place throughout Great Britain. In London the 'National Fascisti' posted placards declaring that they were organizing to smash the Reds. Troops were being moved about, and there was even a possibility that 'warships at Malta and elsewhere' would be recalled.[20] The Duke of Northumberland had a letter in the *Morning Post*, which was headed 'COAL WAR PLOT — MINERS UNDER THE THUMB OF MOSCOW. THE VANGUARD OF REVOLUTION.' The Duke wrote, 'In this great crisis the issues are not between Capital and Labour, Employer and Employed; they are between those who love their country and those who are in league with its enemies.'[21] On the Saturday night the B.B.C. broadcast a message from the Prime Minister. 'Be steady, Be ready,' a pompous voice repeated, 'Remember that peace on earth comes to men of good will.'[22] The Civil Commissioner and the O.M.S. were actively organizing. Miss Lintorn-Orman, founder of the British Fascists had sent off a telegram to all her commanders on the Friday, which they would be acting on by that Saturday. It read, 'In the event of a crisis stand by the local authorities.'[23] All this was happening while the workers were showing their readiness for battle out in the streets. What then were their leaders doing? Still 'pleading', or 'grovelling' to use Thomas's words. Two letters were sent to the Prime Minister by Walter M. Citrine, Acting Secretary of the General Council. The first offered, in the event of a strike, to co-operate in the distribution of essential food supplies: the second announced that negotiations would thereafter be undertaken by the General Council, because the miners had decided to hand over the conduct of the dispute to them; a readiness to discuss the dispute was also stressed. It was Thomas who persuaded the General Council to send these letters.[24]

Police arresting a woman (in foreground) at an incident in Hammersmith Broadway (Photograph by courtesy of the T.U.C. Library)

1st May 1926

The Rt. Hon. Stanley Baldwin, M.P.,
  10 Downing Street, Whitehall, S.W.1.
Dear Sir,

     Mining Lock-out — Essential Food-Stuffs.

     I am directed to inform you that in the event of the strike of unions affiliated to the Trades Union Congress taking place in support of the miners who have been locked out, the General Council is prepared to enter into arrangements for the distribution of essential food-stuffs.

     Should the Government desire to discuss the matter with the General Council they are available for that purpose.

     The General Council will be glad to learn your wishes in this respect.

     Yours faithfully,
        Walter M. Citrine.

1st May 1926

The Rt. Hon. Stanley Baldwin, M.P.,
    10 Downing Street, Whitehall, S.W.1.
Dear Sir,

Mining Lock-out.

I have to advise you that the Executive Committees of the Trade Unions affiliated to the Trade Union Congress, including the Miners' Federation of Great Britain, have decided to hand over to the General Council of the Trades Union Congress, the conduct of the dispute, and the negotiations in connection therewith will be undertaken by the General Council.

I am instructed to say that the General Council will hold themselves available at any moment should the Government decide to discuss the matter further.

Yours faithfully,
    Walter M. Citrine.

The text of them was read to the Miners' Federation office over the phone, and a copy sent round by hand. Baldwin invited the T.U.C. representatives to meet him in No. 10 Downing Street at 8.30 p.m. At 9 p.m. Arthur Cook heard quite by accident that the Negotiating Committee of the T.U.C. were closeted with the Prime Minister.[25] After there had been some discussion of the Samuel Report by the nine members of the negotiating committee and six cabinet ministers, Baldwin had suggested that there should be further discussions with three from the trade union side, and three members of the cabinet. Arthur Pugh, J.H. Thomas, and Alonzo Swales (of the Engineers) were confronted by Baldwin, Birkenhead and Steel-Maitland (the Minister of Labour). Walter Citrine and Sir Horace Wilson were present to keep a record of the discussions. The discussions spilt over into the Sunday morning, and in Baldwin's words, 'what both sides wanted was to get to a position where they could secure an assurance that the Trades Union Council, on behalf of the miners, would say that they felt confident that, given a fortnight, a settlement could be arrived at on the basis of the report. Had the Government been able to get that assurance they would have risked it.' When the reader recalls all that had gone before, and knows what the miners had suffered, he will agree that such a conclusion by the Prime Minister (or Thomas, who agreed with Baldwin's account), was absurd. When

A.B. Swales (left) and Ernest Bevin M.P. (right) arriving at T.U.C. Headquarters in Ecclestone Square for consultations during the 1926 General Strike (Photograph by courtesy of the T.U.C. Library)

the three members of the General Council returned to their headquarters in Eccleston Square on Sunday 2 May to tell the rest of
the members, Bevin was suspicious. He believed that 'under it all
there was no doubt that the settlement provided for a reduction of
wages or an increase in hours.' Consequently he pressed them as to
whether there had been any private understanding to this effect:

> I questioned Mr Thomas very closely on this last point, and
> while they kept saying it might or might not involve that, to
> act in a perfectly straight manner, I came to the conclusion
> that was really what it meant . . . and the Prime Minister
> would be satisfied in advance so far as a reduction was
> concerned, irrespective of what might happen afterwards.[26]

When Cook arrived at the meeting he was naturally, furious.
(Citrine had phoned him at 2.30 a.m. on Sunday morning.) The
Negotiating Committee pressed him to recall the Miners'
Committee, who had all gone to their respective districts to
organize the strike which the T.U.C. had already agreed should
take place. Cook pleaded with his colleagues not to commit the
miners to a policy in contradiction of the one agreed upon.[27]
Thomas replied that the miners had, like every other union,
entrusted the General Council with the conduct of affairs and he
pointed out that if they wanted support from people like the
railwaymen, who had already accepted wage reductions, they
would have to be prepared to make concessions themselves.[28] Cook
then left the meeting, without any decision being made as to what
to do next. Thomas then rang Baldwin at five o'clock to tell him
that the miners had been recalled, and that the General Council
would only make a final decision when they arrived, but that
meanwhile the General Council had accepted the proposals and
would like further discussions.[29] The Prime Minister agreed to
meet the trio at 9 p.m. that Sunday evening, 2 May 1926 (why the
long delay?). According to George Lansbury seven members of
Baldwin's Cabinet (Churchill, Joynson-Hicks, Cunliffe-Lister,
Cave, Bridgeman, Amery and Chamberlain) had threatened to
resign if the negotiations were not broken off soon.[30] Certainly a
new formula was presented to the Trade Unionists which was
asking to be refused. It was drafted by Lord Birkenhead, and it
read: 'We will urge the miners to authorize us to enter upon a
discussion with the understanding that they and we approach it

with the knowledge that it may involve some reduction in wages.'

'We accept it,' said Thomas, 'never mind what the miners' or anybody else say.' By 'we' he meant the T.U.C. and, as he emphasized, the General Council of the T.U.C. was the body responsible for negotiations.[31] The Miners' Executive had arrived meanwhile, and had been taken to the Chancellor's room in No. 11 Downing Street. There they found the rest of the General Council, soon joined by the trio which had conducted the negotiations. Thomas said nothing about the Birkenhead formula, and it was never shown to the General Council at all.[32] Instead they discussed the original draft, and one new one formulated by Bevin. Just before the latter had been finalized, the Prime Minister's secretary entered the room and asked the Negotiating Committee to return. Thomas said, 'Yes in a minute', but the messenger returned and insisted. Thomas, Swales, Pugh, and Citrine returned to the Prime Minister's room.[33] A phone call had been received by Birkenhead. His comment was, 'Bloody good job.'[34] It proved to be the excuse some members of the Cabinet had been waiting for. A note previously drawn up by the Cabinet was 'stiffened', and Baldwin was left to hand the note to the trade union leaders. Baldwin was taut, 'The task of the peace-maker is hard,' he said, passing the note over. Because of an incident of which he had just heard, he said the Cabinet had to break off negotiations, but after all their efforts to find a solution, he felt that he had to tell them personally. 'Goodbye, I am sorry.' Very solemnly he shook each of the three flabbergasted men by the hand.[35] Bewilderment soon turned to anger. After hours of negotiation the trio had been rejected. The note was even more of a deliberate provocation than the Birkenhead formula. It told them: 'It has come to the knowledge of the Government, not only that specific instructions have been sent (it knew of these instructions for more than 36 hours) but that all overt acts have already taken place, including gross interference with the freedom of the press.' It demanded 'a repudiation of the actions referred to that have already taken place and unconditional withdrawal of the instructions for a general strike.'[36]

The General Council were shown the letter, none knew about any 'overt acts' or of any 'interference' with the press. When it came to their knowledge that the machine-room men had refused to print a provocative article for the *Daily Mail* (despite pressure from the Secretary of N.A.T.S.O.P.A. for them to resume work), the gathering of tired men was transformed from one seeking a way

out, to one determined to justify the miners' case. After two hours
of debate a letter, signed by Pugh and Citrine was delivered to the
Cabinet Room, only to find the door locked and the lights out.
There was nothing to do but return to Eccleston Square, from
where the reply was dispatched at 3.30 a.m. on Monday, 3 May
1926. Bevin, a few hours later, approached the Miners' Executive
with a formula which he hoped would be acceptable to them and
the Government. Smith, Cook, and Richardson accepted his idea,
but the full executive rejected it by 12 votes to 6. The key line of
Bevin's proposal was that any agreement should be subject 'to the
maintenance of a national minimum and the Seven Hours Act.'
Having been defeated by the miners, Bevin took his draft to the
General Council, arguing that as the miners had handed over their
powers, they must accept the General Council's ruling as final.
They accepted it, so Bevin dashed to the Commons and saw his
proposals delivered to MacDonald. Bevin even went to the extent of
getting in touch with the Ministry of Labour, and urged him to get

Dispatch riders waiting outside T.U.C. Headquarters in Ecclestone Square
(Photograph by courtesy of the T.U.C. Library)

the Prime Minister to put forward his proposals in the House that
evening. Sir Horace Wilson, the Permanent Secretary of the
Ministry of Labour saw the proposals next, but when he was told
that the men were not prepared to accept a reduction in wages, the
Government was not interested.[37] The Leader of the Labour Party
made no reference to them either. It was quite clear that the

Government did not want a way out, but all these underhanded activities by the various trade union leaders, made it quite clear that the workers were defeated before the strike began. That evening of Monday 3 May the whole world was staggered by the response to the strike call. Even the Durham miners who had been out on strike for eight months came out again.[38] There was a clear risk of adding to the 1½ million unemployed, yet twice this number came out in support of the miners. This fact is often lost sight of. The stoppage of work was a mass, unselfish act, carried out for the most part with quiet dignity. Middle class reaction was different. Many of them, thrown out of work by the strike, became Special Constables, which was of course a paid job. £2. 6s. 3d. per week, plus 2s. 6d. a day for food, was offered to the strike breaker, whereas the pit labourer from Wales had been locked out because he refused to accept £1. 11s. 7½d a week. Others, especially university students, volunteered to drive buses, trams, or even trains. Often to get a single tram out of the depot, there would be more police than passengers.

The first unit (A Company) of volunteers equipped with steel helmets, truncheons and armlets leaving their headquarters in Buckingham Gate as the new Civil Constabulary Reserve (Photograph by courtesy of the T.U.C. Library)

To get some idea of the support to the miners given by the railwaymen, the company's own figures are revealing. Of 15,062 engine drivers employed by the L.M.S., 207 reported for work on the first day of the strike; of 14,143 firemen, only 62; of 9,979 guards, only 153. On the first day of the strike, the L.M.S. succeeding in running 3.8% of its normal passenger service. By the end of the strike, this percentage had been raised to 12.2%. But this was largely with the aid of volunteer crews. The continued solidarity of the men is more accurately reflected by the figures for goods trains which, on the last day of the strike, represented no more than three per cent of the L.M.S.'s normal traffic. The L.M.S. was the biggest of the four railway networks.

In London, not one of the General Omnibus Company's 3,293 buses was moved on the first day of the strike; on the 11 May despite extensive use of volunteer drivers, the number still did not exceed 526. No more than 100 of London's trams were ever got on the roads on any one of the nine days of the strike. In the London Docks, not a single cargo was touched for the first four days and the work of unloading was only then begun by volunteers with the aid of the navy and under the cover of fully-armed detachments of troops, equipped with machine-guns and armoured cars.[39]

The strike breakers were urged on to greater efforts by all shades of reaction. The *Yorkshire Post* published a letter from a Captain Leo Gosson, of Hillcrest, Potternewton, which epitomizes their views. It concluded: If miners, or any others, think only of short hours, and high wages for doing as little work as possible, with no thought or care as to how it comes about, or the consequences thereof, the only way out is to teach them — by discipline. The Conservative Party, to which I belong, have a huge majority, and can find a good and considered way out of this stupidity. Moral: Pass an Act — then discipline. England is too precious to stand this nonsense.[40]

That this letter reflects Government opinion at the time is born out by the Illegal Strikes Bill considered by the Cabinet on Saturday, 8 May. Its intention was to kill the prospect of any sympathetic strike, and as the miners were the only workers who were protecting their own standard of living it proposed to freeze the funds of all the other unions. This secret Bill was only revealed to the general public in December 1967. It never came into force because it was decided to defer consideration of the Bill until 12 May.[41] On that day the General Strike was betrayed.

What was the Negotiating Committee of the T.U.C. doing, may well be asked, during all this activity. Thomas was carrying on with his pleading to the Tories to 'make a last effort', to avert the 'greatest calamity'. Winston Churchill told the Commons that the

T.U.C. had only to cancel the general strike and withdraw the challenge, and they would immediately begin to endeavour to rebuild the economic prosperity of the coal industry.[42] Mr Arthur Henderson and others visited Churchill in a last minute effort to find the elusive formula. As they entered Churchill asked 'Have you come to say the strike notices are withdrawn?' 'No, we . . . .' 'Then there is no reason to continue this discussion.' 'Do you think this is Sydney Street again?' said Henderson vehemently.[43] Certainly Churchill was fighting a class war, and using all the weapons at his disposal. The American *Evening World* (quoted in the *Yorkshire Post* 4 May) summed up the whole situation: 'The Baldwin Ministry has failed to bring about a settlement, and seemingly has taken its stand with the mineowners. This sinister feature of the situation is a fact that means the beginning of a bitter class struggle. It has been a genius of the English, throughout their history to find a way. This time they have failed.' *The British Gazette*, published on the presses of *The Morning Post* by His Majesty's Stationary Office, became Churchill's propaganda sheet. The first issue was published on the 5 May 1926. An example of this paper's class hatred is typified by the following:

A long line of motor lorries swinging into Hyde Park during

Armoured car acting as convoy escort to food lorries. The leading lorry has 'FOOD ONLY' clearly chalked on the side, this was respected by the strikers who strongly criticized the Government's intimidatory demonstrations of military force (Photograph by courtesy of the T.U.C. Library)

the week and bore sure witness to the fact that the strikers had
suffered early defeat in their attempt to starve London. Each
of the rumbling waggons, and there were more than 100 of
them, was piled high with bags of flour. The convoy looked
like the commissariat of a victorious army, and the illusion was
heightened by the sight of soldiers perched high on their
loads, some of them smoking, most of them smiling, and all of
them going about their job with the casual good humour
characteristic of the British private in peace and war. As escort
to the lorries 20 business like armoured cars — each of them
manned by men of the Tank Corps, wearing their characteristic black caps — rattled along at intervals in the column. .
. . There were few people in the streets, but as dockland grew
closer an occasional knot of strikers on picket duty gazed in
amazement at the column. Troops had descended on their
objective before the enemy had time to realize that they were
there.[44]

Such provocative words and actions, especially when one considers
that the T.U.C. had offered to move essential foodstuffs, roused
the anger of some of the workers, but surprisingly few. Buses were
burnt or overturned, trams were stoned, and even a train was overturned by eight Northumberland miners.

The *Leeds Mercury* reported the news like this:

DASTARDLY OUTRAGE TO THE FLYING SCOTSMAN.
DELIBERATE SMASH NEAR NEWCASTLE.
WOMEN PASSENGERS COURAGE.

ANOTHER TRAIN WRECKED IN A TUNNEL NEAR
EDINBURGH. TWO KILLED. PASSENGERS AND
RESCUERS GASSED.

The deaths had been on a train 'manned by a volunteer crew and
the engine driver being a man in the employment of the railway
company, but not a regular driver . . . ' The smash near Newcastle
and the train wreck in Edinburgh were coupled together in the headline so that the skimming headline reader was led to believe that the
deaths occurred as a result of the 'dastardly outrage' near Newcastle.

The strikers killed no one, but — besides troops with fixed
bayonets, armoured cars, submarines, cruisers, special constables
and fascists — poverty too provoked dissent and it is a wonder that
all these acting together did not bring about the bloody revolution
men like Northumberland constantly predicted.

Submarines (including the one with large gun in foreground) generate electricity at the Royal Albert Docks with soldiers guarding the supply cables (Photograph by courtesy of the T.U.C. Library)

The fascists usually were glaringly obvious: they had the full backing of the establishment. Poverty however, rarely showed itself, and the establishment denied responsibility for it. A short letter in the *Yorkshire Evening Post* was a rare exception to the 'out of mind out of sight' attitude then prevalent, yet the unemployment was typical of the times.

> Sir,
> My husband has been out of work for 16 months and has had no employment benefit for 13 months. I went for relief and received a grocer's ticket for a family of six. It works out daily at two loaves, 10d; ½lb. margarine, 4d; 2oz. tea 3d; ½lb. sugar 2d; pint of milk 3½d.
> This does not allow for rent or coal. We are forced to go into debt.
> Leeds. 5 May 1926.   'Sympathy'

The fascists on the other hand found favour in Mr Churchill's paper. On 6 May it told its readers:

> To effect a consolidation of the old and the new factors is Italy's task today under the Fascist regime. The Cabinet, having yesterday completed a scheme for the creation of a new Ministry of Trade Corporations, is now hammering out administrative details whereby masters, . . . workers, province-wide, can be amalgamated in the framework of the state so that production can proceed with the highest efficiency consistent with the best conditions for the men and reasonable returns for the capitalists.

The same paper on the 8 May provided the English employer with further food for thought:

> The strike in England, instead of causing unrest among Italian workmen, serves as a warning against industrial suicide and as an inspiration to masters and men to collaborate. An outstanding example is provided by the agrarians in the Leghorn district who have for a considerable time been divided in an economic dispute. The strike lesson in England led to an immediate re-convocation of the parties and the sitting was prolonged until the question in dispute was settled. The following message was sent to Signor Mussolini — 'While in England there is a strike, we have after a ten hours sitting concluded a series of agreements for the provinces of Leghorn in the spirit of collaboration with the firmness of imperial Italy and the invincible Duce.'

On the 12 May the *British Gazette* discovered a 'Vast Soviet Scheme':

> Arnold Rechberg, a German businessman, writing in the *Nation* this morning, states that he has evidence that the English strike is only one side of a vast Soviet scheme. Russia has prepared carefully for the English strike for a long while, though the trade union leaders did not know that for the most part they were playing the game of the Kremlin and thought they were merely defending the economic interests of the working class.

In the same issue in bold print it had the following:

> FOR WHOSE BENEFIT? A Question for Trade Unionist. The Council of the T.U.C. make a great virtue of returning the Soviet's cheque for thousands. So money to subsidise the strike in this country *was* offered from this source!
> Why?
> Was it to serve a British interest?

The Times on 6 May had already provided a more rational account. It stated simply:

> Soviet Support For Strikers.
> Red Trade Unions throughout the U.S.S.R. are organizing contributions to support the British strikers.

The money if accepted, could not have served the British Communist Party. The national leaders were arrested before the strike began, and throughout the strike raids were made on communist rooms to get rid of the local leaders. In Shipley the police raided a communist dance, siezing copies of *The Leeds Weekly Citizen* and leaflets intended for distribution amongst soldiers.[45] In

Shapurji Saklatvala, a member of the millionaire Tata family, was also Communist M.P. for Battersea and was arrested for saying 'Tell the army boys they must refuse to fight us,' in his May Day speech of 1926. He was imprisoned for two months (Photograph by courtesy of Battersea Library).

Salford police raided several premises and arrested seven members of the Communist Party.[46] Similar items relating to arrests throughout the country were to be found in the press during and after the strike.

Without a communist movement the strike would have been just as solid and it would take another book to prove it, but it is plain from literature printed before and after 1926, that the Communists did not have a great deal of support amongst the rank and file of the labour movement. The general strike was a culmination of years of discontent, much of which has been described in these pages and much more could have been added.

The British Worker was published to counter the Government paper, and the General Council of the T.U.C. stressed that there should be no local editions. This did not prevent such papers appearing, but these were frowned upon by head office.

The British Worker kept from the workers the secret negotiations of their leaders, and when the Government side leaked any information to the press, strong denials followed. The Birkenhead formula, mentioned earlier and which Thomas accepted, was but one distasteful affair. On Monday, 3 May 1926 Thomas said in the Commons:

> The General Council (of the T.U.C.) had never asked for a subsidy as a permanent solution of the present difficulty. The only thing the General Council had asked the Prime Minister since Monday last was that negotiations should be given a fair chance because they could not conduct negotiations under threat of a lock-out. The breakdown took place on that and that alone. The lock-out came into operation at midnight on Friday night. There were forty-thousand men who finished their shift on Friday afternoon, and it was not until 1.15 on Friday afternoon that the first national offer was made by the employers. What they then offered was eight hours a day and 20 per cent minimum wage. The meanest part of the business was in demanding that the miners' representatives should agree in advance to a reduction of wages.
>
> What they asked for was a chance to discuss the whole situation. The position taken up on behalf of the miners was that there should be no lock-out of men without giving a chance for negotiation. He did not believe two per cent of the people would vote for a revolution, but he was a blind fool who could not see that these people be driven by circumstances into courses they did not desire. This was not only not a revolution; it was merely a plain economic industrial dispute where the workers said they wanted justice.
>
> Was it too late yet to avert what he believed to be the greatest calamity to the country? He appealed for a last effort to be made.[47]

After other speakers such as MacDonald, and Churchill had spoken, Thomas asked if there was any possibility of the situation being covered on the lines of lock-out and general strike notices both being withdrawn. He did not ask for an answer at that moment. The House adjourned at 11.08. p.m.[48]

> When the House adjourned Thomas had an interview with the Attorney General (Sir Douglas Hogg). He then had a short conference with the miners' Executive, who were meeting in

the Committee Corridor of the House. He returned immediately afterwards to Sir Douglas Hogg's room. What these movements portended was obscure, for neither Mr Thomas nor anybody else concerned would indicate.

The above are the actual words reported in the *Leeds Mercury* of 4 May 1926.

Only Thomas and Hogg knew what was discussed if we are to believe the Chairman of the General Council of the T.U.C., but according to the *British Gazette* report of the 7 May 1926, 'for the first time the representatives of the Trades Union Council mentioned the phrase "reduction of wages" in a tentative proposal.'

Baldwin told the House on the 3 May, 'that another effort was made to see whether it was possible to obtain the sort of assurance the Government thought was essential,' but the actual formula was not disclosed. It was not until the 5 May that Baldwin claimed the document was not a Government document. 'It was a formula reached by discussion between the permanent officials and the T.U.C. to see if it would be accepted by the miners.' Mr Thomas said the formula referred to by the Prime Minister, was a document which, while it represented the general view and *common agreement of those who had been negotiating*, had to be subscribed to the Negotiating Committee, then to the General Council, and then to the miners. Mr A. Steel Maitland said that when the Prime Minister asked the General Council if they had the power to take decisions for the miners they said they had not.[49] These last two statements are in contradiction of the actual attitude taken by the Negotiating Committee of the T.U.C. who throughout acted, and made decisions, without the miners representatives being present. But more of that later. The Birkenhead formula, after being revealed to trade unionists for the first time in the House of Commons on 5 May, (not even Bevin nor any others on the General Council knew about it, except Thomas and perhaps Swales, Citrine and Pugh), it appeared in full in *The British Gazette* of 7 May. *The British Worker*, four days later, published a complete denial of there ever being a Birkenhead formula. Pugh stated that there was 'no such formula . . . ever dictated by the Trade Union representatives, nor assented to by them or in their possession.' A year later, Citrine denied the existence of the document when he had been acting as secretary to the trio. Pugh, on 11 May replied to an article published in the *British Gazette* that same day, written by none other than Sir Douglas Hogg. (See appendices pp.200-205). Had Thomas made some secret agreement with the Attorney-

General on the 3 May, and had Hogg 'blown the gaff'? It shall perhaps never be known, but it is certainly very odd that Thomas did not deny the document in the House when he had ample opportunity, and Pugh was only roused to reply to Hogg's *British Gazette* revelations of the 11 May when he could have challenged a front page account on the 7 May. (The reader can follow this discussion for himself in the various papers referred to.)

The speeches of J.H. Thomas and Ramsey Macdonald were too whimsical and lacking in political commitment to repeat here, but we shall follow the actions of the former which led to the eventual betrayal of nearly four million workers. Sir Herbert Samuels wired Baldwin and asked if there was anything he could do. The reply was appreciative but negative. Samuels had made a dash from the continent to Folkestone. There he had been met by Major Segrave, who had sped the former chairman of the coal commission to London. He then phoned Thomas from the Reform Club. On the

Herbert Smith and W.P. Richardson thoroughly dejected after the General Strike, 14 May 1926 (Photograph by courtesy of R. Page-Arnot)

following day, Friday 7 May, the T.U.C. negotiating committee sat down in the millionaire home of Sir Abe Bailey in Bryanston Square. There, for three days, in the home of this wealthy friend of Thomas, a formula acceptable to both the miners and the Government was discussed. Despite the fact that this committee had said they could not act without the miners, no miners were present, and none knew of the meetings. They were not told until the Sunday, and it was not until Monday that Pugh and Citrine took Herbert Smith, Cook and Richardson to meet Sir Herbert Samuels.

On the Saturday Thomas was invited to a luncheon party at Wimbourne House, near the Ritz. Lord Wimbourne had decided to try to get the two sides together, so the story goes, but again the miners were neither informed nor invited. Lord Londonderry (descendant of the man who was so reluctant to part with women and child labour down his pits), and Lord Gainford, both leading coal owners, were present. Lord Reading, a former Viceroy of India, was there and Mrs Snowdon represented her husband Phillip. Both Birkenhead and Churchill were told of this meeting.[50] That same evening Baldwin promised: 'when the time comes, and I hope it soon may, to discuss terms upon which the coal industry can be carried on . . . to see that . . . justice is done both to the miners and the owners.' Such absurd remarks were typical of the man. He reasserted that the general strike was an attack upon the community, but denied unequivocally that the Government was 'fighting to lower the standard of living of the miners or of any other section of the workers.' This last remark was belied by later events, especially with his addition, 'Cannot you trust me to ensure a square deal for the parties, to secure even justice between man and man?'[51] It is even more absurd when it is remembered that the Illegal Strikes Bill was discussed that very day.

The Wimbourne episode proved of no value to the strikers, but instead strengthened the Government's belief that the strike would be called off soon. Wimbourne's secretary, Selwyn Davies, had called upon Thomas at Dulwich on the Sunday night, because Baldwin had asked for very special attention to be paid to the text of his broadcast of the previous evening, implying that his words might have been influenced by the Wimbourne meeting. On Monday morning Davies turned up again at Dulwich and persuaded Thomas to go with him to Wimbourne House. With Lord Reading's help a formula was being prepared which sought to get a definite assurance from Baldwin. It was then that the miners' leaders were invited to attend. Three hours discussion failed to make any impression on Smith's angry insistence that he would not consider any reduction in wages, whatever assurances were given about reorganization. Sir Herbert Samuels, with the help of Lord Reading and Thomas, had drawn up a memorandum, which the General Council told the Miners' Executive they regarded as a satisfactory basis for reopening negotiations. This was discussed on the Monday evening and rejected by the miners. Thomas and Bromley even threatened to take their men back immediately if the strike were not called off. 'Take them back,' retorted Smith.[52]

On the following day, 11 May, the *Daily Mail* issued a leaflet and a leading article calling for the arrest of the members of the General Council. Cook issued a statement to the press which was ignored by *The British Worker*. It was printed in *The Times* next day. It read:

> Executive has reviewed the position in the light of messages received from all over the coalfields appealing to the Executive to stand firm against any compromise on either hours, wages or a national agreement. On behalf of the Executive, I desire to inform the miners and the general public that we are as firm today as we were when the miners decided unanimously, after the question had been refered to every district, that there were to be no reductions in wages. In the words of the President, Mr Herbert Smith, 'we have nought to give.'

Also on 11 May Mr Justice Astbury, gave his judgement in the case where Mr Havelock Wilson, General Secretary of the Seamens' Union, had taken out an injunction against the secretaries and other officials of certain branches of the union to restrain them from calling on their members to strike. He declared 'the so-called general strike . . . illegal, and contrary to law, and those persons inciting or taking part in it are not protected by the Trade Disputes Act of 1906.' A few days earlier, (6 May) Sir John Simon had come to a similar conclusion, stressing that 'every trade union leader who has advised and promoted that course of action is liable in damages to the uttermost farthing of his personal possessions.' With all these details at the back of their mind the General Council behaved in an almost hysterical manner towards the miners' leaders. They insisted that the miners accept the Samuel Memorandum; they told the full Committee on Tuesday evening that a unanimous decision had been arrived at. The Memorandum had been amended and agreed upon by the Negotiating Committee of the General Council.

In a long speech, Mr Pugh solemnly and seriously declared that the General Council had decided that these proposals must be accepted by the miners' representatives as a basis for negotiation, and that they would call off the strike. They had guarantees that satisfied them that the Government would accept these proposals, and that on the strike being withdrawn the lock-out notices would also be withdrawn, and the miners should return to work on the status quo (with, of course, a reduction in wages to come after resumption of work). We were told these proposals were unalterable, could not be amended, that we had to accept them en bloc as this was the unanimous decision of the T.U.C.

Cook later wrote of the occasion in his book. Naturally Smith and Cook were very suspicious of such 'guarantees', and repeatedly asked Thomas and Pugh to define them. Thomas, true to form, eventually pleaded: 'You may not trust my word, but will you not accept the word of a British gentleman who has been Governor of Palestine?' The miners, and other delegates, pressed for assurances that all the strikers would return to work together on the same conditions as when they left, in accordance with the unanimous decision taken at the outset to avoid victimization. Thomas said, 'That was all right', but the doubts persisted. Then with the inference that the miners should not meddle in the affairs of other unions, Thomas declared: 'I have seen to it that the members of the railways will be protected.'[53] (He had not, as we shall see.) Absolutely disatisfied the miners adjourned as a committee to a room in the Labour Party offices next door, to consider the position. They rejected the General Council's ultimatum just after midnight. While they were in the Labour room a telephone call from Downing Street asked Mr Citrine 'when the negotiating Committee would be done.' When all the trade unionists left Eccleston Square in the early hours of the Wednesday morning, Thomas left on his own a little behind the others, and out of the shadows a figure emerged at his side; it was Selwyn Davies. Thomas told him the strike was off and at once the news transmitted to Baldwin. *The British Worker* that day carried this headline. 'THE TERMS OF PEACE: MINERS ENSURED A SQUARE DEAL.' In truth it should have read: THE TERMS OF THE SURRENDER: MINERS BETRAYED.

On that fateful Wednesday, 12 May 1926, Sir Herbert Samuels sent a letter to Arthur Pugh.

Dear Mr Pugh,
As the outcome of the conversations which I have had with
your Committee I attach a memorandum embodying the conclusions that have been reached.
I have made it clear to your committee from the outset that I
have been acting entirely on my own initiative, have received
no authority from the Government, and can give no
assurances on their behalf . . .[54]

Lord Reading had insisted on Thomas calling off the strike; his
reason, unknown to Thomas at the time, was his information that
the cabinet had decided to arrest the trade union leaders if the
strike was not called off.[55]

When Pugh and the rest of the General Council deputation went
to Downing Street at noon on Wednesday the Prime Minister was
therefore not unprepared for their visit. He had assembled there
the War Minister, the First Lord of the Admiralty, the Minister of
Labour, the Secretary for Mines, and Earl Birkenhead, the
Secretary for India, among other members of the cabinet. Despite
being forewarned earlier in the day by Thomas, the Prime Minister
had to go through the motions of possessing power over the lower
orders. He 'refused to see them until he had ascertained the object
of their visit. In the first place, therefore, the deputation was met
by Sir Horace Wilson, the Secretary to the Ministry of Labour,
who was informed that the General Council had decided to
terminate the General Strike. It was after this definite announcement had been made, without any reservation or condition, that
Mr Baldwin saw the deputation.'[56]

The British Gazette, a toy Churchill used, talked of surrender and
the King's appeal for lasting peace. They thought that the class war
had come to an inglorious end, but they had overlooked the
fighting spirit of the working class. They carried on with the
battle. Their leaders had led them into a trap, but they had not
recognized it just yet. Pugh told the Prime Minister that the
general strike had terminated in order that negotiations could
proceed. That evening Mr Baldwin broadcast to the nation:

The General Strike . . . has ended, as I made it plain in my
speech a few nights ago that it must end, without conditions
entered into by the Government. No Government, confronted
by such a menace, could enter into a conditional negotiation,

the very undertaking of which would involve treachery to the accepted basis of our democratic Constitution. Having said this, I must make it plain that I adhere both to the spirit and letter of the speech which I delivered to the nation a few days ago. Our business is not to triumph over those who have failed in a mistaken attempt. It is rather to rally them together with the population as a whole in an attempt to restore the well being of the nation.

The British Worker of the 13 May never mentioned the disagreement with the miners. On Wednesday, 12 May, a Government statement was issued, and printed in all the national papers on the following day: 'His Majesty's Government have not power to compel employers to take back every man who has been on strike, nor have they entered into any obligation on this matter.' *The British Gazette* had a significant headline 'Reinstatement, No Obligation Incurred.' It then carried a large type notice, a notice which was plastered all over the country offering State protection to all blacklegs.[57] (See poster/handbill on p.152). The *Daily Mail* had the headline we can expect knowing now something of its history: 'Surrender of the Revolutionaries'. Under further headlines 'For King and Country' and 'Revolution Routed' it declared that the T.U.C. which was a 'barely disguised Soviet was now hurriedly effacing itself.' It spoke of the people who had arranged the strike with their heads 'stuffed with theories which emanated from half witted Germans and Russians such as Marx and Lenin.'

Just as the Government and the more belicose press had been amazed at the solidarity of the strikers at the beginning (as some trade union leaders were terrified), they were even more alarmed at their response to the 'surrender'. Thomas on the 13 May told the House that at least 100,000 *more* workers were out at the moment of speaking than had been the case when the General Council cancelled the strike 24 hours before, and this despite the fact that the strikers had returned to some degree in the interval. Mr Baldwin on the same day declared: 'I will not countenance any attempt on the part of any employer to use the present occasion for trying in any way to get reductions in wages below those in force before the strike began, or to get an increase of powers.' J.H. Thomas refused to believe that the Prime Minister was aware of the fact that the Government themselves had broken not only the spirit but the letter of his broadcast speech, of his statement to the

TO ALL WORKERS IN ALL TRADES

ADDITIONAL GUARANTEES

Official

Every man who does his duty by the Country and remains at work or returns to work during the present crisis will be protected by the State from loss of Trade Union benefits, superannuation allowances or pensions. His Majesty's Government will take whatever steps are necessary in Parliament or otherwise for this purpose.

STANLEY BALDWIN.

H.M. STATIONERY OFFICE.

Baldwin's Poster/Handbill that was widely distributed on the 12 May

House that day. He read out a copy of an Admiralty order: 'Following the Admiralty decision as regards men on strike; established men are not to be allowed to enter, but are to be suspended until further notice.' Then he quoted the War Office Notice: 'Notice to employees at War Office Department establishments. Men who have remained at work and men who have returned to work by Wednesday May 12th., will be given preference in employment irrespective of their former length of service . . . Attention is drawn to the provision of the regulations that all awards under the superannuation acts are subject to the condition that discharge at a person's own desire or due to his own default forfeits all previous service.' And another notice was quoted from Tillings Garage of Bromley Road: 'Drivers and conductors who are willing to resume work will, until further notice be paid at the same rate as volunteers, viz., 15s a day for a driver . . . This arrangement will only continue until further notice. The unions having broken this, they should understand quite plainly that we do not propose to make a further agreement with the existing union . . .' Thomas then stated that Carter Paterson had given notice that their men could only resume duty with a reduction of 4s per week. He had got so many that he needed not to go into them. It was sufficient for him to say that there was not a town in the country within which these incidents had not taken place. That Thomas was not exaggerating was confirmed by other pages in *The Times* of the 14 May, which had reported the speech referred to. It told its readers that in Glasgow 'there is a disinclination on the part of employers to welcome their men back to work. Railwaymen who presented themselves were told each case is being considered on its merits. The result was that in certain districts of Glasgow this morning there were processions of men carrying placards, bearing the words, "Down With Thomas", and declaring that the railwaymen had lost the strike.'

The workers had expected a united return to work but, on 13 May, *The British Worker* issued another official manifesto:

> The General Council considered the practicability of securing a resumption of work by the members in dispute at a uniform time and date; but it was felt, having regard to the varying circumstances and practices in each industry, that it would be better for each Executive Council itself to make arrangements for the resumption of work of its own members.

Without warning the strikers were thrown upon the resources of their own individual unions, with the dreadful suspicion, growing hourly into certainty, that the Miners' Executive had not consented to the termination of the strike, and that their own sacrifices and solidarity had apparently been rendered for nothing. The sight of little paper slips which so many men received on their return to work, requiring their individual signature to a statement whose full significance was by no means clear, was like a red rag to a bull. Angry men refused to sign, took these provocative forms back to their local leaders, and pledged themselves not to return until all strikers in their own groups were unconditionally reinstated.

This happened all over the country, and it is impossible to detail every situation. One such protest showing the typical reaction of thousands should illustrate the attitude of the workers and their great feeling of class solidarity.

In Manchester the tramwaymen were to report for duty on Wednesday at noon. At the required hour, 15 men and five boys out of a force of 5,000, turned up at the tram sheds. The others went to Hyde Road in full strength, not to report for duty, but to march in procession to the centre of the city, headed by their band and carrying banners declaring their determination to support the miners with many of the strikers wearing war medals. As they marched they were joined by contingents of other trades on strike, until the procession, marching four abreast was nearly half a mile long. To this mass meeting came the first news of the end (reported in good faith by a Labour City Councillor), as the acceptance *by the Government* of the Samuel Memorandum. When the more correct terms of the settlement came through later the indignation was great.[58] A tramway worker in Glasgow, who had been with the tramways department for four years, was told that his services were no longer required because he joined the strike. He was Robert Downie, winner of the V.C. in the First World War.[59]

In the mining areas of South Wales the news of the end of the strike was received, at first in a spirit of scepticism, mixed with displeasure. It spread up the valleys by telephone at a great pace. At Pontypridd the men, refusing to believe the story, gathered outside the headquarters of the strike committee and waited for hours for official confirmation. Many of them described it as a trick to break down their solidarity.

There was no rejoicing among the miners higher up the valleys. They assumed that their troubles had not been settled at the end of the strike. A number of them had not been employed for months. They saw no prospect of an improvement in their condition and felt that they were being left alone again to solve their own problems.[60]

On Thursday, 13 May, the B.B.C. at 10 a.m. broadcast the following:

> As far as London was concerned, the calling off of the General Strike seemed to have made little difference to traffic this morning. Few of the strikers have returned to work and the strike service of trains and buses is still in force, volunteers acting as drivers and conductors. No trams were running in the early morning and the scramble to get to work was as bad as ever. The newspapers again appeared in attenuated form.
>
> While the general strike public as a whole took no pains to conceal their satisfaction at the calling off of the strike, the action of the T.U.C. seems to have caused some dissatisfaction among some of its adherents. A tour through Canning Town and Poplar shortly before midnight disclosed the fact that the inhabitants of these parts were not at all pleased with the state of affairs. Crowds paraded the streets, but the police kept them on the move, and only in one or two instances was actual violence threatened. The dockers had withdrawn their pickets from the docks, but the gates remained closed and very little activity was noticed within them.[61]

On Friday, 14 May, the civil war psychosis which gripped certain members of Baldwin's Cabinet showed its ugly face.

> Poplar, the dock section of London, was being patrolled . . . by armoured cars, posses of mounted police and hundreds of constables of groups of not less than three . . . . The shops . . . [are] . . . closed and the shutters drawn by the terrified people. Policemen [are] lining the streets keeping back mobs of cursing men, whose anger is at the boiling point. Dozens of their comrades were under arrest, and many are in hospitals, including the Mayor of Poplar and a Catholic priest, who are nursing wounds inflicted by the police . . . eye-witnesses, including the Vicar of St. Michael's Church, declared that it was the police who opened the hostilities. A meeting was going on in front of the Poplar Town Hall, when a motor lorry full of police, followed by mounted men, drove straight through the crowd. To quiet the men the Vicar, Father

Grose, took charge of the meeting . . . . Then a squad of policemen issued from the neighbouring police station and charged the crowd with nightsticks, chasing some a quarter of a mile towards the docks. When the priest, upholding a crucifix, approached the police and tried to explain that the meeting was peaceful, he was struck down.

A stampede followed, and in the melee the police raided the headquarters of the N.U.R. branch adjoining, where a crowd headed by Mayor Hammond, were singing at a piano or playing games. About thirty policemen drew their sticks, and when Hammond, saying he was Mayor, tried to explain, he was struck on the head, while the police swept on and cleared the place.[62]

Only the day before the Prime Minister had bandied the word 'democracy' about as if it had some meaning, and told the House that their business was 'not to triumph over those who have failed in a mistaken attempt.' The working class fighting spirit had been overlooked, but when they refused to be forced back to work, the State machine retaliated with brutal violence. It should be pointed out that a large food convoy passed through Central London on the very day the Prime Minister was speaking, (Thursday) from the docks, 'accompanied by armoured cars and steel-helmeted soldiers with rifles at the "ready".'[63] It was a class war all right, and the only weapon the working class had was their solidarity. Of course, the 'other side' showed all the signs of working together to smash the workers, but the vast majority were paid for their services.[64] One Major-General John Vaughan, polo manager at Ranelagh, went to the authorities and offered to raise a troop of 25 or 30 mounted 'specials' through his club. News of the troop spread quickly and some 3,000 men visited Scotland Yard, eager to join the new force. Scores were ready to provide their own horses, many offered two or more. A Master of Foxhounds telegraphed that he was prepared to provide the authorities with all the horses in his hunt, and they were ready to take to the road. The troop were horsemen to a man — ex-officers of cavalry and artillery, yeomanry officers, polo and hunting men, accustomed to discipline. Their dress and equipment were a khaki topee, trench coat, riding breeches and boots, and long baton.[65] These gentlemen, who instead of a fox or stag suddenly found new pleasure in hunting down workers, provided their services free.

Trouble breaks out in Hammersmith Broadway as a milk lorry passes through, a man is being led away by the police in the foreground whilst mounted police ride into the crowd (Photograph by courtesy of the T.U.C. Library

Talk of 'democracy' and the desire to 'protect the constitution' may have *sounded* right but when it is recalled that Sir F.E. Smith, speaking of the Ulster Volunteer movement at Armagh, 4 October 1913, said, 'We shall make England realize that it (the establishment of Home Rule Parliament) can never be done, the more easily the more swiftly, and the more triumphantly your Volunteer movement advances. I hope to see at an early date those men who have undergone the necessary discipline and drill with real rifles.'[66] 35,000 magazine rifles and 2,500,000 rounds of ammunition were taken into Ireland with the full support of this man, in order to resist 'democracy' and the 'constitution'. He was later to become Lord Birkenhead, writer of the famous 'formula' in the coal dispute. When Pugh, Thomas and the rest stood before him, ready to betray the whole working class movement, he found it 'so humiliating that some instinctive breeding made one unwilling to even look at them.'[67]

So determined were the rank and file to see that justice was done for the miners, that despite everything they continued the strike. The railway unions were forced to declare a new strike by the action of the ranks. This was admitted in the *Railway Review* of 21 May. It told how a meeting 'was hurriedly arranged between the three railway Trade Union Executives at 2.00 p.m. on Thursday

(13th), when it was known that everywhere the men had refused to accept the conditions offered them when reporting for duty, left no option but to call a further strike and to offer negotiations to the companies.'[68] After these negotiations had teminated two days later, a telegram was despatched to the Branches of the N.U.R.

Cartoon 'The Striker's Return' from *Punch* May 1926

Employer: Glad to see you back, my lad; but you'll understand that in the circumstances we can't run to a fatted calf.

with the incorrect assertion, 'Complete reinstatement secured without penalties. All members should report for duty immediately. Full details to follow.'[69] Five months later (12 October), Thomas spoke against the proposal to place an embargo on the movement of coal, and against a levy on union funds in aid of the coal miners who were still out. He said his union could not pay any levy because 'they had 45,000 men out who had not gone back to work since 1 May, and 200,000 who were working three days a week.' The membership of the N.U.R. was 327,374, which meant that about 75% of the members of the union had NOT received the 'satisfactory settlement' which Thomas had promised.[70]

Workers everywhere, with the exception of the miners, returned to work where jobs were offered with many at reduced rates of pay or altered conditions of work. Thousands found themselves unemployed, many to remain so for years. Victimization was carried out with great ruthlessness by employers. The Government in July 1926 introduced a Bill giving the Ministry of Health authority to supersede Guardians who offered too much relief by others appointed from the Ministry. The miners remained on strike until November, so that they were particularly hard hit by this Act, introduced by Neville Chamberlain. The Labour Exchanges were instructed to disqualify those who withdrew their labour, from unemployment benefits on the grounds that they had left their employment without just cause.[71] As early as 17 May, it was assumed that poverty would drive the miners back to work. The tone of *The Times* report of that date suggests this.

There has been a *subdued* tone in the chief centres of South Wales during the weekend. There is *very little fight* left in the men. Some of them like the Cardiff dockers, are planning the overthrow of the 'blackleg' with whom they will have to work, but the majority are anxious to get back. Evidence of the *sober mood to which they have been brought* is to be found in the fact that there were no cases in the Cardiff and Swansea Police courts yesterday, and that in the Newport Petty Sessional Division, which embraces several mining industrial areas, there were no cases of violence and disorder.

The men realize that all of them will not get back to work at once and signs of distress are appearing. Already Boards of Guardians throughout South Wales have been overwhelmed with applications for relief. In the Pontypridd Union which includes the Rhonda Valleys, 40,000 people have already applied. At Risca an out relief station of the Newport Union, over 1,000 people tried to enter application on Friday, and particulars were only taken from about 80. The Chapel vestry, used an office by the relieving officers was described by a Guardian as 'den of riotous people.' (Author's italics)

Five days later, the same paper, in a report from Newport, said that:

. . . over 2,000 miners marched in procession from the Western Valley and from several villages near it with the avowed intention of demanding admission to the workhouse, while a deputation presented their needs to the Guardians. Some of the men came from Crumlin at the head of the valley 12 miles away . . . led by a colliery band. After a long hot march they were stopped by the Mayor and Chief Constable of Newport. They were eventually persuaded to wait at Bassaley while a deputation went on to lay their case before the Emergency Committee of Guardians . . . . *This sort of demonstration has not been unexpected.* It has arisen partly out of the ruling that strikers may not be relieved, but it has been hastened by the fact that the Guardians of Crickhowell, a neighbouring Union have ignored the Ministry's instructions and the judgement in the Merthyr case, and have relieved the miners . . . .. This does not solve the problem of the single man who is often a lodger and has no friends who can help him. The Guardians explained today that they would not relieve single men unless they *were destitute and on the point of collapse*, but the Guardians undertook to see that the relieving officers administered the law as humanely as possible.

Also in that newspaper was found the attitude of Yorkshire miners to Poor Law Relief. 'So great is the dislike of Poor Law Relief even amongst the recipients that they willingly sign a form authorizing a stoppage of 2/6d a week from wages after the resumption of work until the amount advanced by the Guardians is discharged.' After seven months of strike activity a miner who *did* get work had to repay a debt which took him many years, some were still paying back the money received in 1921 when the 1926 lockout began. (The *Yorkshire Evening Post* 3 May 1926 pointed out that Leeds Co-op advanced money in 1921, 'but every penny has been repaid . . .

```
-----------------------------------------
    PARISH OF LAMBETH : BOARD OF GUARDIANS
-----------------------------------------
```

E. A. GREEN
Collector.

Guardians' Offices,
Brook Street,
Kennington, S.E.

1 7. AUG 1927   *192___*

Dear Sir,

The Guardians have had under consideration the question of taking legal proceedings to recover the amount of out-relief advanced by way of loan during the General Strike in May 1926.

According to my Ledger there is the sum of _____ still due from you, which I shall be glad to receive at an early date so as to avoid the possibility of proceedings being taken against you in respect thereof.

Yours faithfully,

Ea Green

Collector.

Mr, *H E Parker*

24 Cranfield Villas

West Norwood S.E 27

No. F496   **PARISH OF LAMBETH.**

240

Guardians' Offices,
BROOK STREET, KENNINGTON, S.E. 11

27. AUG 1927

_____ day of _____ 19____

Received of Mr. *H E Parker* _____ the sum of

_____ pounds *One* shillings

and _____ pence on behalf of the above-named Parish in respect

of Maintenance of *Relief advanced Since of a/s.*

Ea Green

Collector for the said Parish.

£ : 1 : 0

Correspondence and receipts from Board of Guardians in the Parish of
Lambeth (Courtesy of Sheila Ferguson)

whereas there are still thousands of pounds still owing to Lancashire and South Wales Societies.') An actual copy of the type of intimidating letter sent out by some Guardians can be seen on p.161 (note the date, and the receipt for payment). Many Guardians were not quite as ruthless, and letters have been received which show that in some cases debts were forgotten. The rates paid by the Boards of Guardians were laid down by Mr Chamberlain in his infamous circular 703. It laid down a maximum scale of 12/- for a wife, and 4/- for a child. With rents around 10/- and coal at 2/6 a cwt., only 3/6 was left to feed three people. *The Socialist Review* for September 1926, reported that at Pontypool the scale of relief was 10/- for wife and 4/- for a child, which was to be reduced by 25% the first week, 50% by the second, and by 75% for the third week, and thereafter it was abolished altogether in the fourth. Bolton Board refused out-relief altogether, and simply told the miner's wife and their children that they would have to leave home and enter the workhouse, or go without any assistance whatsoever. Such repressive measures left their mark on the British working class, and thousands of children in particular suffered extreme hardship, misery and humiliation. There seems little doubt that this deliberate rout of the workers was the result of a determined effort to make sure that they would never again dare to challenge capitalism. The Trades Dispute Act of 1927, was to prove that Sir John Simon had been wrong in 1926 when he declared a general strike illegal then, and it was also to make a mockery of all the speeches by the 'man of peace', Mr Baldwin. Arthur Pugh, who had led the surrender of the workers, told a convention of the American Federation of Labour at the end of 1927 that: 'The Act actually lays it down that a worker who refuses to accept employment under a common understanding with other workers in any strike which under its provisions may be deemed to be illegal becomes guilty of a criminal offence. It is almost unthinkable that a British Government should go so far in the direction of industrial serfdom.'[72]

It should not however be assumed that the miners, who were left alone in the struggle, just gave up the fight. They organized soup kitchens, set up committees to provide meals, held concerts to raise funds; 'at homes' were held organized by wealthy sympathizers. In much of this work the strikers were helped by many from the middle classes, especially shopkeepers and small traders. John Galsworthy, the novelist, sent £100 to the strike fund, for example, but these were exceptions rather than the rule. Emma Noble, a member of the Society of Friends, and her husband, an Engineering Union President, pioneered help for the distressed families in the Rhondda. Working class families who were fortunate to be in work, offered to take in miners' children.

That the miners were eventually beaten into submission by poverty, there is little doubt. Neville Chamberlain wrote in his diary on 20 June: 'They are not within sight of starvation, hardly of under-nutrition . . . they are not living too uncomfortably at the expense of the ratepayer.' He really knew little of the realities of the situation: the stubborn pride of the miners fooled more than him. Their poverty persisted well into 1939, when many other people discovered how appalling their conditions of life really were. Cook, the miners' leader, made concessions to the Government. They would accept the Samuel Commission's recommendations; but the owners, as before, would have none of it. The justice between man and man so glibly spoken of by Baldwin was as empty as the findings of many other Royal Commissions, and Prime Ministers' pledges. A Coal Mines Bill suspended the seven-hour day for five years. The strike remained unbroken. Again the miners appealed to the Government to intervene. Churchill told them that the question of giving financial help to the industry 'had long since passed out of the sphere of practical politics.' To this Herbert Smith replied: 'After your statement I do not think we need detain you long. You seem to be of the same mind as the employers. I am not here to make a petition. If that is what you think I am here for you are mistaken. I am here to get an honourable settlement . . . . We can carry this fight on a bit further yet.'[73] But they could not carry on much further, and when a settlement was finally reached the miners lost everything for which they had fought. They were forced to accept district agreements when they had wanted to retain a national agreement; hours of work were increased but in most cases wages were reduced; the owners were able to keep wages down by having a large pool of unemployment.[74] The Liberal *Daily News* realistically summed up the situation the miners were forced into. 'There need be no attempt to disguise the fact that the document they (the miners) are now asked to authorize represents a complete surrender to the owners, whose uncomprimising attitude in the last few days must have disgusted thousands of decent minded people. Clearly they wanted a fight to a crude and brutal finish, utterly regardless of the interests of the public or any other interest save their own selfish resolve to drink the last dregs of a transient and dismal victory . . .

The owners, or the majority of them, must be given up as the most reactionary, shortsighted and ungenerous of all our great industrial bodies.'[75]

Joynson-Hicks, who had been so outspoken in defiance of the Asquith Cabinet over Ulster in 1913, told the General Council of the Primrose League on 20 May 1926: 'Having got through the strike, and having once and for all laid the bogey of the General Strike, it would be easier for future Governments to deal with the threatened strikes. All they would have to do would be to say, "Look at 1926. We burst your bogey. We have shown the impossibility of holding the country to ransom at the hands of any organized body of opinion." '[76]

Trade Union membership fell, the funds of many were exhausted and some were in debt. Whilst the unions were weak and

A.J. Cook (seated on table) and Ramsey MacDonald (on right) at the T.U.C. Conference, Bournemouth 1926 (Photograph by courtesy of the T.U.C. Library)

unemployment high, the Trades Disputes and Trade Union Act of 1927 was pushed through Parliament. Fascism made no rapid progress until about 1932 when Sir Oswald Mosley organized the British Union of Fascists. After the brutal outrages at the Olympia meeting of June 1934, the Conservative M.P. for South Islington said in the House: 'The young men who have joined the Blackshirt movement . . . are the best elements in this country.' All the anti-fascists arrested for assault on the night of Olympia were fined or imprisoned: all the fascists were discharged or bound over.[77] *The Daily Mail* 4 March 1935, printed an article under the banner head-line, 'THE BLACKSHIRTS ARE MARCHING ON.'[78] No-one can predict what would have happened if the working class had not organized to resist the blackshirts in the 30s. The fascist movement found during the General Strike that authority was on their side; they were strengthened by this knowledge later. Fortunately not all Conservative M.P.'s supported the member for South Islington. Mr Geoffrey Lloyd M.P. who had witnessed the Olympia outrages said in the *Yorkshire Post* 9 June 1934: 'I could not help shuddering at the thought of this vile bitterness, copied from foreign lands, being brought into the centre of England. I came to the conclusion that Mosley was a political maniac, and that all decent English people must combine to kill his movement.'[79]

Mr Lloyd was the Private Secretary to Stanley Baldwin, then Lord President in Ramsey MacDonald's National Government. Yet Stanley Baldwin, by his handling of the General Strike, and his failure to stand up to men like Joynson-Hicks, Birkenhead, Chamberlain, Churchill and the rest, provided the seed bed for the growth of fascism in this country.

The photograph overleaf, taken in 1929, shows non-unionists being escorted from the pit in the Garw Valley, during another coal strike. It symbolizes the solidarity of the working class in those years of struggle against the capitalist state machine. Despite such a huge protective force for blacklegs, only three men turned up for work. Our children ought to be told more of the heroic struggle of their forefathers to win better working conditions. It is a subject which is all too often neglected in our schools.

Three non-unionists at Garw Valley in South Wales are given a massive police escort (Photograph by courtesy of R. Page-Arnot).

Notes to Chapter 7

1. *Socialist Review*: February 1926. From 'Whither England', by Leon Trotsky, p.36.
2. Arnot, R.Page: *The Miners*, Allen & Unwin, 1953. p.409.
3. Arnot, R.Page: *The General Strike, Its Origin and History*, London, 1926. p.118.
4. Crook, Wilfred Harris: *The General Strike. A Study of Labor's Tragic Weapon in Theory and Practice* The University of North Carolina Press, 1931. p.339.
5. *Socialist Review*: July 1926. An article written by R.J. Schmidt, Chief of Publications and Research Dept., of the Netherlands Federation of Trade Unions.
6. Crook, W.H.: *Op.Cit.* pp.337 and 338. Mr. Crook points out that 'the International Miners' Federation had not pledged itself to stop the export of coal to Britain.' Cook did not say they had. What he did say was confirmed by the article quoted above in footnote 5 published by the *Socialist Review*.
7. Crook, W.H.: *Ibid.* p.339.
8. Crook, W.H.: *Ibid.* p.339.
9. Martin, Kingsley: *The British Public and the General Strike*, Hogarth Press, 1926. p.31.
10. Arnot, R.Page: *The General Strike.* p.121.

11. Arnot, R.Page: *The Miners*. pp. 412 and 413.
12. Arnot, R.Page: *The General Strike*. p.126.
13. Arnot, R.Page: *Ibid*. p.126.
14. Crook, W.H.: *Op.Cit*. p.357 and
    Arnot, R.Page: *Op.Cit*. pp. 128 to 132.
15. Arnot, R.Page: *Ibid*. p.132 and
    Blaxland, Gregory: *J.H. Thomas: A Life for Unity*, London, 1964.
    p.188.
16. Crook, W.H.: *Op.Cit*. pp.348/9 and
    Fyfe, Hamilton: *Behind the Scenes of the Great Strike*. London, 1926. pp.
    13 to 15.
17. Crook, W.H.: *Ibid*. p.349.

18. Bullock, Alan: *The Life and Times of Ernest Bevin*, Vol.I, Heinemann,
    1960. pp. 300 and 301.
19. Arnot, R.Page: *The General Strike*. pp.132/133, and 140.
20. *The Sunday Times*, 2 May 1926.
21. Martin, Kingsley: *Op.Cit*. p.28.
22. Symons, Julian: *The General Strike*. London, 1957, p.177.
23. *Sunday Worker*, 2 May 1926.
24. Blaxland, Gregory: *Op.Cit*. p.189.
    Bullock, Alan: *Op.Cit*. p.307, and
    Cook, A.J: *The Nine Days. The Story of the General Strike told by the
    Miners' Secretary*. London, 1926. p.9.
25. *The Leeds Mercury*, 4 May 1926.
26. Bullock, Alan: *Op.Cit*. p.309.
27. Cook, A.J: *Op.Cit*. p.10.
28. Blaxland, Gregory: *Op.Cit*. p.191.
29. Blaxland, Gregory: *Ibid*. p.191.
30. *Lansbury's Labour Weekly*, 22 May 1926.
31. Blaxland, Gregory: *Op.Cit*. p.192.
32. Fyfe, Hamilton: *Op.Cit*. p.21.
33. Bullock, Alan: *Op.Cit*. pp.311/312.
34. Camp, William: *The Glittering Prizes. A study of the First Earl
    Birkenhead*. London. p.193.
35. Blaxland, Gregory: *Op.Cit*. p.192.
36. Blaxland, Gregory: *Ibid*. p.192 and
    The Daily News, 4 May 1926.
37. Bullock, Alan: *Op.Cit*. pp.313 and 314.
38. *The Sunday Times*, 2 May 1926.
39. Bullock, Alan: *Op.Cit*. p.317.
40. *The Yorkshire Post*, 4 May 1926.
41. *Daily Express*, 30 December 1967.
42. *The Leeds Mercury*, 4 May 1926.
43. *Lansbury's Labour Weekly*, 22 May 1926.
44. *The British Gazette*, 8 May 1926.
45. *The Daily Chronicle*, 14 May 1926. (The arrests referred to took place
    on the 6 May.)
46. *The Daily News*, 15 May 1926.
47. *The Leeds Mercury*, 4 May 1926.
48. *The Leeds Mercury*, 4 May 1926.

49.   *The Yorkshire Post*, 6 May 1926.
50.   Mowat, Charles Loch: *Britain Between the Wars, 1914-1940*, London, 1955. pp. 321 to 326 and
      Blaxland, Gregory: *Op.Cit.* pp.198.
51.   Mowat, Charles Loch: *Op.Cit.* p.322.
52.   Blaxland, Gregory: *Op.Cit.* pp.198 to 201.
53.   Cook, A.J., *Op.Cit.* p.20. Arnot, Mowat, Blaxland and Crook all confirm his statements.
54.   Arnot, R.Page: *The General Strike.* p.224.
55.   Blaxland, Gregory: *Op.Cit.* p.202.
56.   *The Times*, 13 May 1926.
57.   *The British Gazette*, 13 May 1926.
58.   Crook, W.H.: *Op.Cit.* p.448.
59.   *Sunday Worker*, 23 May 1926.
60.   *The Times*, 13 May 1926.
61.   Arnot, R.Page: *The General Strike*, pp.232 and 233, refering to a B.B.C. 10 a.m. news report.
62.   Crook, W.H.: *Op.Cit.* pp.454 and 455.
63.   Crook, W.H.: *Ibid.* p.453.
64.   *The Times*, 13 May 1926.
65.   *The Times*, 22 May 1926.
66.   Crook, W.H.: *Op. Cit.* p.384.
67.   Camp, William: *Op. Cit.* p.194.
68.   Crook, W.H.: *Op. Cit.* p.452.
69.   Crook, W.H.: *Ibid.* p.458
70.   Crook, W.H.: *Ibid.* p.461
71.   *Yorkshire Post*, 19 May 1926.
72.   Crook, Wilfred Harris: *Op. Cit.* p.488.
73.   Arnot, R. Page: *The Miners.* pp.475 and 476.
74.   Arnot, R. Page: *Ibid.* pp.457 to 519 for a very full account.
75.   *The Daily News*, 22 November 1926.
76.   *The Times*, 21 May 1926
77.   Mullally, Frederick: *Fascism Inside England*, London, 1946. pp.48 and 49.
78.   Mullally, Frederick: *Ibid.* p.57.
79.   Mullally, Frederick: *Ibid.* p.36.

Epilogue

One or two news items not included in the book give extra emphasis to the theory that the General Strike *was* a Class War. They are added here.

The Times, 13 May 1926.

Special Constables and Volunteer Workers. A Government Suggestion. The Home Secretary announces that further recruiting of Special Constables as an emergency measure is suspended, but special constables already enrolled should hold themselves available for duty until released by the chief officer of the police concerned. The Government feel sure that all employers who have been assisted in meeting the requirements of the emergency by volunteer labour will recognize the great civic service which these men have performed, and will desire to deal generously with them. It is suggested that employers dispensing without notice with the services of any paid volunteer should follow the course which the Government propose to pursue, and grant a gratuity of at least two days pay.

"National Police Fund".

On the first day over £10,000 received from such sources as the Stock Exchange (£1,050) Anglo Persian Oil (£5,000).

The Times, 19 May 1926.

Triumphal March.

The march of the First (Guards Brigade) to Waterloo Station yesterday after emergency strike duties in the East End of London, enabled the people of London to demonstrate their appreciation of the part played by the troops in maintaining food supplies from the docks.

The Sunday Times, 16 May 1926.

  Power of the Middle Class the Key of Politics.*

The story of the strike has revealed the immense numbers and power of the English middle class, and shown that though politicians hardly recognize its existence except for the purposes of taxation, it still holds the key of politics.

---

* The second edition of this newspaper carried this point at the top of the front page.

Appendices

Appendix I

REPORT BY MR CHESTER JONES
ON
CERTAIN DISTURBANCES AT ROTHERHITHE ON JUNE 11TH, 1912, AND COMPLAINTS AGAINST THE CONDUCT OF THE POLICE IN CONNECTION THEREWITH

Sir,

On the 14th June last I received a letter from Sir Edward Troup enclosing a transcript of the shorthand notes of a Deputation which had waited on you to lay a complaint in regard to the conduct of the Police in the neighbourhood of Lower Road, Rotherhithe, on the evening of Tuesday the 11th June. Sir Edward, in his letter, informed me that you had requested me to hold an inquiry into the matter of the complaint and to furnish you with a report thereon.

In pursuance of this request I held a preliminary meeting in the Council Chamber of the Bermondsey Town Hall on Monday the 17th June, in order to settle the procedure to be adopted.

I came to the conclusion that the interests of justice would be best served if I appointed a solicitor to collect the evidence of all persons desiring to give evidence against the Police, and to present this evidence before me.

I appointed Mr. Lewis Margetts for this purpose.

He collected the evidence and examined the witnesses, who were cross-examined by Mr. Muskett on behalf of the Police. Mr. Muskett called the witnesses for the Police, and they were cross-examined by Mr. Margetts.

The cases, both for the Police and the public, were put most ably and fully before me.

I sat on eight different days, the evidence on some of these occasions being taken in the evening in order to give an opportunity to witnesses of attending without interference with their work.

I heard in all 136 witnesses; 81 of these were called by Mr. Margetts. Mr. Muskett called 55 witnesses, 12 being members of the public and 43 Police Officers. These Police Officers were, in part, members of the M Division, that is, the local Police, and, in part, members of the V, W, D and R Divisions who had been brought into the neighbourhood as special aid rendered necessary on account of the Transport Workers' Strike.

The disturbances, the subject of the inquiry, happened on the evening of Tuesday the 11th of June, and the scene of the disturbances was the Jamaica Road commencing at New Church Street, proceeding eastward along Union Road and then along Lower Road as far as Rotherhithe New Road.

Some of the side streets were also involved.

The route that I have mentioned is that along which the vans containing meat coming from the Docks pass nightly. These vans are usually accompanied by Police.

Since the commencement of the strike, a considerable number of persons seem to have collected on the route nightly and to have abused the drivers of the vans, but, until the night in question, there does not appear to have been any appreciable amount of violence.

On this night a considerably larger crowd than usual assembled on the portion of the route at and adjoining Mill Pond Bridge, where there is an open space, sometimes used for meetings.

Having regard to the evidence on both sides I should put this crowd at about 3,000 persons.

Further, there appears to have been in this crowd an organized band of roughs, approaching 100 in number, who were described by a Police Sergeant on duty on the spot as 'Lodging House Boys,' and not the ordinary workmen on strike.

The attitude of this crowd gradually became very threatening, stones, broken glass, and other missiles were thrown at the drivers of vans and at the Police accompanying them. A party of Police 40 strong, marching from Tower Bridge to Rotherhithe Police Station, were pelted with missiles. I might here mention that close upon 100 glasses were missed from the Public Houses in the vicinity. There was a very considerable proportion of women and children in the crowd, and the disorder took place to some extent under the protection of their presence. Superintendent Waters stated that a woman, with a baby held aloft in her arms, stood in front of a van proceeding along the Jamaica Road, compelling the driver to stop, while two or three men endeavoured to pull the driver from his seat. The Superintendent also stated that he saw a young woman throw a glass at a carman which fortunately missed him.

This threatening demeanour of the crowd, remarks that were heard made by members of the crowd to the effect that they meant having the meat vans that night, and private information to a similar effect led the Superintendent to the conclusion that, if the meat convoy was to be got through that night without riot and probable loss of life, it was necessary to clear the streets, and he gave orders for this to be done.

The opinion that I have formed, after hearing and considering all the evidence, is that the Superintendent was justified in giving the orders that he did.

In pursuance of these orders, about 10.30 p.m., a body of over 100 Police with Inspectors and Sergeants marched from Rotherhithe Police Station to Mill Pond Bridge and crossed the Jamaica Road, thus dividing the crowd. An endeavour was made to persuade the crowd to disperse quietly. This was met with shouts and booing, with throwing of stones and other missiles.

The Police then commenced to disperse the crowd by force, driving some up West Lane, some along the Jamaica Road, and some in an opposite direction along Union Road.

It was as to the conduct of the Police during this dispersal that complaints were made by some of the witnesses.

During the evening, prior to the Police leaving Rotherhithe Station, there had been some rain, and more threatened. Consequently on leaving the Station some of the Officers wore their capes, some carried them tightly folded as when worn on the belt, and some carried them wrapped loosely on the arm.

It was alleged that in dispersing the crowd a great number of the Officers struck right and left with their capes in a brutal way and without discrimination.

I do not believe this to have been the case, but I have come to the conclusion that some few of the Officers when they met with a determined opposition did strike the members of the crowd with their capes, and, taking into consideration all the circumstances, I cannot say that their action was not justified. 'Better use capes than truncheons,' as one of the Officers said.

Unavoidably, in the course of such proceedings the innocent suffered with the guilty, and there is no doubt that several persons who had taken no part in the disorderly conduct before referred to were knocked down or otherwise roughly handled, and I am not surprised at their being indignant.

The effect of this action of the Police on the crowd as I said before was to drive them in three directions. The Police followed up and the crowd dispersed, some of them down the side streets. In some cases the Police followed down these side streets and it was here that some incidents occurred for which I can see no explanation.

John Herbert Marney stated that he kept a provision shop at the corner of Southwark Park Road and Slippers Place. (This is up a side road about 160 yards from the scene of the disturbance at Mill Pond Bridge.) He said that about 11 o'clock on the evening in question he heard a noise; he went out and saw a number of persons being chased by the Police to within 60 or 70 yards of his shop. Being his closing time he determined to put his shutters up; while putting his shutters up a Policeman ran round the corner and struck him several blows with a cape which knocked him down. He has an artificial hand, the little finger of which was broken. A second Constable struck his wife with a cape. This, put quite shortly, was the effect of his evidence. Marney was corroborated by two witnesses. I feel convinced that some such incident did take place, and the Police were not able to give any explanation or throw any light on the matter.

Another incident that happened in Culling Road was as follows:—

Walter Albert Maxwell, residing in Culling Road, is a porter in a fruit warehouse in Arthur Street East, London Bridge. He met his brother-in-law, George Ings, a printers warehouseman in Culling Road about a quarter to 11. They both say the Police came round the corner and asked them what they were doing there; they answered that they lived down the road. The Police ordered them away and struck at them with capes; they ran home followed by the Police; they were struck at in the forecourt of their house, and, as they entered the house, a Policeman made a lunge at them with his cape and the cape fell into the passage. The Police kicked the door, it came open and the cape was handed out. This account was practically confirmed by James William Coade, a Nonconformist Minister residing opposite the house occupied by Maxwell and Ings. Again I am of opinion that some such incident must have taken place, and again no light is shed upon it by the Police.

Another incident occurred in New Church Street. About 1 o'clock on the morning of the 12th, some time after the crowd had dispersed and all disorder was at an end. Frederick John Edwards, coal porter, stated that he was saying 'Goodnight' to four friends at the corner of New Church Street and Jamaica Road. A Sergeant of Police came over and said to him 'Get out of it.' As he was moving away he was struck a blow on the side of the face with the Sergeant's cape. One of Edward's friends said 'That wasn't asked for,' and the Sergeant said 'If you don't clear out, you'll get the same.' This statement is corroborated by two people in the employment of the Anglo-American Cold Storage Company, and by two carmen. On the part of the Police, several officers were called who were on duty at or about the time mentioned. Their evidence is to the effect that no such incident took place, and one goes so far as to say that if it had taken place he must have seen it. I am of opinion that some such incident must have taken place; it is impossible to believe that all these persons can have conspired together to fabricate a false charge of this description.

Allegations were made in respect of incidents alleged to have occurred near the Rotherhithe Tunnel immediately after the dispersal of the main crowd at Mill Pond Bridge. It was alleged that while there was no disorder in the road and no unusual crowd a young woman named Lily Abner was assaulted by a Police Officer striking her with his cape. Although every opportunity was given to her to attend, Lily Abner presented herself on no occasion to give evidence at the inquiry. Several persons gave evidence as to the assault, one of whom, an employee of the Borough Council, alleged that he himself had been assaulted by the same Officer striking him with a cape. It was also stated that other persons were similarly assaulted at the same time and place.

I had some difficulty in coming to a conclusion as to these incidents, as the evidence of some of the witnesses was undoubtedly embroidered.

I think the real truth is that after dispersing the main crowd at Mill Pond Bridge a small body of Police pursued a remnant of the crowd along Union Road, and when near the Tunnel with a view of effecting a final dispersal, some of this body did strike with their capes (unnecessarily in my opinion), and some innocent persons suffered in consequence.

Complaints were made as to the action of the Police in clearing away a crowd near the 'Red Lion' Public House at the corner of Rotherhithe New Road. I do not think these complaints were well founded. The Police were justified in clearing away this crowd for reasons similar to those I have given in respect of the Mill Pond Bridge crowd, and here again the innocent had to suffer with the guilty.

As the outcome of all this trouble nobody seems to have sustained any injury that, by any stretch of the word, could be called serious. I directed Mr. Margetts to make inquiries of the doctors in the neighbourhood as to persons they might have been called upon to attend in consequence of injuries received during the disturbance. As the result of the inquiries Mr. Margetts called Dr. Richmond, of 95 Lower Road, Rotherhithe. He said that he had attended some five or six persons who alleged that they had been injured in the crowd. None of these injuries could be called in any way serious. One woman far advanced in pregnancy told the doctor that she was knocked down by a Policeman's cape and while she was lying on the ground a policeman kicked her in the stomach. This woman was called as a witness and gave evidence to a similar effect, as also did her husband. I came to the conclusion they were exaggerating and that the real truth was that the woman was in the crowd at Mill Pond Bridge and in the dispersal before referred to she got knocked down and perhaps trampled on. Although the consequences might have been serious I am glad to say that in the result no great harm has been done.

The local police or M Division were spoken well of by nearly all the witnesses, and, excepting one case, all the alleged excesses were stated to have been committed by the divisions who were called in as special aid during the strike.

In some of the cases in which all allegations were made against the Police, particular officers were named as being guilty of misconduct. I do not consider it would be fair in this report to say whether in my opinion the charges had or had not been made out against any particular officer. The witnesses at the inquiry could not be put upon their oath; the inquiry was naturally conducted without too strict an adherence to the rules of evidence, and under these circumstances it would not be right for me to express any opinion that might possibly prejudice any officer in the event of a charge being preferred against him in a Court of Criminal Jurisdiction.

It is to be observed that most if not all of the Police who took part in the dispersal of the crowd had done their ordinary day's work, and would have gone off duty at 10 o'clock but for the condition of the streets before mentioned.

I have not dealt in this report with all the cases of alleged assault in the side streets, but I have selected those in which the evidence was most definite and satisfactory. In the other cases the witnesses did not impress me favourably, but, having regard to the fact that I have come to the conclusion that the Police were blameworthy in the cases with which I have dealt specifically, I cannot say that in my opinion the complaints in all the other cases were without foundation.

Very few arrests were made, but on three of the persons arrested dangerous weapons were found.

To sum up, the position is this: there was a large and dangerous crowd collected at Mill Pond Bridge; it was necessary for the Police to clear this crowd away; they did so, and in the process some persons were necessarily roughly handled, and I think no blame attached to the Police for what occurred at Mill Pond Bridge; in the subsequent pursuit some members of the Police Force employed were guilty of excesses, and some persons have undoubtedly a right to complain of the treatment they received.

CHESTER JONES
Old Street Police Court, E.C.
July 19th, 1912.

Appendix II

So Ill Remembered

MANUFACTURING POVERTY

Terms like 'disinflation' and 'deflation' may mean little to the person whose most intricate financial calculation is to fill in a football pool coupon. Deflation is a financial operation through which the credit and money which keep goods in circulation and create buyers for them are reduced. In 1920 the banks embarked upon that policy. They demanded the repayment of credits previously advanced by them to industrialists and manufacturers. In order to repay the banks, stocks of goods had to be turned into cash as quickly as possible. When that policy became general, everyone was getting rid of his stocks of goods, and prices slumped so heavily that sellers could not get enough to cover their costs of production. As a result, manufacturers stopped making goods, closed down their factories and threw their employees out of work. They then demanded reductions in wages in order to reduce their costs of production. **From 1921-1923 it was calculated that wages fell by £500,000,000 per year, but at the other end of the scale, the capital value of fixed interest bearing securities increased by £712 millions.** Deflation, therefore was a measure by which wages were reduced, certain types of profit were increased, and unemployment was manufactured or aggravated.

The newspapers of the early 1920s remind us of the social and economic consequences of 'deflation.' Speaking in Glasgow on 19th January, 1922 (just about two years after deflation was started), Mr. Austin Chamberlain, Tory Chancellor of the Exchequer, said:—

'We are confronted with economic and financial difficulties greater even than those which fell upon our country at the conclusion of the Napoleonic wars. Nearly 2,000,000 of our people are unemployed; the trade of the country is stagnant, the purchasing power of Europe does not exist; the whole machinery of exchange and trade has been destroyed.'

(You might remember that quotation when the Tories claim that they could have handled the post-war difficulties better than anyone else.)

So large a proportion of the working population received either unemployment pay or public relief that *The Times* commented on the 23rd December, 1922:—

'More than half the Nation is receiving help in one form or another from public funds.'

EAST IS EAST . . .

At the end of 1920 the daily newspapers made depressing reading. The social and human results of deflation appeared in the news columns — not in the city pages. At the bottom end of the social scale, which included thousands of ex-service men, were those who bore the burden of austerity; at the top end were those who flaunted extravagance in the haunts of the rich.

'Between 250 and 350 of the unemployed of Camberwell will march to Camberwell workhouse in Gordon Road and claim admission as inmates — the authorities are making beds ready for the influx.' — (*Daily Chronicle* (now the *News Chronicle*) 10th November, 1920.)

'The Ritz menu card for instance will be adorned with birds and real feathers, and will contain ten heavy courses of exhausting dimensions. The West End on Christmas night will be a swirl of the most riotous splendour.'

That contrast continued to exist year after year and no Housewives League rose to protest against it. In Christmas, 1922, there was still austerity — for some:—

An advert in the Glasgow Press appealed: 'The Christian Volunteer Force — a hungry Christmas . . . the blackest we have ever known . . . cruel hunger . . . bitter cold and squalid misery.'

'The exodus to the Riviera which started a few weeks ago, is now in full swing and I believe not a berth can be booked on the Train de Luxe . . .' — (21st December, 1922.)

SORRY — NO HOPE

Whilst there was some uneasiness about these inequalities there was no Tory plan to expose or abolish them. Indeed as late as on 16th July, 1929, Mr. Churchill is found saying:—

'. . . **on questions of economic law it does not matter at all what the electors think or vote or say. The economic law proceeds.** You may vote by overwhelming majorities that you can cure unemployment by public works on public money, but that will not have the slightest effect on the results whatever they may be, which you achieve by your programme.'

Mr. Churchill bowed before 'economic laws' as he had not done when he restored the gold standard in 1925 and knocked the bottom out of our coal export trade.

And some like Viscount Lymington opposed Unemployment Insurance as being bad for the independent spirit of the British people:—

'. . . But evil is not only done by adding £12,250,000 to the state commitments of this country. That is the least of it. The worst is the attack on the independence and the moral fibre of the people of this country. This is eating into the stubborn independence of our English character.' — ('Hansard,' 21st November, 1929.)

We can never understand why the Lymingtons never themselves experimented with the development of moral fibre through semi-starvation.

In the same paper that recorded beanfeasts of the well-to-do, Mr. Lloyd George offered a deputation of the unemployed cold comfort as he gave reasons why he could do little to help them:—

'The difficulties are difficulties of limitation and restriction . . . that is the restriction of cash which we are all suffering from, whether local authorities, governments or individuals.' — (*Glasgow Herald*, 23rd December, 1920.)

DROWNING IN PLENTY

Starvation in the midst of plenty became only too common in the 1920s, partly because the Government accepted the view that, if left to itself, private enterprise would solve its own problems. Because the Government refused to plan, the farmers planned in their own way to get the best price they could for their products. Today, because the market is planned and the price guaranteed, it is difficult to imagine such a circular as the following being sent out (Circular 172 of the National Farmers' Union):—

'Important — Milk Position.

Under present conditions, the central milk committee of the Union strongly advise the policy of keeping all surplus milk off the market, and, in all cases where no contract has been signed, to refuse to sign such a contract. **The County Milk Committee have already advised producers to keep back one-third of their supplies** and to utilise it on the farm, and the continuance of this policy is also strongly urged.' — C.A. Wright, County Secretary, Farmers' Union, 6th April, 1922.

This method of equating supply and demand was so much admired that the *Fruitgrower*, 21st September, 1922, reported a meeting of South Lincolnshire potato growers where the speaker explained that there was a surplus of potatoes in the country, and suggested that growers might copy the example of the milkmen last March 'when it was decided to withhold a portion of the supply from the market. **He saw no reason why farmers should not agree to feed these to pigs or to allow one-third of the potatoes to rot.**'

In the year in which milk and potatoes were destroyed. *Glasgow Evening News*, 24th November, 1922, reported:—

'The sudden death of a fourteen months old child in the Northern District of Glasgow provides a poignant example of the dire straits to which unemployment has reduced many working class families in the city . . . a distressing state of affairs was found in the house . . . there was no food . . . and without exaggeration it may be said that the entire family was starving. The total income of the household was 15s. per week.'

AUSTERITY FOR SOME

In those days if the unemployed did not already know what austerity meant they soon found out. Their rates of pay were (1922):—

              Man .... 15s.
              Wife .... 5s.
              Child .... 1s.

Even so, influential voices were raised against the 'dole' as it was called. We found the Tory *Morning Post* saying, 20th October, 1922:—

'THE DOLE SYSTEM CANNOT BE ABOLISHED AT ONCE, BUT IT MAY BE REFORMED SO THAT IT SHALL NO LONGER BE SAID THAT IT IS LESS PROFITABLE TO WORK THAN TO DO NOTHING.'

A man, wife and four children could then receive the magnificent sum of

24s. per week in this non-austere world of the 1920's. It remained for Mr. Churchill and Mr. Lloyd George to carry the comment farther in the 1930's, when the minority Labour Government raised the allowances a few shillings per week. Mr. Churchill accused the Government of 'making this country a vast soup kitchen for the unemployed,' and Mr. Lloyd George thought it had 'crossed the border line of prudence between providing against starvation and the temptation of men not to seek work.'

Not only was the world an austere place for some, but it was considered proper that it should be so. It was the fear of austerity and starvation that kept the worker in his place, and prevented him getting ideas beyond his station in life.

Occasionally the unemployed lost heart and became angry, bitter and rebellious:—

'Following a meeting of a Committee sitting to find work and raise funds for the unemployed in Norwich, a great crowd attacked the windows of a grocery store in the centre of the city and scattered the goods.'

It was far easier to attribute an occasional outburst of anger to the 'paid agitator' as everyone who tried to organise the unemployed was called in those days, than to think out a policy to relieve the austerity of the unemployed. So the out-of-works took to demonstrations and hunger marches which made every socially-minded citizen self-conscious and ashamed as he saw them proceeding from workhouse to workhouse on the road to Westminster. As Mr. Tom Johnston, M.P., put it:—

'Some of the hunger marches in London presented a pitiable and heart-rending spectacle. Emaciated, starved, ragged, beaten, hopeless, not from these will come a social revolution. The press placards were yelling 'Moscow' and 'Communist Plot' but God knows the poor victims in that procession were concerned for a square meal — and for a Soviet, not at all.' — (*Forward* 2nd December, 1922).

LIVING WITH AUSTERITY

Nor was this austerity a temporary feature of our social life. Between the two world wars, the average rate of unemployment was over 14 per cent of the population. In the late 1930's the B.B.C. ran a series of talks called 'Time to Spare.' Several unemployed men and their wives broadcast, and the talks were afterwards published in book form. Perhaps Members of the Housewives' League who complain that the existing rations are less than they can properly live on, will try to manage on the fare described in some of these talks.

'I feel if I get half-a-pound of tea every week for three weeks, then I can make do the fourth week with a quarter of a pound. In ways like that I save a penny or two. I manage to get a two-pound jar of jam once a month, and make it last the four weeks. Some weeks I can get a quarter of a pound of bacon for threepence to threepence halfpenny. Now that eggs are cheap, I use quite a lot. We very, very rarely get cheese. We all like it but it is a bit of a luxury. When there are birthdays we have it. I can't manage more than one box of matches a week — that's all we ever use. Many a time we've sat in the dark — it is gas-light, and we haven't a penny for the slot maybe, or we haven't a match. Rather than let people know, we sat in the dark.' — (Page 34.)

Rationing gives us a guaranteed minimum of food, but there was no guarantee for the unemployed.

'My husband never changes his dole money, but although he doesn't keep a halfpenny pocket money, still we can't manage. And we don't waste nothing. And there's no enjoyment comes out of our money — no pictures, no papers, no sports. Everything's patched and mended in our house. We're both of us always occupied in the home. I haven't had a holiday for thirteen years. My husband's never been to a football match. When people talk about the talkies I don't know what they mean. I've never been, but I've no desire to go — it's all gone.' — (Page 30.)

Austerity here does not mean trimming off the luxuries — it means near starvation.

'It's the women who suffer. The man brings the dole in and he's finished — the woman's got all the rest. Many a week he's given it me and I've just said "Put it in the fire." It's just like an insult to a mother to bring in 33s. to keep her home and five children.

I've often said to my husband, "Don't you feel ashamed at bringing this amount to keep all these on?" And he'd say, "What can I do?" He'd work if he could get it. I'm not blaming my husband. I don't know who to blame, but I wonder who I should blame. If only men in authority would realise what a struggle it is for us women, maybe they'd do something.' — (Page 31.)

There is stark misery in those bitter sentences.

'It's terrible to think that our children haven't got a chance. Setting aside the lack of food or warmth, they run short in other things, too. We can't keep things from them, and some of them worry like little old men. Some get to feel different from other children, because they can't have what others are having. A little boy wants what other boys are having; he comes to you and says, "Can't I have so-and-so, like all the other boys have got?" And he can't understand why you say "No." But there just isn't the money for it. Or a little girl has to speak on Open Day at school, and she hasn't a white dress like her little mates. Children from better-to-do families don't mean to be unkind to others, but they sometimes rub it in. So, though we plan and manage as best we may, we can't give them ordinary childhood. We cannot even give them a sure hope of getting work when they leave school — but we try never to discourage them. My bigger boy comes to me sometimes and says: "You just wait till I start work, Daddy," or something like that, to cheer me up.' — (Page 80.)

Austerity here is hardship and self-denial without any solid prospect of relief.

'We don't have a Sunday dinner — we have potatoes. We do get meat on Fridays, once a week, when the money comes in. We get fourpennyworth of stewing beef. **It's mainly bread and "marge" we live on — and jam sometimes for the children at tea.** I boil rice sometimes for a change from potatoes. I spend about six shillings and twopence a week on bread and two shillings and sevenpence on margarine. Then we have fourpennyworth of cheese or tripe, and sixpennyworth of vegetables. Sugar comes to about one shilling and eightpence. We don't buy eggs, however cheap they are, because they aren't filling. Sometimes I get threepence worth of cut oranges at the market for Sunday tea, because I know fruit is good for

children. They're called "cut oranges" because they've had the bad parts
cut off.

'There's many a time I puts my children to bed a bit early in case they'll
ask for a bit of bread and I'm afraid it won't last for breakfast. You daren't
reckon up from one day to another what you've got.' — (Page 84.)

All the little extras we enjoy even in these austere days play no part in
the dietary of poverty.

Appendix III

WAGES AND PRICES

To begin with wages and prices. Table I. (overleaf) shows the relation between prices and real wages between 1900 and 1923. Column (*a*) gives the level of nominal wages, expressed as a percentage of 1900. Up to the beginning of the war this figure is taken from an average compiled by the Board of Trade for forty-seven trades, which is generally accepted by economists as being a fairly true index of wages generally. From 1914 onwards this index is not available, and we have used an index figure compiled by Professor Bowley from the information given monthly in *Labour Gazette*. Professor Bowley's figures only go as far as 1920; but adopting his method of calculation for subsequent years we find that the figure we reach for 1923 is the same as that given by the Ministry of Labour for that year.

Column (*b*) gives the average figure of unemployment among Trade Unionists during these years. (This figure has been used, rather than the general index of unemployment, because the latter did not exist before the Insurance Acts. The Trade Union figure is, if anything, slightly lower than the general figure, so the error, if any, is against the workers.)

Column (*c*) combines these two figures so as to show the *actual money wages* (expressed as percentage of 1900) which the average worker could expect to earn in each of these years. The following is the method of calculation. In 1900 the unemployment percentage was 2.5; that is to say, for every 100 jobs 102.5 men were competing. Or in other words, each man could only expect 100 ÷ 102.5 = 97.8 per cent. of full-time wages. In 1901 he could only expect 100 ÷ 103.3 = 96.8 per cent.; and so on for each year. If we express the *actual money wages* throughout as percentages of 1900, we find that in 1901 a man could expect to earn 98.2 per cent. of what he earned in 1900, in 1902 96.3 per cent., and so on. When the unemployment percentage is less than 2.5, as during the war, the rise in the *actual money wages* will appear higher than in nominal wages; during a slump it will appear much lower. This, of course, as every worker will know, reflects the facts.

This column, it should be observed, takes no account of either overtime or short time earnings. To make a proper calculation of actual earnings these should be included; but in the absence of any figures at all they cannot be. We can only observe that overtime increases earnings in good trade, and short time decreases them in bad. If they were included the drop in wages between 1920 and 1921 would be even more sudden than it appears.

Column (d) gives a comparative table of retail food prices. It is regrettable in the extreme that there was no cost-of-living figure compiled for the years before the war. The Board of Trade, up to 1914, gave an index figure of retail prices in London, and the figures for the last nine years have been compiled by adding on the percentage rise in food prices shown by the Ministry of Labour. This is not satisfactory, because the Ministry of Labour does not base its figure on quite the same commodities, but it is the best that can be done. If there had been a proper 'cost-of-living' figure before the war, it might have shown a point or two less increase, as rents immediately before the war were not rising*; but unfortunately there was not. In any case, rent does not form a very large item, so that the margin of error is not great, but it should be observed that the column does not show the increase in the price of all working-class necessities, but only of food — by far the most important item.

In column (e) we have combined columns (c) and (d) so as to show the course of real wages, i.e. wages expressed in terms of food prices, since 1900. As in the previous column, the reader must remember that only the price of food is taken into account. Were it possible to include all items the figure for real wages would be a little higher up to 1918, but would then drop more sharply.

TABLE I
EARNINGS AND FOOD PRICES, 1900-1924

Year	(a) Nominal Wages	(b) Unemployment Percentage	(c) Actual Wages (combined) (a) and (b)	(d) Retail Prices	(e) Real Wages
1900 . .	100	2.5	100	100	100
1901 . .	99.0	3.3	98.2	100.4	97.8
1902 . .	97.8	4.0	96.3	101.0	95.3
1903 . .	97.3	4.7	95.2	102.8	92.5
1904 . .	96.8	6.0	93.5	102.4	91.3
1905 . .	97.3	5.0	95.0	102.8	92.4
1906 . .	98.7	3.6	97.6	102.0	95.7
1907 . .	102.1	3.7	100.9	105.0	95.1
1908 . .	101.5	7.8	96.5	107.5	89.8
1909 . .	100.3	7.7	95.4	107.6	88.2
1910 . .	100.7	4.7	97.5	109.4	88.2
1911 . .	100.9	3.0	100.4	109.4	91.8
1912 . .	103.4	3.2	102.7	114.5	89.7
1913 . .	106.5	2.1	106.9	114.8	93.1
1914 . .	107.0	3.3	106.1	116.8	90.7
1915 . .	115.0	1.1	116.5	154.1	82.1
1916 . .	125.7	0.4	128.3	188.0	69.9
1917 . .	147.1	0.7	149.7	238.3	62.0
1918 . .	189.9	0.8	193.0	245.3	78.2

*   But food since the war shows a less rise than other items in the budget.

1919 . .	227.4	2.4	227.6	244.1	93.2
1920 (mid)	278.2	2.4	278.4	301.3	92.4
1921 (end)	230.0	15.3	204.4	216.0	94.6
1922 (end)	185.1	15.4	164.3	204.4	81.2
1923 (end)	180.9	11.5	166.2	204.4	81.3

The startling fact which emerges from this table is that *not once since* 1900 has the rise in working-class wages come near the rise in food prices; and more than this, the discrepancy has been growing steadily year by year, the steady level of wages during the war period being more than offset by the violent rise of prices. 1921, the first year of the slump, when prices fell faster than wages, was about the best year since 1907, but in 1922 the capitalists, aided by continued unemployment, recaptured their lost advantage, and down comes the figure with a bump. *Since* 1900 *British capitalism has been giving its workers a less and less amount of the necessities of life.*

Table II. puts these facts another way. In 1904 the Board of Trade conducted an inquiry into the 'standard and working-class budget,' which has been used as a basis for the cost-of-living figure ever since. This is not the place to discuss the many criticisms of this budget which have been made in working-class circles. In the absence of any other figure, we are bound to make our calculations from it. This 'standard family' in 1904 spent 22s. 6d. a week on food out of a total expenditure of 36s. 10d. Assuming, as it is pretty safe to assume, that the 'standard family' spent all that it received, we proceed to calculate in column (*a*) what the same quantities of food would have cost during the remaining years, and (*b*) what total income a man earning 36s. 10d. a week in 1904 could reasonably have expected in each of those years. We find that whereas in 1900 he might have received 39s. 5d. and had to pay out 22s. for his food, leaving him with 17s. 5d. to cover rent, clothes, heating, lighting, and all other expenses, in 1923 he would have got 65s. 6d., out of which his food would have cost him 45s. This leaves for all other necessities 20s. 6d., only about 3s. more than in 1900, to pay for all these other necessities, which at 1900 standards would have cost him about 34s. or 35s. If for a moment we leave income calculations out of account, and take only the expenditure on food, we find that to provide for his family — not an ideal set of meals, but one equivalent to the average standard in 1904 — a wage-earner at the end of 1923 would have had to spend 45s. a week. How many are there whose wages, allowing for time out-of-work periods, come nowhere near 45s. per week — *i.e.*, are insufficient to buy the food, let alone the rest of the necessities of life, which the average family ate in 1904.

The chart on p.189 puts the whole position pictorially. The curve of nominal wages we have omitted as misleading; and have included only the curves of actual wages, of retail prices, and of real wages. We need not enlarge upon the implications of the chart; the curve of real wages, dropping slowly till the war, then suddenly after its outbreak, and finally stabilising itself (in 1923) at little more than four-fifths of the 1900 standard, speaks for itself.

TABLE II
COST OF FOOD AND AVERAGE INCOME, 1900-1924

Year	(a) Cost of Standard Working-Class Food Budget s. d.		(b) Income of Average Family (1904) basis s. d.
1900	. .	. .	22 0	. .	39 5
1901	. .	. .	22 1	. .	38 8
1902	. .	. .	22 2	. .	37 11
1903	. .	. .	22 5	. .	37 6
1904	. .	. .	22 6	. .	36 10
1905	. .	. .	22 7	. .	37 5
1906	. .	. .	22 5	. .	38 6
1907	. .	. .	23 2	. .	39 9
1908	. .	. .	23 7	. .	38 0
1909	. .	. .	23 7	. .	37 7
1910	. .	. .	24 0	. .	38 5
1911	. .	. .	24 0	. .	39 7
1912	. .	. .	25 1	. .	40 6
1913	. .	. .	25 2	. .	42 2
1914	. .	. .	25 8	. .	41 10
1915	. .	. .	33 11	. .	45 11
1916	. .	. .	41 4	. .	50 7
1917	. .	. .	52 5	. .	59 0
1918	. .	. .	54 0	. .	76 1
1919	. .	. .	53 8	. .	89 4
1920 (mid)	. .	66 3	. .	109 9
1921 (end)	. .	47 6	. .	80 7
1922 (end)	. .	45 0	. .	64 9
1923 (end)	. .	45 0	. .	65 6

The Value of Unemployment Pay

'But,' someone will say, 'your figure of earnings is incorrect. You have forgotten the dole! If you take unemployment into account at all, you must take into account the money which the State and the employers so generously provide to assist the unemployed.' For the first ten years of our table this criticism has no weight, for there was no out-of-work benefit provided except by Trade Unions, for which, of course, the workers had already paid out of income. Between 1911 and 1920 the effect is almost impossible to ascertain, for the Insurance Acts applied to so few trades. But from November, 1920, onwards the bulk of the workers were insured, and fortunately we have some figures available.

According to the Ministry of Labour (*Report on Unemployment Insurance*) the total amount paid out (deducting the percentage paid for by workers' contributions) between November 1920 and June 1922 was £82¼ million, or just under £33 million per annum. Dividing this by 11 million, which is roughly the number of insured persons, we get £3 per annum or 1/1.8 pence per week, which is the average value of the unemployment benefit which does not come out of his own contributions to the insured worker in a time of very bad trade. Uninsured persons, such as agricultural labourers, of course, get nothing at all, and the figures take no account of the workers who have lapsed from benefit and no longer remain on the books. Still, we may say that during 1921 and 1922 the State and the employers between them increased the average insured worker's wages by about 1s. 2d. a week. It seems a cheap form of insurance against social revolution.

Of course, we do not intend to imply that the working-class as a whole lived during the slump on the wages we have calculated and the dole. Some part of the difference was made up by the Boards of Guardians. But the relief given by the Guardians was in theory at least individual relief, given to prevent a particular family from starving, and cannot properly be made the subject of a general calculation. In any case, our concern is not to find out what means there are by which a particular worker can supplement an inadequate income, but what provision capitalist industry makes for a living wage. Our figures show that year by year since 1900 British capitalist industry has been providing less and less of the necessities of life to its own workers.

THE WORKERS' STANDARD.

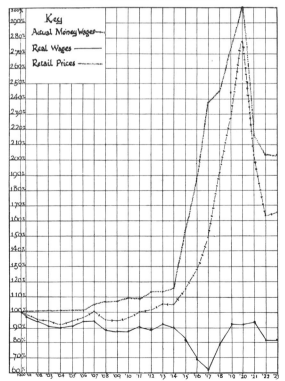

Appendix IV

THE MINES FOR THE NATION

FOREWORD
BY THE
President of the Miners' Federation of Great Britain

As President of the Miners' Federation of Great Britain, which directly represents the interests of about four million people, I declare, after a life-long experience as a practical miner, that the only hope for the Miners of Britain to achieve a proper standard of life, and for the nation to receive a plentiful, cheap and uninterrupted supply of coal, is through the re-organisation of the coal industry upon the basis of public ownership as advocated in the speeches contained in this little pamphlet.

No industry has been the subject of such exhaustive inquiry as the coal industry, and I am convinced that a careful study of the evidence given at the Coal Industry Commission, 1919, and at the recent Inquiry presided over by Lord Buckmaster, will conclusively prove my contention.

The present methods of winning, distributing, and using coal are un-economical to a degree. The work of a miner is hard and dangerous. To have any chance of earning a living and of combating the dangers which surround him he must possess muscular strength, nerve, intelligence, good eyesight, and quick hearing. The miner accepts the risks of the industry in search of a living, but he also knows that he is a national asset.

It should be the duty of any Government to ensure that advantage is taken of his practical experience in the mine by giving him a share in the control of the industry in which he invests his life, and further, to remedy by legislative enactment the gross social injustices and the extravagant and wasteful methods of winning and using coal which the speeches contained herein so graphically describe.

Such action will, however, be undertaken only by a Labour Government possessed of a majority in the House of Commons, and I commend the arguments contained in this booklet to the electors in the confident belief that after a perusal thereof they will unhesitatingly register their votes in favour of the Nationalisation of the Mines and Minerals of this country.

HERBERT SMITH.

THE CASE FOR NATIONAL OWNERSHIP
By T.I. MARDY JONES

The Nationalisation of Mines has been discussed for many years and carried unanimously in Labour Conferences for years past, but I think it is true to say that it has now entered definitely into the region of practical politics, especially as the result of the debate on the Mines Bill last May. With the advent of a Labour Government we are able to see the possibility of it being carried out in the near future.

It is generally recognised that coal is likely to remain the basic fuel and source of motive power of modern industry for a long time to come, as it has been for the past two centuries. Scientists are agreed on that, and the experiments of fuel research confirm it, and although it is true that in recent years there has been an enormous increase in the output of the oilfields of the world, which has displaced coal as fuel up to a certain point, nevertheless it is recognised that the oilfields of the world can never compete seriously with the coalfields. If the oilfields of the world were doubled or even trebled, they would not replace coal as fuel by 10 per cent. of the world's demand for fuel, and many of the oilfields of the world are likely to be exhausted within the next generation or so. When you compare that with the coal resources of the world you realise there is enough coal, practically in all the continents, to last for many centuries; and in our own land we have coal resources which will last for hundreds of years even if the coal output were double what it is today.

But the test of the value of our coal supplies is not their duration in point of time; the test of their value is: How long can Britain maintain her production of coal for export and as power at competitive prices with other coal producing countries whose coal and manufactures compete with British coal and British manufactures in the competitive markets of the world? And if the British coal industry fails to stand this test, it will decline, and the whole superstructure of the British commercial system will decline in the same ratio.

But fortunately for us, the British coal industry has three great advantages over all its rivals.

First, British coal is the best quality coal in the world — Bituminous, semi-Bituminous and Anthracite.

Secondly, our British coalfields are better situated in relation to the home and foreign markets than the coalfields of our rivals.

Thirdly, British coalminers and British managerial and technical staffs, with all their faults, are the best in the world, and the most efficient and experienced in the world.

Yet these three great advantages, which ought to have kept Britain easily ahead, have been seriously hampered for the last 200 years as the result of three handicaps. The first is the dead weight of the landlord system and the royalty system. The second is that of the 1,500 colliery companies, most of them are too poor or too stupid to amalgamate as effective economic units for large scale production. The third great handicap is this: the fact that British coal seams are highly explosive and most dangerous in character, and many of our colliery companies for generations past have been either too poor or too mean to meet the cost of adequate precautionary measures for safety and health, and as the result, the cost of production in Great Britain has been increasing steadily against us compared with the other coal producing companies of the world.

It is a remarkable fact, which is now generally admitted, that during the 200 years that private enterprise has been free to exploit our coal resources, they have exploited recklessly the best seams of coal and they have allowed to waste underground at least four thousand million tons of coal, which at £2 per ton, gives us a value of 8,000 million pounds, or more than enough to pay off the whole of our National War Debts, and Mr. Lloyd George has just informed us that this has not yet been redeemed.

The royalty owners in the same period of time have extracted at least £400,000,000 in royalties alone, while many, many thousands of our miners are being sent to their doom by explosions and floodings as the result of the present system, whilst the housing conditions in all our older coalfields are a national disgrace. It is no wonder, therefore, that when Mr. Smillie and the other members on the Sankey Commission disclosed the terrible conditions and the inefficiency and waste of existing mining that Mr. Justice Sankey should have put on the black cap and passed the death sentence on our existing system.

These are the words that Mr. Justice Sankey used, in which he was supported by three disinterested Commissioners:—

'Even upon the evidence already given, the present system of ownership and working stands condemned, and some other system must be substituted for it — either nationalisation or a method of unification by national purchase and/or by joint control.'

And Lord Gainford, speaking for the coalowners, rejected unification with joint control, and the Miners' Federation of Great Britain has also rejected that proposal. We should impress the public mind that the bitterness created in the hearts of the mining population, due to generations of tyranny and greed under the present system, makes it impossible to bolster it up much longer, with its waste and inefficiency.

The only alternative to nationalisation is unification by private enterprise, but if you get unification by private enterprise, then you get a huge coal trust in each coalfield — a menace to the national interests. The only 'Trust' the nation dare trust is the nationalisation scheme on the lines outlined in this proposal. The only hope of the future for the whole of British commerce is to take it out of the hands of the private exploiters and re-organise the whole coal industry and its ancillary trades in the interests of the producer, the consumer and the community.

Nationalisation, therefore, holds the field, and the decks are to be cleared for action, and we have a right to expect the Labour Government to take up this question and introduce a Bill with the whole weight and influence of a Government behind it.

If we carry nationalisation, the effect of the savings in cost of production that we shall be able to effect under a scheme of nationalisation of this character will be so tremendous, owing to economies and increased efficiency in the production of coal and the more scientific use of coal, that we can provide abundant supplies of cheap coal and motive power to consumers. We can, by the better utilisation of the coal that is consumed, conserve our coal resources by the elimination of waste in production and consumption, and last, but not least, there will be a sufficient margin of saving under such a scheme to secure for the miners a living wage and a higher standard of life than they have ever experienced under private enterprise, together with a status as free men and not as wage slaves in the industry in which they risk life and limb.

In addition, it is proposed in our scheme that we should utilise the coal supplies in great super power stations to generate electric energy in each coalfield for all industrial and domestic purposes. We can also carbonise certain classes of coal of a high volatile character to produce oil fuel and motor spirit, and for by-products which are now being imported into this country from abroad.

Once the coalowner and the royalty owner are eliminated from the coal industry, you will bring about a revolution in the mental and moral outlook of the miners themselves. The miners will be prepared to give that willing service the Prime Minister spoke about when they know that the product of their labour is not going to enrich the coalowner and the royalty owner, but is going to benefit the nation.

THE CASE FOR THE MINERS
By A.J. COOK
Secretary of The Miners' Federation of Great Britain

The question of mines nationalisation is not an academic one. It is a real bread-and-cheese question, not only to the miners, but to all other workers as well. I want to put it plainly and clearly that this is not a miners' question, although the miners, like the agricultural workers, are the first to suffer as direct productive workers in this country, and any investigation proves that the miner, as a direct productive worker, is suffering more today in relation to his conditions than any other section of the community. That is granted, and I do not want it to be misunderstood. When the miner looks round at the railwayman, the docker, the teacher, it is not because the miner is jealous, for the miner feels that the teacher, the railwayman, and the docker is entitled to a living, but not at his expense.

What is the condition at the present moment? We have in this industry double the number of men that were at work in 1894. With their dependants there are four million people, or one-tenth of the total population of Great Britain, who are dependent directly on the mining industry. When the miners are not working, who suffers? The railwaymen, the dockers and others.

Some people say that the miners are lazy. That is not true. When people talk about 'ca'canny' in the mines — well — they ought to go down there. I have worked among the miners for 20 years, and if there is one complaint I have to make against the miner it is his love for work. There are one hundred thousand men who are not allowed to work, one hundred thousand who have as much right to live as the man who does work, one hundred thousand men whose children have a right to sustenance.

But this is not the worst. There are one hundred thousand men in the mining industry who are idle today, with more and more on notice week by week, and before this winter is over there will be thousands more. We have men coming to the pit two or three days a week, men who are getting up in the early hours of the morning and going to the pit, only to see the notice 'No work today.'

And those people who talk about the miners' 7-hour day do not know what they are saying. I want to put it to you that it is not 7 hours from bank to bank. The miner has to get up and down the pit, which often takes three-quarters of an hour. He has to be down by seven o'clock and he does not get up until two, and today there are men who are working, not seven hours, but eight and eight and a-half hours.

Go to the mining villages and see what the conditions are. See the houses tumbling down right and left, see the subsidences and see what wastage of gas takes place — twenty or thirty per cent. of the gas wasted owing to the present wicked method of mining. And the result is huge cost and waste. Look at the mining industry; examine it from a business point of view, in Scotland, Durham, Yorkshire, Wales — live in it as some of us have lived in it, and then you will forgive us for being rebels. We cannot be anything else.

Why do we ask for nationalisation? Because we want to live the lives of decent men and women. Our women are slaves. There is no greater slave than the miner's wife. Why? Because under private ownership there is no consideration for social life and no consideration for housing. Thank God for the Sankey Commission. Thank God for the Welfare Committees. That has brightened the lives of some of our people. We want nationalisation. First, for the sake of economic security, and secondly, because we want safety. Under private ownership our men are murdered. Safety is not the first consideration, but the last. We have Mine Inspectors and Mine Managers and Technical Advisers that are equal to any in the world, but they are tied by private owners, the men who run the mines run them from London simply for profit, and safety is the last consideration.

Sixty per cent. of the accidents are preventible. Explosions ought to be a thing of the past. Our worthy President recently pointed out how they could be prevented. There are many managers who tell us they would like to work hand in glove with us. We do not blame them. We blame the system. Miner's agents come to me, and they have come to others and begged us to send a deputation to the Directors asking for more timber, or to send a deputation to the manager for more safety appliances. In spite of the Mines Act, there are mines today where there are no safety appliances. Acts of Parliament dealing with safety come to nothing where there is no industrial organisation to see them carried out.

Consider also what the country is losing from a business point of view. I have seen as many as twenty, thirty or forty tons of coal absolutely thrown away in one week. There are millions of tons of small coal in which there is heat and power which are wasted. Coal is God's or nature's gift — not to the coalowner, but to the community. We say to the Labour Government,

'You supported the Bill that was brought in, and you must support us now.' We ask not only the Labour Government, but every Trade Union in this country to support the miners in this demand, because if you do not save the miners you will be damned, but if you will save the miners you will save yourselves.

I would like to give you some figures. In 10 years the colliery owners have made £219,000,000 clear profit. Last year — 1923 — they made £27,000,000 profit, and the miner's wages did not exceed 10/- a day when he worked. There are not many of you who would go down a pit for £10 a week, and there are very few people who write against us in the Press who would go down for £10 a day. The pick would be different from the pen if they only had to use it.

Now take royalties. I think my friend pointed out that they averaged from £6,000,000 to £7,000,000 or even £8,000,000. They have had more in royalties than would buy the pits at their valuation twice over. Who gets them? These are the men that make us rebels: Lord Durham, £38,000 a year — and he 'toils not, neither does he spin'; Lord Dunraven, £64,000; the Duke of Hamilton — another man who works hard — £115,000; the Duke of Northumberland, £82,000; and the Marquis of Bute, £115,000.

No industry in the country has been under the searchlight to the same extent as ours. We had our Sankey Commission and we had our Buckmaster Commission. We have no complaint against Mr. Justice Sankey or Lord Buckmaster. They said then that we should have the industry on the industry's valuation. In 1907 a valuation was taken, and that called for £128,000,000 to buy it out. But it has gone up since then. During the Sankey Commission Sir Josiah Stamp, who is not a Socialist, put it at £135,000,000. Since then, despite the fact that they say the mines do not pay, that they are living on their losses, they say now that the present estimate is £200,000,000. They tell us now that their pits do not pay. Well, if they do not pay, let them give them up. I appeal to you as a miner — not as we appeal when we get an explosion — we do not want your sympathy. It does not carry us anywhere. The Labour Government, we say, should welcome this resolution. I ask you men and women to go back to your constituencies and make this a live issue, and I promise you that my organisation will help you by getting you the information you require. The men of this important industry demand that a measure framed on the lines suggested shall be got on to the floor of the House of Commons as quickly as possible.

Appendix V

SUPPLEMENT
TO
THE LONDON GAZETTE

Friday, the 30th of April, 1926.
Published by Authority.

SATURDAY 1 May, 1926

BY THE KING
A PROCLAMATION.
GEORGE R.I.

Whereas by the Emergency Powers Act, 1920, it is enacted that if it appears to Us that any action has been taken or is immediately threatened by any person or any body of persons of such a nature and on so extensive a scale as to be calculated, by interfering with the supply and distribution of food, water, fuel or light, or with the means of locomotion, to deprive the community, or the essentials of life, We may, by Proclamation, declare that a state of emergency exists.

And whereas the immediate threat of cessation of work in Coal Mines does, in Our opinion, constitute a state of emergency, within the meaning of the said Act:

Now, therefore, in pursuance of the said Act, We do, by and with the advice of Our Privy Council, hereby declare that a state of emergency exists.

Given at Our Court at Buckingham Palace, this Thirtieth day of April, in the year of our Lord one thousand nine hundred and twenty-six, and in the sixteenth year of Our Reign.

GOD SAVE THE KING.

Appendix VI

GENERAL STRIKE PLAN BEFORE UNIONS

How Labour's General Staff Proposes to Organise the Great Fight

ORDERS MUST BE OBEYED

The plans drawn up by the General Council for the co-ordination of all trade union activity during the General Strike were presented to the Executive members at the Memorial Hall, London, yesterday.

The unions, it is proposed, will be called out by sections, as follows:—

Transport, including all affiliated unions connected with transport, i.e., railways, sea transport, docks, wharves, harbours, canals, road transport, railway repair shops and contractors for railways, and all unions connected with the maintenance of, or equipment, manufacturing, repairs, and groundsmen employed in connection with air transport.

Printing Trades, including the press.

Productive Industries

(a)   Iron and Steel.

(b)   Metal and Heavy Chemical Groups. Including all metal workers who are engaged, or may be engaged, in installing alternative plant to take the place of coal.

Building Trade. — All Workers engaged on building, except such as are employed definitely on housing and hospital work, together with all Workers engaged in the supply of equipment to the building industry, shall cease work.

Electricity and Gas. — The General Council recommend that the trade unions connected with the supply of electricity and gas shall co-operate with the object of ceasing to supply power. The Council request that the Executives of the Trade Unions concerned shall meet at once with a view to formulating common policy.

Sanitary Services. — The General Council direct that sanitary services be continued.

Health and Food Services. — The General Council recommend that there should be no interference in regard to these, and that the Trade Unions concerned should do everything in their power to organise the distribution of milk and food to the whole of the population.

With regard to hospitals, clinics, convalescent homes, sanatoria, infant welfare centres, maternity homes, nursing homes, schools, the General

Council direct that affiliated unions take every opportunity to ensure that food, milk, medical and surgical supplies shall be efficiently provided.

Trade Union Discipline

(a) The General Council direct that, in the event of the trade unionists being called upon to cease work, the trade unions concerned shall take steps to keep a daily register to account for every one of their members. It should be made known that any Workers called upon to cease work should not leave their own district, and by following another occupation, or the same occupation in another district, blackleg their fellow Workers.

(b) The General Council recommend that the actual calling out of the Workers should be left to the unions, and instructions should only be issued by the accredited representatives of the unions participating in the dispute.

Trades Councils. — The work of the Trades Councils, in conjunction with the local officers of the trade unions actually participating in the dispute, shall be to assist in carrying out the foregoing provisions, and they shall be charged with the responsibility of organising the trade unionists in dispute in the most effective manner for the preservation of peace and order.

Incitement to Disorder and Spies. — **A strong warning must be issued to all localities that any person found inciting the Workers to attack property, or inciting the Workers to riot, must be dealt with immediately. It should be pointed out that the opponents will in all probability employ persons to act as spies, and others to use violent language in order to incite the Workers to disorder.**

Trade Union Agreements. — The General Council further direct that the Executives of the unions concerned shall definitely declare that in the event of any action being taken and trade union agreements being placed in jeopardy, it be definitely agreed that there will be no general resumption of work until those agreements are fully recognised.

Procedure

Those proposals shall be immediately considered by the Executives of the trade unions concerned in the stoppage, who will at once report as to whether they will place their powers in the hands of the General Council and carry out the instructions which the General Council may issue from time to time concerning the necessary action and conduct of the dispute.

And, further, that the Executives of all other affiliated unions are asked to report at once as to whether they will place their powers in the hands of the General Council and carry out the instructions of the General Council from time to time, both regarding the conduct of the dispute and financial assistance.

(Signed) A. Pugh, Chairman.
Walter M. Citrine, Acting Secretary.

I.L.P. CALL for SOLIDARITY

By Fenner Brockway
(Gen. Sec., Independent Labour Party)

May Day this year is the most important in all the history of the working-class movement. Nothing else matters except the fullest support for the miners. The government and coalowners are fighting for the whole capitalist class; the miners are fighting for the whole working class.

We must have solidarity and discipline in the rank and file, and courage and determination among the leaders. With these we can win, although the forces ranged against us will be greater than ever before.

N.C.L.C. FOR ACTION

The National Council of Labour Colleges calls upon all present and ex-students, tutors, and officials to co-operate with Trades Councils and with local T.U. officers participating in the dispute. This appeal is signed by A.A. Purcell, John Hamilton, and J.P.M. Millar.

Appendix VII

British Gazette, May 7th 1926

NEGOTIATIONS UNDER MENACE

T.U.C.'s Plans For Paralysing The Life Of The Nation

Cabinet's Refusal to be Intimidated

Mr. J.H. Thomas's Responsibility.

(By a Cabinet Minister.)

In the House of Commons on Wednesday Mr. J.H. Thomas said: 'At eleven o'clock on Sunday night we had, not a formula, but the Prime Minister's own words, in writing. The Trades Union Council not only accepted it, but said that they would take the responsibility of telling the miners that they had accepted it . . . as being a common basis of settlement.'

The object of this is to lead people to believe that the disputing parties were within an ace of a peaceful settlement at eleven o'clock on Sunday night, and that, but for the Government taking offence at the stopping of the *Daily Mail*, the whole catastrophe of a General Strike could have been avoided. This suggestion is quite untrue. It would have been easy at any moment in the negotiations to put off the General Strike for a fortnight or three weeks by paying an additional subsidy to the coal trade. For £23,000,000 the Government has bought nine months' delay. Another £2,000,000 or £3,000,000 would have made that nine months into ten.

But was there any real prospect of our being any nearer a settlement at the end of the tenth month than at the end of the ninth? That was the question with which the Government were confronted. They were quite prepared to buy a further short period of time, if there was any reasonable assurance that it would lead to a settlement. They were not, however, willing to throw more money into the gulf of mere procrastination. This attitude was definitely adopted by the Cabinet during the afternoon, and was plainly and fully explained by the Prime Minister and his two colleagues to the three representatives of the Trades Union Council when they met at nine o'clock on Sunday evening.

What then was the 'formula' which Mr. Thomas and his two colleagues expressed their willingness to accept and to endeavour to persuade the

Miners' representatives to agree to? It was published for the first time on Wednesday night:

'We will urge the miners to authorise us to enter upon a discussion with the understanding that they and we accept the report as a basis of settlement, and we approach it with the knowledge that it may involve some reduction in wages.'

An effort made by the Government representatives to obtain a more definite undertaking failed. Mr. Thomas and his colleagues intimated that they had already gone to the uttermost limit. In these circumstances the Prime Minister and his two colleagues, without agreeing in any way, and having throughout the interview repeatedly stated that the Cabinet alone could decide, left the meeting and returned to the Cabinet, which all the time was assembled and waiting.

The Cabinet was of opinion that the so-called 'formula' constituted at least a verbal advance upon anything previously stated. For the very first time the representatives of the Trades Union Council mentioned the phrase 'reduction of wages' in a tentative proposal. But on the main question there was no solid ground to justify a further prolongation of the coal subsidy, to which the Government had publicly and repeatedly declared themselves deliberately opposed.

The formula was, in the words which Sir Edward Grey used on a more memorable occasion, 'far too narrow an undertaking.' As the Prime Minister said in the House of Commons on Wednesday night, 'We were where we had always been without any acceptance or likelihood of acceptance.'

MR. THOMAS'S 'PISTOL'

So far we have been dealing only with one of the sets of circumstances with which the Government were confronted. It is now time to turn to the other sequence of events which became increasingly dominant. On Saturday the General Committee of the Trades Union Congress had published in great detail their organised plans for wrecking the industry and paralysing the life of Great Britain by a General Strike, and had announced that this would begin at midnight on Monday. During the course of Sunday the Cabinet learned that definite instructions had been sent to all the Unions affected, ordering the men to cease work at the end of Monday's shift. THEY KNEW THAT EVEN THIS SAME, Mr. J.H. THOMAS, WHO WAS STRIVING SO EARNESTLY FOR PEACE, HAD APPROVED THE ORDERS WHICH WERE IN A FEW HOURS TO HOLD UP THE WHOLE RAILWAY COMMUNI-CATIONS OF THIS ISLAND. The Cabinet were therefore negotiating with a pistol at their heads.

The Government have not shown themselves in the past 'afraid of being called afraid.' On the contrary, nine months ago they faced not only the deep misgivings, and even disapproval of a large majority of the Conservative Party in Parliament and in the constituencies by assenting to the Coal Subsidy, but they also faced the taunts of those who declared that the Government had 'given way to the threat of a General Strike.'

Nevertheless it was impossible to leave the nation under the impression that the Government, after the positive declarations which they had made against the renewal of the subsidy, had in fact at the last moment collapsed under the brutal threat of a General Strike. Nothing but the most unmistakable undertakings by the Trades Union Council and the Miners' Federation, that the prolongation of the subsidy for a fortnight would lead to the acceptance by the Miners of the Commission's Report, including the clauses which require sacrifices from them, could have justified a further departure by the Government from their declared position.

VAGUE ASSURANCES.

The only assurances forthcoming were the vague and limited assurances of the 'formula'. The Cabinet decided that this was no foundation for the further payment of the subsidy in the face not only of a General Strike, but actually of overt acts which had already begun.

Let us imagine for a moment what would have happened if we had taken the opposite course. The General Strike would not have been averted; it would only have been postponed. No settlement of the coal problem was in sight. There was no assurance of any kind of permanent peace. The miners had not yet been persuaded even to agree to the phrase, 'may involve some reduction.'

Even if they had done so, it would have bound them to nothing. They could argue indefinitely that no sacrifices should be required from them until after the reorganisation of the industry had at least been definitely set in hand. This was bound to take a good many months. They would have had no inducement to settle. On the contrary they would have had the strongest encouragement to resist.

It would have been universally proclaimed that the threat of a General Strike was one which no Government dared face. A blow would have been struck at the national confidence, the consequences of which were incalculable. At the end of the fortnight the parties would still have been disputing in a labyrinth of words; and the Government, bankrupt in public respect, would have found it difficult, if not impossible, to avoid renewing the subsidy from month to month in the hopes of purchasing a little longer immunity.

Appendix VIII

British Worker May 11th Issue 7

THE REAL TRUTH OF THE COAL NEGOTIATIONS

Chairman of General Council Replies to Sir Douglas Hogg

In the Government publication, the *British Gazette*, of this morning, appears an article by the Attorney-General, Sir Douglas Hogg, which purports to state the truth of the coal negotiations. As one who has been directly associated with those negotiations, I claim the right to speak with a degree of authority on this matter which neither the Attorney-General nor anyone else with second-hand information can possibly possess.

The initial cause of the deadlock was the mineowners' arbitrary attitude in refusing to conduct national negotiations as recommended in the Commission's Report, and their action in giving notices to enforce a general reduction in wages.

From the moment the mineowners issued lock-out notices to their work-people, the question at issue, so far as the General Council was concerned, was the withdrawal of those notices as a condition preliminary to the conduct of negotiations. From that we have never receded.

The Government representatives insisted that the mineworkers must first decalre themselves definitely as willing to accept a reduction in wages. In these circumstances, and in view of the inevitability that there would be a stoppage throughout the coalfields on May 1 if the notices and demands of the mineowners were pressed, the General Council decided to call a conference of the responsible Executives of the unions affiliated to Congress to take their decision upon the course to be adopted in supporting the miners to resist the demands made upon them.

The decision of the Conference held on Thursday, April 29, was one of supporting the miners and instructing the General Council to proceed with negotiations with a view to an amicable settlement, but subject to the condition that the threat of a lock-out must be removed so that negotiations could be carried on under proper conditions. It was under these instructions that the Negotiating Committee of the Council proceeded with its efforts on the Thursday evening, and continued during the following day.

It is significant, in view of the statement of Sir Douglas Hogg as to the Government's excuse for breaking off final negotiations, that the General Council Committee persisted in its efforts until nearly midnight on Friday, April 30, despite the fact that, while this was proceeding, scores of thousands of men throughout the coalfield had already been locked out. The Committee failed to induce the Government to get the notices withdrawn, or to depart from their attitude of demanding, as a preliminary condition to negotiations, that the miners must definitely agree to a wages reduction.

Despite the request that had been made by the miners in their earliest discussions with the Mineowner's Association that they should be informed of what was proposed in the form of reductions, it was not until the afternoon of Friday, April 30, when the lock-out was actually operating, that proposals were received through the Prime Minister, which involved a substantial all-round reduction of wages and an increase of hours to eight per shift.

REFUSAL TO WITHDRAW NOTICES

Our Conference of Trade Union Executives was kept waiting hour after hour during the whole of Friday. At midnight we had to report that, not-withstanding all our efforts, it had been found impossible to give effect to their resolution to get the lock-out notices withdrawn. Negotiations had completely broken down, and as the majority of the men had already been locked out, nothing remained but to give the fullest support to the miners in resisting the atrocious demands which had been made upon them under the pressure of the lock-out. The Conference on the following day decided on a course of definite action in support of the miners. At the same time the General Council intimated to the Prime Minister that, even at that stage, they were ready to make a further effort at negotiations.

The result was a meeting of our Committee with representatives of the Government on Saturday night and in the early hours of Sunday morning the Government representatives submitted the following formula for our consideration:—

'The Prime Minister has satisfied himself as a result of the conversations he has had with the representatives of the Trades Union Congress that, if negotiations are continued (it being understood that the notices cease to be operative), the representatives of the Trades Union Congress are confident that a settlement can be reached on the lines of the Report within a fortnight.'

The Trade Union representatives agreed to arrange to discuss the situation with their full body as well as with the Miners' Executive. Owing to the latter having left London to be present in their districts to advise their members in consequence of the lock-out having come into operation, not expecting anything to transpire that would require their presence during the Sunday, our Committee found that the Miners' Executive were not available, but immediately telegraphed to them to return to London.

SUNDAY NIGHT'S ULTIMATUM

Meanwhile the discussions with the Government representatives were reported to the General Council, and consideration given to the formula referred to. This having been done, an intimation was sent to the Government that our Committee desired a further meeting to discuss the situation. The meeting took place on Sunday evening, and we intimated that while we could accept the formula in principle, there were certain of its terms which our General Council required should be further considered.

Arising from this many exchanges of opinion took place as to a suitable formula. As the miners' representatives were now present in the building we left the Government representatives so that we could consult the miners, and were actually making an arrangement when, without warning, we received the ultimatum of the Government that in consequence of what had transpired with the *Daily Mail* newspaper, and that, as certain of the Unions had advised their members with regard to a strike, negotiations were broken off.

I desire to make special reference to the statement by Sir Douglas Hogg, which reads as follows:—

'In the course of a two hours' discussion, the Trade Union leaders dictated what they stated to be the utmost they were prepared to submit to the miners. It was in these words:—

' "We will urge the miners to authorise us to enter on a discussion with the understanding that they and we accept the Report as a basis of settlement, and we approach it with the knowledge that it may involve some reduction of wages." With this resolution in their pockets the Congress representatives went off to consult with the miners, who by this time had got back to town, and the Ministers on their side returned to report to the Cabinet.'

The foregoing statement, I have no hesitation in saying, is a gross misrepresentation of the facts. While, as I have indicated, the matter was explored by the meeting, no such formula was ever dictated by the Trade Union representatives, nor assented to by them or in their possession.

The only formula was that written by the Government representatives, quoted above and handed to us in the early hours of Sunday morning. It was this which we proceeded to discuss with the miners, and upon which we were making progress towards an arrangement when the Government's ultimatum put a stop to the proceedings.

I repeat, and I defy contradiction, (1) that the breakdown of the negotiations was, in the first instance, due to the failure of the Government to obtain a withdrawal of the lock-out notices, and its insistence upon a prior agreement by the miners to accept a reduction in wages as a preliminary to giving effect to the terms of the Commission's Report by negotiations; (2) that the second attempt on the part of the General Council to get negotiations on foot was defeated by the action of the Government in closing the door to negotiations while we were actually discussing arrangements with the Miners' Executive — and this because of the action taken by the printers in regard to the *Daily Mail*, an action which was quite unknown to our representatives while we were in the Government building, and which was promptly repudiated as soon as the facts were brought to our notice.

I leave it to the public to decide whether, in the statement which appears in the Government publication, Sir Douglas Hogg has justified the title to his article 'The Truth of the Coal Negotiations.'

Arthur Pugh

Bibliography

BIBLIOGRAPHY

Amery, L.S: *My Political Life*. Vol. 2. Hutchinson, 1953.

Arnot, R. Page: *The Coal Crisis: Facts from the Samuel Commission, 1925-26*. The Labour Research Dept. 1926.

Arnot, R. Page: *The General Strike: Its Origin and History*. The Labour Research Dept. 1926.

Arnot, R. Page: *The Miners: Years of Struggle*. A History of the Miners' Federation of Great Britain (from 1910 onwards). George Allen & Unwin, 1953.

Ashton, T.S. & Sykes, Joseph: *The Coal Industry of the Eighteenth Century*. Manchester University Press, 1964.

Bagwell, Philip S: *The Railwaymen*. Allen & Unwin, 1963.

Bennett, Richard: *A Picture of the Twenties*. Vista Books, 1961.

Beresford, M.W. & Jones, G.R.J: *Leeds and its Regions*. Arnold, 1967.

Birkenhead, The Earl of: *Frederick Edwin, Earl of Birkenhead*. Thornton Butterworth. 1933.

Blaxland, Gregory: *J.H. Thomas: A Life for Unity*. Muller, 1964

Briggs, Asa: *Social Thought and Social Action*. Longmans, 1961.

Brockway, Fenner: *Socialism Over 60 Years. The Life of Jowett of Bradford*. Allen & Unwin, 1946.

Bullock, Alan: *The Life and Times of Ernest Bevin*: Volume 1: *Trade Union Leader: 1881-1940*. Heinemann, 1960.

Camp, William: *The Glittering Prizes. A Study of the First Earl Birkenhead*. MacGibbon & Kee

Cole, G.D.H: *A Short History of the British Working Class Movement: 1789-1947*. Allen & Unwin, 1960.

Cole, G.D.H. & Postgate, Raymond: *The Common People: 1746-1946*. University Paperback, Methuen, 1961.

Collingwood, R.G: *The Idea of History*. Oxford. 1946

Concise Dictionary of National Bibliography, The, Part 2. 1964.

Cook, A.J: *The Nine Days: The Story of the General Strike told by the

Miners' Secretary. Cooperative Printing Society. 1926.

Crook, Wilfred Harris: *The General Strike. A Study of Labor's Tragic Weapon In Theory and Practice*. The University of North Carolina Press, 1931.

Cross, Colin: *The Fascists in Britain*. Barrie and Rockliff, 1961.

Fyfe, Hamilton: *Behind the Scenes of the Great Strike*. Labour Publishing Co. 1926.

Glasgow, George: *General Strikes and Road Transport*. Geoffrey Bles, 1926.

Hammond, J.L. & Hammond, Barbara: *Lord Shaftesbury*. Frank Cass, 1969.

Laver, James: *Between the Wars*. Vista Books, 1961

Lewis, E.D: *The Rhondda Valleys*. Phoenix, 1959.

Macleod, Iain: *Neville Chamberlain*. Muller, 1961.

Martin, Kingsley: *The British Public and the General Strike*. Hogarth Press, 1927.

Mowat, Charles Loch: *Britain Between the Wars, 1918-1940*. Methuen, 1955.

Mullally, Frederick: *Fascism Inside England*. Claud Morris, 1946.

Petrie, Sir Charles: *The Life and Letters of the Right Hon. Sir Austin Chamberlain*. Cassell, 1940.

Robertson, John: Chairman of the S.M.W.U: *Scotland's Shame. How the Miners Live and Work*. Reformers Bookstall, 1919.

Simon, Brian: *Education and the Labour Movement*. Lawrence and Wishart, 1965.

Symons, Julian: *The General Strike*. Cresset Press, 1957.

Toole, Millie: *Bessie Bradock, M.P.* Robert Hale, 1957.

Newspapers and Magazines

The Times, 30 May 1919.
   9 July 1925.
   17 July 1925.
   3 August 1925.
   7 August 1925.
   1 October 1925.
   17 November 1925.
   13 May 1926.
   22 May 1926.
   21 May 1926.

Glasgow Evening News, 24 November 1921.

The Daily Mail, 2 August 1925.
The Economist, 21 October 1922.
The Sunday Times, 2 May 1926.
The Sunday Worker, 2 May 1926.
The Leeds Mercury, 4 May 1926.
The Daily News, 4 May 1926.
The Yorkshire Post, 4 May 1926.
The Daily Express, 30 December 1967.
The Yorkshire Post, 6 May 1926.
       19 May 1926.
The Daily News, 22 November 1926.
The Social Democrat, November 1925
The Bradford Pioneer, 27 May 1927.
Forward, 2 December 1922.
The Labour Magazine, May 1925.
       December 1925.
The Fascist Bulletin, 21 November 1925.
The New Dawn, 13 March 1926.
The Socialist Review, February 1926.
       July 1926.
       September 1926.
       December 1926.
Hansard, 9 November 1906, 21 November 1929, 13 April 1933.

Index

Index